THEORY OF GRAPHS

AMERICAN MATHEMATICAL SOCIETY
COLLOQUIUM PUBLICATIONS
VOLUME XXXVIII

THEORY OF GRAPHS

BY

OYSTEIN ORE

AMERICAN MATHEMATICAL SOCIETY
190 Hope Street, Providence, Rhode Island
1962

Library of Congress Catalog Card Number: 61–15687

PHOTOLITHOPRINTED BY CUSHING - MALLOY, INC.
ANN ARBOR, MICHIGAN, UNITED STATES OF AMERICA

TABLE OF CONTENTS

FOREWORD

The present book has grown out of courses on graph theory given from time to time at Yale University. A first set of lectures on binary relations and graphs was presented before the American Mathematical Society at its summer meeting in Chicago, 1942. Since the manuscript to these lectures was not completed for publication at that time due to more urgent tasks it seems appropriate that this book should appear in the Colloquium Lecture Series of the society.

Graph theory as a mathematical discipline was created by Euler in his now famous discussion of the Königsberg Bridge Problem. However, Euler's article of 1736 remained an isolated contribution for nearly a hundred years. About the middle of the last century a resurgence of interest in the problems of graph theory took place, centered mainly in England. There were many causes for this revival of graph studies: The natural sciences had their influence through investigations of electrical networks and models for crystal and molecular structure; the development of formal logic led to the study of binary relations in the form of graphs. A number of popular puzzle problems could be formulated directly in terms of graphs and thus came the realization that many such questions include a mathematical nucleus of general importance. Most celebrated among them is the Four Color Map Conjecture which was first laid before the mathematicians by De Morgan around 1850. No other problem has occasioned as numerous and ingenious contributions to graph theory. Due to its simple formulation and exasperating evasiveness it still remains a powerful incitement to the examination of graph properties.

The present century has witnessed a steady development of graph theory which in the last ten to twenty years has blossomed out into a new period of intense activity. Clearly discernible in this process are the effects of the demands from new fields of applications: game theory and programming, communications theory, electrical networks and switching circuits as well as problems from biology and psychology.

As a consequence of these recent developments the subject of graphs is already so extended that it did not seem feasible to cover all its main ramifications within the framework of a single volume. In the present first volume of an intended two volume work the emphasis has been placed upon basic concepts and the results of particular systematic interest.

There exist very few books on graph theory; the mainstay has been the book by D. König (1936), which for its time gave a most excellent introduction to the subject. Strangely enough, until now there has been no book in English, in spite of the fact that many of the most important contributions to the subject are due to American and English writers. An effort has been made to present the subject matter in the book in as simple a form as possible. Almost all proofs have been revised; a considerable number of new results are also included. A systematic terminology is introduced which it is hoped may prove acceptable.

For the benefit of the reader a considerable number of problems have been included. Many of these are quite simple; others are more in the nature of proposed research problems; these have been marked with an asterisk.

The second volume will be devoted to more special topics: planar graphs, the four color conjecture, the theory of flow, games, electrical networks, as well as applications to a number of other fields in which graph theory is a principal tool.

Oystein Ore

Yale University
April 1960

CHAPTER 1

FUNDAMENTAL CONCEPTS

1.1. Graph definitions. The first problems in graph theory dealt with configurations of points with lines joining them. In these considerations it was immaterial whether the lines were straight or curved continuous arcs between two endpoints; where they were located; whether they were long or short. The fact that they connect two given points is the only essential element.

This leads to the definition of a graph as an abstract mathematical concept: There shall be a set V consisting of the points which shall be considered to be connected in some fashion. We call V the *vertex set* and the elements $v \in V$ are *vertices*. A graph

(1.1.1)
$$G = G(V)$$

with the vertex set V is a family of associations or pairings

(1.1.2)
$$E = (a,b), \qquad a,b \in V$$

which indicates which vertices shall be considered to be connected. In keeping with the geometric image of a graph each defined couple (1.1.2) shall be called an *edge* of the graph; the vertices a and b are called the *endpoints* of the edge E.

One may use a different terminology. When two sets V_1 and V_2 are given one can form the set of all pairs

$$(v_1, v_2), \quad v_1 \in V_1, \quad v_2 \in V_2.$$

This set is called the *product space* and denoted by $V_1 \times V_2$. In our case each pair of vertices (a,b) is an element of the product space $V \times V$. Thus we can say that the graph G in (1.1.1) with the given edges (1.1.2) is a subset of the product space $V \times V$.

This definition of a graph must be supplemented in one essential respect. In the definition (1.1.2) of an edge one may or may not take into account the order in which the two endpoints occur. If the order is immaterial

$$E = (a,b) = (b,a)$$

we say that E is an *undirected edge*. On the other hand, if the order is to be taken into consideration we shall call E a *directed edge*. In this case a is the *initial vertex* and b the *terminal vertex* of the edge E. We may also say that E is an *outgoing edge* or an *edge issuing from* the vertex a while E is an *entering edge* or an *incoming edge* to the vertex b. Both for a directed and undirected edge we use the terminology that the edge E in (1.1.2) is *incident* to the vertices a and b while conversely a and b are incident to E.

In the applications a graph is usually interpreted as a *network* in which the vertices of G are *nodes* or *junctions*. Two of them, a and b, are joined by a continuous curve, even a straight line, when and only when an association (1.1.2) holds. In the geometric diagram the nodes shall usually be indicated by small circles while the direction of an edge, if required, is shown by an arrowhead on the curve representing the edge (Figure 1.1.1).

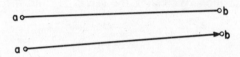

Figure 1.1.1.

A graph is called *undirected* when every edge is undirected, while in a *directed graph* all edges are directed. In Figure 1.1.2 one finds examples of undirected graphs.

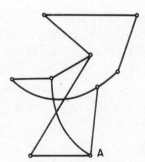 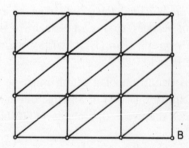

Figure 1.1.2.

The illustrations in Figure 1.1.3 represent directed graphs.

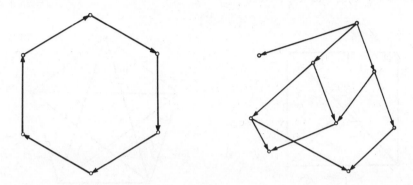

Figure 1.1.3.

There are cases when it is natural to consider *mixed graphs* with both directed and undirected edges. For instance, a city map may be considered to correspond to a graph in which the streets are the edges and the street intersections the vertices. Then some streets may be one-way streets with a prescribed traffic direction while in other streets two-way traffic is permitted and so no direction is introduced.

We have already pointed out that in drawing the geometric diagram of a graph one has great freedom in the choice of the location of the vertices and in the form of the arcs joining them. This may make the diagrams of the same graph look quite different. We shall say that two graphs G and G' are *isomorphic* when there is a one-to-one correspondence between their vertex sets V and V' such that corresponding vertices are joined by edges in one of them only if they are also joined in the other. If the edges are directed their directions must also correspond. In the following it is immaterial which image of the graph is used since isomorphic graphs have the same graph properties. In Figure 1.2.1 one finds illustrations of isomorphic graphs for the case of the graphs formed by the edges and corners of the Platonic solids.

A vertex not incident to any edge is called an *isolated vertex*. In defining the vertex set of a given graph it is often convenient to restrict this set V to the non-isolated vertices. A graph consisting only of isolated vertices is called the *null-graph*; it may be denoted by 0. Another special graph of importance is the (undirected) *complete graph*

$$(1.1.3) \qquad\qquad U = U(V)$$

whose edges are all pairs of possible associations (1.1.2) for two different vertices a and b in V. In Figure 1.1.4 one finds diagrams for the complete graphs with vertex sets of four and five elements.

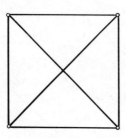
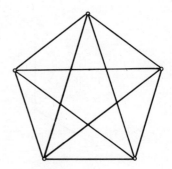

Figure 1.1.4.

In a *directed complete graph* $U^{(d)}$ there is a pair of edges, one in each direction, joining any two different vertices a and b.

The preceding definition of a graph with its corresponding image is sufficient for many problems in which graphs make their appearance. However, for some purposes it is desirable to enlarge the graph concept somewhat.

First, one may admit edges for which the two endpoints are identical

$$(1.1.4) \qquad\qquad L = (a, a).$$

Such an edge (1.1.4) shall be called a *loop*. In the graph diagram it may be introduced as a circular arc returning to the vertex a and passing through no other vertices (Figure 1.1.5). A loop is usually considered to be undirected.

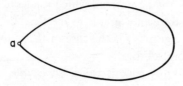

Figure 1.1.5.

One can enlarge the complete graph U in (1.1.3) to a *complete graph with loops* U_0 by adding a loop at each vertex, that is, the edges of U_0 are all pairs (1.1.2) with $a = b$ also permitted.

Secondly, one can extend the graph concept by permitting a pair of vertices to be joined by several distinct edges

(1.1.5) $E_i = (a, b)_i$

as indicated in Figure 1.1.6.

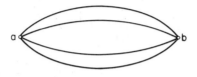

Figure 1.1.6.

For a directed graph there may be several edges in each direction

$$E_i = (a, b)_i, \ E_j' = (b, a)_j$$

connecting a and b (Figure 1.1.7).

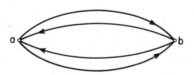

Figure 1.1.7.

To give an illustration of a case in which these concepts appear natural let us take some team competition, for instance, the record of the games in a baseball league. The vertices of the corresponding graph are the teams. A pair of teams A and B are connected by one edge for each time they have played. In case A wins over B this edge may be directed from A to B, and in the opposite direction when B wins over A; in case of a tie the edge may be undirected.

To every graph G there exists a *converse graph* G^* obtained by reversing the direction of the edges in G. To every directed graph there is also an *associated undirected graph* G_u whose edges are the same as those in G but with directions omitted. Sometimes it is desirable to change an undirected graph G into a directed graph G_d by the process of *duplication*: one replaces each edge in G by a double edge with the same endpoints; to the two edges in such a pair one assigns opposite directions.

A graph is called *planar* if it can be drawn in the plane in such a manner that all intersections of edges in the diagram are vertices of G. The graph in Figure 1.1.8a is planar while 1.1.8b is not.

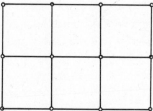
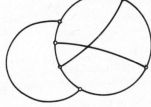

Figure 1.1.8a.   Figure 1.1.8b.

PROBLEMS

1. Show that the two graphs in Figure 1.1.9 are isomorphic.

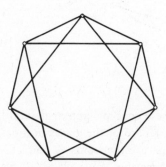
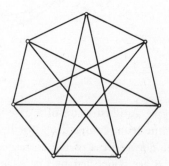

Figure 1.1.9.

2. *The three houses and the three wells.* Three bad neighbors have three wells for common use. Can one construct separate non-intersecting paths from each house to each of the wells?

1.2. **Local degrees**. A graph is *finite* when it has a finite number of edges, and it is *infinite* when it has an infinite number of edges. According to this definition a finite graph could have an infinite number of vertices, all but a finite number of them being isolated. However, the usual situation is that in a finite graph also the number of vertices is finite.

Let G be an undirected graph. The number of edges having a given endpoint a we shall designate by

$$(1.2.1) \qquad\qquad\qquad \rho(a).$$

This number is called the *local degree* or simply the *degree at a*. If all $\rho(a)$ are finite the graph is *locally finite*. We observe that in counting the edges at some vertex a the loops may introduce a certain ambiguity since they may be counted as a single or as a double edge. Depending on the problem under consideration either type of count may be appropriate. Thus in each case we shall have to indicate whether a *single* or *double loop count* shall be used.

We shall derive a few simple formulas concerning the local degrees. The number of edges in G connecting the vertices a and b we denote by

$$(1.2.2) \qquad\qquad\qquad \rho(a, b) = \rho(b, a).$$

When G has no multiple edges there are only the alternatives

$$\rho(a, b) = 0, \quad \rho(a, b) = 1$$

for the *multiplicities* (1.2.2). Evidently each local degree (1.2.1) is the sum of the multiplicities at a

$$(1.2.3) \qquad\qquad\qquad \rho(a) = \sum_b \rho(a, b), \qquad\qquad\qquad b \in V.$$

The number of edges in G we denote by

$$(1.2.4) \qquad\qquad\qquad v_e = v_e(G).$$

Since each edge is counted in two local degrees, namely both at a and at b, it follows that

$$(1.2.5) \qquad\qquad\qquad 2 \cdot v_e = \sum_a \rho(a), \qquad\qquad\qquad a \in V$$

or also according to (1.2.3)

$$(1.2.6) \qquad\qquad\qquad 2 \cdot v_e = \sum_{a,b} \rho(a, b), \qquad\qquad\qquad a,b \in V.$$

One verifies that the formula (1.2.5) remains valid when there are loops, provided they are counted double in the local degrees (1.2.1). The formula (1.2.5) shows that the sum on the right is always even, hence in the ordinary number theoretical way of expressing this as a congruence, we can write

$$(1.2.7) \qquad\qquad\qquad \sum_a \rho(a) \equiv 0 \ (\text{mod}\, 2), \qquad\qquad\qquad a \in V.$$

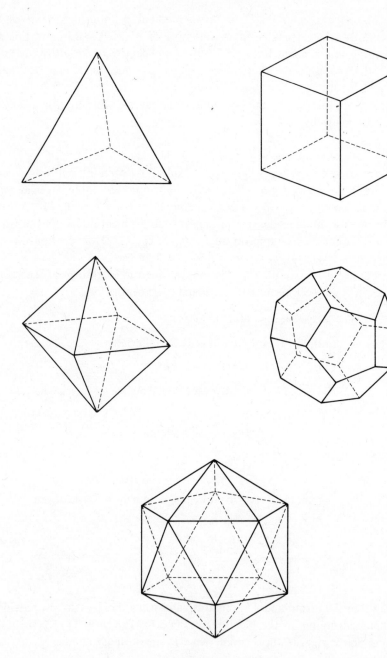

Figure 1.2.1a

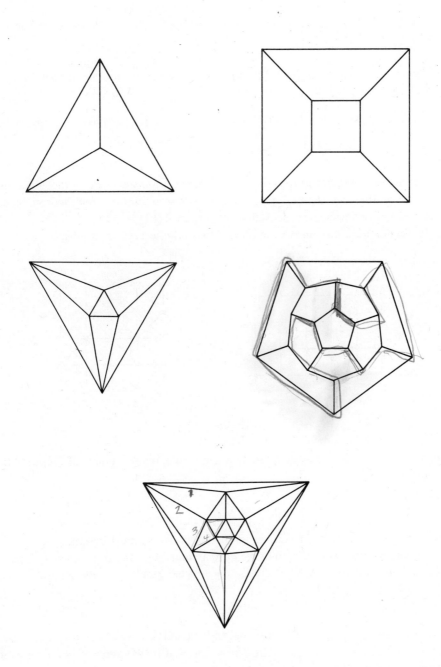

Figure 1.2.1b

The sum (1.2.7) remains even when one omits all vertices a with even local degree $\rho(a)$. Thus we conclude:

THEOREM 1.2.1. *In a finite graph there is an even number of vertices for which the local degrees $\rho(a)$ are odd.*

A graph is called *regular of degree n* if all local degrees have the same value

$$(1.2.8) \qquad\qquad \rho(a) = n, \qquad\qquad a \in V.$$

As examples of regular graphs one may take the graphs defined by the edges and corners of the five *regular polyhedra* or *Platonic solids*: tetrahedron, cube, octahedron, dodecahedron, icosahedron (Figure 1.2.1).

In Figure 1.2.2 one finds examples of two infinite regular graphs.

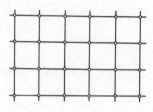 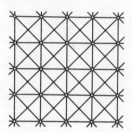

Figure 1.2.2.

From the formula (1.2.5) one concludes that in a regular graph of degree n the number of edges is

$$(1.2.9) \qquad\qquad v_e = \tfrac{1}{2} \cdot v_v \cdot n$$

where v_v is the number of vertices in G. If n is odd v_v must be even.

In the preceding considerations we have assumed that the graph was undirected. Let us turn next to the case where G is a directed graph: here we denote by

$$(1.2.10) \qquad\qquad \rho(a), \quad \rho^*(a)$$

respectively, the number of outgoing and incoming edges at a vertex a. These numbers (1.2.10) we call the *local degrees* of G at a. We agree to count possible loops at a once in each local degree. As an analogue to the multiplicities (1.2.2) we now have two *multiplicities*

(1.2.11) $\rho(a, b), \ \rho^*(a, b)$

denoting respectively the number of edges in the direction from a to b and from b to a. This definition shows that

(1.2.12) $\rho(a, b) = \rho^*(b, a).$

The number of outgoing and incoming edges at the vertex a are then expressed by the sums

(1.2.13) $\rho(a) = \sum_b \rho(a, b), \quad \rho^*(a) = \sum_b \rho^*(a, b),$ $b \in V.$

For the number of edges in G we use the same notation (1.2.4) as before. The definition of the local degrees (1.2.10) then gives two expressions

(1.2.14) $v_e = \sum_a \rho(a) = \sum_a \rho^*(a),$ $a \in V$

for the number of edges. According to (1.2.13) we can also write them in the form

(1.2.15) $v_e = \sum_{a,b} \rho(a, b) = \sum_{a,b} \rho^*(a, b),$ $a, b \in V.$

A directed graph shall be called *regular of degree n* when all local degrees (1.2.10) have the same value

(1.2.16) $\rho(a) = \rho^*(a) = n,$ $a \in V$

for every vertex a. The expression (1.2.14) for the total number of edges then becomes

(1.2.17) $v_e = n \cdot v_v,$

where as before v_v is the number of vertices in V. In Figure 1.2.3 one finds examples of regular directed graphs of degrees 1 and 2.

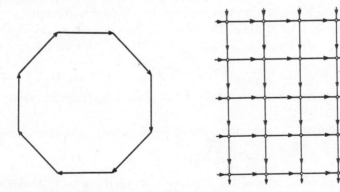

Figure 1.2.3.

In a directed or undirected graph G let A be a subset of the vertex set V. The set of all vertices which are endpoints of edges with initial vertex in A we shall call the G-set of A and denote by $G[A]$. In particular, $G[a]$ is the set of vertices which are endpoints of edges from a. One has $a \in G[a]$ if and only if there is a loop at a. The *converse G-set* $G^*[A]$ consists of all vertices from which there is an edge with endpoint in A.

PROBLEMS

1.   Determine the degree and the numbers of vertices for the graphs of the five Platonic solids.

2.   Generalize the regular graphs in Figure 1.2.2 to three dimensions or to n-dimensional space and determine the degree of these graphs.

1.3.   **Subgraphs.** A graph H is called a *subgraph* of the graph G and we write $G \supset H$ when the vertex set $V(H)$ of H is contained in the vertex set $V(G)$ of G and all edges of H are edges in G. The null graph is considered a subgraph of every graph. Any single edge is a subgraph. In general, one may obtain all subgraphs H of G by selecting for the edges in H all possible families $\{E\}$ of edges in G. Thus H is directed or undirected according to the corresponding properties of G.

A particularly important type of subgraphs are the *section graphs*. Let A be a subset of the vertex set V of G. The section graph $G(A)$ defined by A is the subgraph whose vertex set is A and whose edges are all those edges in G which connect two vertices in A. When $A = V$ the section graph is G itself. For a single vertex $A = a$ the graph $G(a)$ consists of the loops at a.

The *star subgraph* defined by a vertex a consists of all edges in G having an endpoint at a. The loops at a may or may not be included in the star.

To any subgraph H of G there exists a unique *complementary graph* $\bar{H}$ consisting of all edges in G which do not belong to H. We shall indicate this by writing

$$(1.3.1) \qquad\qquad \bar{H} = G - H.$$

A subgraph H is said to *cover* G when H has at least one edge at every vertex of G.

Next let H_1 and H_2 be two subgraphs of G. We define their *sum graph*

$$(1.3.2) \qquad\qquad H = H_1 + H_2 = H_1 \cup H_2$$

to be the subgraph which consists of all edges in H_1 or H_2 or both. Analogously, the *intersection graph*

$$(1.3.3) \qquad\qquad D = H_1 \cap H_2$$

consists of the edges common to H_1 and H_2. These concepts of sum and inter-section of subgraphs we extend to an arbitrary family $\{H_\alpha\}$ of subgraphs: The sum

(1.3.4) $$H = \sum_\alpha H_\alpha = \cup_\alpha H_\alpha$$

consists of all edges in G which belong to at least one of the subgraphs H_α while the intersection

(1.3.5) $$D = \cap_\alpha H_\alpha$$

consists of all edges which belong to every subgraph H_α.

Two subgraphs H_1 and H_2 are (*vertex*) *disjoint* if they have no vertices, hence no edges in common. If H_1 and H_2 are disjoint we say that the sum (1.3.2) is *direct*, similarly the sum (1.3.4) is direct when H_α has no vertices in common with any other. We define further: The subgraphs H_1 and H_2 are *edge disjoint* when they have no edges in common. In this case the sum (1.3.2) is called *edge direct*; also (1.3.4) is an edge direct sum if each pair of graphs H_α and H_β are edge disjoint. As an example we notice that for a subgraph H with the compliment $\bar{H}$ in (1.3.1) one has the edge direct sum

$$G = H + \bar{H}.$$

In the early applications of graph theory to algebraic invariant theory one described a graph by associating a variable x_a to each vertex a. To the edge (a, b) one assigned the difference

$$x_a - x_b.$$

This led to a representation of an (undirected) graph G as a formal product

$$P(G) = \prod_{a,b} (x_a - x_b), \qquad\qquad a,b \in V.$$

But then every subgraph H of G would correspond to a unique factor $P(H)$ of this product, hence the term *factor* for a subgraph which is still used occasionally.

PROBLEMS

1. Determine the number of subgraphs of a finite graph with v_e edges.

2. Determine the number of subgraphs with a given number of edges.

3. What is the number of edges in a complete graph U_0 or U for a vertex set with v_v vertices?

1.4. **Binary relations.** *A binary relation R is defined as an association*

(1.4.1) $$aRb$$

which shall hold for certain pairs of elements in a set V. Thus according to the preceding discussion a binary relation can be represented as a graph on the vertex set V

(1.4.2) $G(R) = G(V)$

such that there exists an edge (1.1.2) in G if and only if the relation (1.4.1) holds in R. Conversely any graph defines a binary relation R on its vertex set when one writes aRb for each existing edge (1.1.2). There is, however, one slight difference between the two concepts. It is usually not appropriate to ascribe a multiplicity to a relation. Thus we see that there exists a one-to-one correspondence between the binary relations and the graphs with single edges on a vertex set V.

We check briefly some of the interrelations between binary relations and graphs. The null graph O corresponds to the *null relation*

$$aOb$$

which holds for no pair of elements. The complete graph U corresponds to the *universal relation*

$$aUb$$

which holds for every pair of elements. Every relation R has a *complementary relation* or *negation* $\bar{R}$ such that

$$a\bar{R}b$$

if and only if (1.4.1) does *not* hold. For instance, when the relation is $a = b$, that is, *a equals b*, the complementary relation is $a \neq b$, *a different from b*. The graph $G(\bar{R})$ is seen to be the *complementary graph* of $G(R)$

$$\bar{G} = U(V) - G(R)$$

with respect to the complete graph U defined on V.

For any relation R there exists a *converse relation* R^* such that

(1.4.3) bR^*a

if and only (1.4.1) holds. The graph $G(R^*)$ is obviously the converse graph of $G(R)$. A relation $R = R^*$ which is its own converse, that is, aRb implies bRa and vice versa, is called *symmetric*. In this case the vertices a and b should be connected by one edge in each direction, but it is simpler to replace them by a single undirected edge so that undirected graphs correspond to symmetric relations.

A relation R is said to *imply* another R', or R' *includes* R when (1.4.1) always has the consequence $aR'b$. This may be written $R' \supset R$; one sees that it is equivalent to

$$G(R') \supset G(R)$$

for the corresponding graphs.

For two arbitrary relations R_1 and R_2 the *intersection*

$$R_1 \cap R_2$$

is the relation

$$a(R_1 \cap R_2)b$$

which holds if and only if simultaneously

(1.4.4) $aR_1b, \ aR_2b.$

The *sum relation*

$$R_1 + R_2 = R_1 \cup R_2$$

holds if and only if at least one of the relations (1.4.4) holds. Thus one must have

$$G(R_1 \cap R_2) = G(R_1) \cap G(R_2),$$
$$G(R_1 \cup R_2) = G(R_1) \cup G(R_2)$$

for the associated graphs.

In the preceding we have defined relations between the elements of the same set V. One can also introduce relations

$$aRa', \qquad\qquad\qquad a \in V, \ a' \in V'$$

between the elements of two different sets V and V'. As an illustration one may take a correspondence τ of the elements in V to elements in V'; here the relation $a\tau a'$ holds if and only if $a' = \tau(a)$ is the image of a under τ. Another basic example is the case where V is a set and V' the family of all subsets A of V, while the relation $a \in A$ denotes that a is an element of A. The graphs of these relations from one set to another will have only edges which connect V with V'. Such graphs are called *bipartite*.

In addition to symmetry there are other relational properties which often appear. A relation R is called *reflexive* when aRa for every $a \in V$. The corresponding graph has a loop at every vertex. Also the converse relation is reflexive. A relation is *antireflexive* when aRa never holds, that is, the graph has no loops. The relation $a \neq b$ is antireflexive; another example is the property of being orthogonal for two vectors.

A relation R is *transitive* when it has the property:

$$aRb, \ bRc \text{ implies } aRc.$$

For the graph this means that when $G(R)$ contains the edges (a, b) and (b, c) it also contains the resultant edge (a, c) (see Figure 1.4.1).

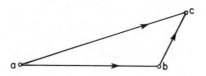

Figure 1.4.1.

We shall return later to a more detailed study of the binary relations from the point of view of graphs. But there are a couple of fundamental relations which appear so universally in mathematical theories that it is advantageous to introduce them already at this stage:

Equivalence relations. A relation R defined on a set V is an *equivalence relation* when it is

1. Reflexive

2. Symmetric

3. Transitive.

All vertices in V equivalent to a given vertex a form a set $R(a)$, the *equivalence block* of a. Since R is reflexive $a \in R(a)$. When aRb and bRx the transitivity shows that aRx so that $R(a) \supset R(b)$. From the symmetry one concludes, therefore, that $R(a) = R(b)$ when aRb. Finally, two different equivalence blocks $R(a)$ and $R(c)$ cannot have any element b in common, because it would follow that

$$R(a) = R(b) = R(c).$$

This proves that the equivalence blocks form a *partition* of V, that is, a decomposition of V into disjoint subsets. An equivalence block $R(a) = a$ consisting of a single element is called a *singular block*, otherwise it is *non-singular*.

Suppose on the other hand that a partition

(1.4.5) $$V = \sum B_k$$

of the set V into disjoint sets B_k is given. Then an equivalence relation with these blocks B_k is defined when one puts aRb whenever a and b belong to the same set B_k. In the corresponding graph $G(R)$ any two vertices in the same set B are connected by an edge while no edges connect different blocks. Therefore

(1.4.6) $$G(R) = \sum U_0(B_k)$$

is the direct sum of complete graphs defined on the various sets B_k.

Partial order. A relation

(1.4.7) $a \geqq b$

is called a *partial order* or an *inclusion relation* when it has the properties:

1. $a \geqq a$.

2. $a \geqq b$ and $b \geqq a$ implies $a = b$.

3. The relation is transitive.

The corresponding graph is therefore transitive with loops and there is at most a single edge connecting two vertices. The graph in Figure 1.4.2 is an example of a partial order.

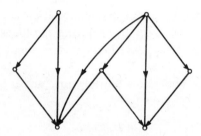

Figure 1.4.2.

A *partially ordered set* is a set in which a partial order is defined.

The inclusion relation (1.4.7) is called an *order relation* and the corresponding set V is *ordered* if in addition to the three preceding conditions also the following fourth is satisfied:

4. For any pair of elements a, $b \in V$ one of the relations $a \geqq b$, $b \geqq a$ holds.

Figure 1.4.3 illustrates the graph of an ordered set.

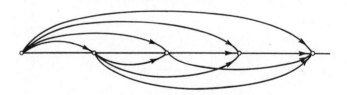

Figure 1.4.3.

For a family of subsets $\{A\}$ of a set V one has the *set inclusion* $A \geqq B$ which denotes that A contains all elements of B. One verifies immediately that this is a partial order. On the other hand one can show that every partial order P is isomorphic to such a set inclusion. To each vertex a in P we associate the set

$P(a)$ consisting of all vertices x with $a \geq x$. From the axioms of partial order one sees that $P(a) = P(b)$ only when $a = b$. Furthermore, if $a \geq b$ the inclusion $P(a) \geq P(b)$ follows from the transitivity; conversely one verifies that this latter set inclusion implies $a \geq b$.

In connection with partial order it must be pointed out that a slightly different concept is also commonly used.

Strict partial order. A relation $a > b$ is called a *strict partial order* or a *strict inclusion* when it satisfies the two conditions.

1. $a > b$ and $b > a$ cannot hold simultaneously.

2. The relation is transitive.

One sees readily that a strict partial order can be considered the intersection of a partial order as defined above and the relation $a \neq b$. Thus one obtains the graph of a strict partial order by removing the loops from the graph of a partial order. Instead of strict inclusion one sometimes uses the term *proper inclusion*.

We notice finally that both for a partial order and a strict partial order the converse is a relation of the same type.

PROBLEMS

1. Let V be the set of positive integers while the relation $a \mid b$ denotes that a divides b. Prove that this is a partial order.

2. Draw the graph of the relation $a \mid b$ for the set of integers from 1 to 20.

3. Draw the bipartite graph for the relation $a \in A$ where A runs through all subsets of a set V with 3 or 4 elements.

1.5. Incidence matrices. In Section 1.1 we defined an edge E in (1.1.2) of a graph G in (1.1.1) to be an element or a point (a, b) in the product space $V \times V$. As usual the elements in this product can be represented in a square array M with the elements of V serving as coordinates along the two axes (Figure 1.5.1).

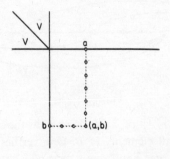

Figure 1.5.1.

At the position with the coordinates (a, b) one places the figures 1 or 0 depending on whether there is or is not a corresponding edge in G. Thus one obtains a finite or infinite *(vertex) incidence matrix* $M(G)$ which completely describes G when the graph has single edges. Usually the notation is chosen such that the elements (a, a) corresponding to the loops lie in the main diagonal of M. If G is undirected both edges (a, b) and (b, a) occur simultaneously and so the undirected graphs correspond to the symmetric incidence matrices.

When G has multiple edges one can replace the symbols 0 or 1 at (a, b) by the multiplicity $\rho(a, b)$ of the edges between a and b as defined in Section 1.2. This gives a description of G by means of a matrix with non-negative integral terms. Conversely, any such matrix can be interpreted as a graph so that any results on graphs can be formulated as properties of these matrices.

This suggests a further extension of the graph concept by including in it all finite or infinite matrices whose terms are real, non-negative quantities. Such matrices occur in various parts of mathematics, for instance, the stochastic matrices in probability and theoretical physics where the system under consideration has a set V of possible states with any pair of states (a, b) connected by a certain transition probability $\rho(a, b)$. Another example is the case where the graph is considered to be a road map on which $\rho(a, b)$ denotes the measured distance between a and b. We shall encounter a number of other instances of this kind where a certain measure or *capacity* $\rho(a, b) \geqq 0$ is associated with each edge.

Graphs may also be described by an incidence matrix of another kind. A graph consists of two classes of concepts, vertices and edges. One can construct a matrix $M_1(G)$ whose lines correspond to the vertices and the columns to the edges. At a location (a, E) in this graph one places the value $\varepsilon = 1$ when a is the initial vertex of the edge E, the value $\varepsilon = -1$ when a is the terminal vertex and $\varepsilon = 0$ when a is not incident to E. When G is undirected one may use only the values $\varepsilon = 1$ and $\varepsilon = 0$. This matrix $M_1(G)$ is the *vertex-edge incidence matrix* of G.

Finally, we shall introduce the *edge incidence matrix* $I(G)$ in which both lines and columns correspond to the edges of G. For the sake of simplicity we assume that G has no loops and undirected single edges. At a position (E, E') in $I(G)$ we place $\varepsilon = 1$ when E and E' are different edges with a common endpoint, and $\varepsilon = 0$ when $E = E'$ or the edges disjoint. Thus $I(G)$ is a square matrix defined by G.

One can take a different view and consider $I(G)$ as the vertex incidence matrix of a new graph, also denoted by $I(G)$, in which the edges E of G are the vertices and the edges of $I(G)$ the pairs (E, E') with $\varepsilon = 1$. We shall call $I(G)$ the *interchange graph* of G. The existence of this graph in which previous edges have become vertices and vice versa explains the duality between vertices and edges which occurs in some parts of graph theory.

The actual construction of the interchange graph $I(G)$ from the diagram of G is simple. On each edge E one selects a fixed point e_E, for instance, the midpoint of E. Then one connects a pair of such vertices (e, e') by a new edge belonging to $I(G)$ if and only if the corresponding edges E and E' have a vertex in common in G. Figure 1.5.1 shows the construction for the tetrahedron graph; one sees that the regular octahedron is the interchange graph for the tetrahedron.

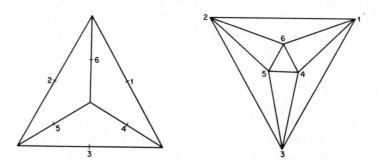

Figure 1.5.1.

Suppose that at a vertex e there are $\rho(e)$ edges $E = (e, e')$ in G. Then in $I(G)$ the midpoint e_E of E is connected by edges to $\rho(e) - 1$ other edges also with an endpoint at e. Thus in $I(G)$ these edges form a complete graph $U(e)$ with $\rho(e)$ vertices. In $I(G)$ each e_E will also be connected to the midpoints of the $\rho(e') - 1$ other edges at e' and these will form another complete graph $U(e')$. The two graphs $U(e)$ and $U(e')$ will have exactly one vertex in common, namely the vertex e_E defined by the single edge E connecting e and e'. Thus $I(G)$ has an edge disjoint decomposition

$$(1.5.1) \qquad\qquad I(G) = \sum U(e), \qquad\qquad e \in V$$

into complete graphs $U(e)$ with $\rho(e)$ vertices such that $U(e)$ has a single vertex in common with each of $\rho(e)$ other complete graphs $U(e')$. It should be noticed that an exception occurs when (e', e) is the only edge at e', hence $\rho(e') = 1$. Then there exists no set $U(e')$.

Suppose conversely that a decomposition (1.5.1) into complete graphs exists for a graph G_1 such that a pair $(U(e), U(e'))$ has at most one vertex in common. Then G_1 can be considered to be the interchange graph $G_1 = I(G)$ of some graph G provided each $U(e)$ has $\rho_1 \leqq \rho(e)$ vertices in common with other blocks $U(e')$. One lets each $U(e)$ correspond to a single vertex e and join e and e' by an edge in G if and only if $U(e)$ and $U(e')$ have a vertex in common. To these edges one adds $\rho(e) - \rho_1$ edges (e, e'') to new vertices e'' at which this is the only edge. The question when a graph is uniquely determined by the interchange graph will be resolved in Section 15.4.

PROBLEMS

1. Construct the incidence matrices for the Platonic graphs.
2. Investigate their interchange graphs.
3. Determine the local degrees and number of edges in a finite interchange graph.
4. Can a star graph be the interchange graph of another graph?
5.* Determine all graphs isomorphic to their interchange graph.
6.* When the interchange graph $I(G)$ is given, is the original graph G uniquely determined?
7.* Investigate the repeated interchange graphs.

CHAPTER 2

CONNECTEDNESS

2.1. Sequences, paths and arcs. Let G be an undirected graph. A *sequence* of edges in G is any finite or infinite series of edges

$$(2.1.1) \qquad\qquad S = (\cdots, E_0, E_1, \cdots, E_n, \cdots)$$

such that consecutive edges E_{i-1} and E_i always have a common endpoint. Thus we can write

$$(2.1.2) \qquad \cdots, E_0 = (a_0, a_1), E_1 = (a_1, a_2), \cdots, E_n = (a_n, a_{n+1}).$$

We mention specifically that the same edge E may appear several times in the sequence (Figure 2.1.1).

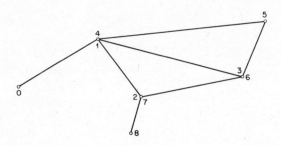

Figure 2.1.1.

If there are no edges in (2.1.1) preceding E_0 we say that a_0 is the *initial vertex* of S while if there are no edges after E_{n-1} then a_n is the *terminal vertex* of the sequence. Any vertex a_i in (2.1.2) which belongs to two consecutive edges E_{i-1} and E_i is an *inner vertex* or an *intermediate vertex*. It should be noted that since edges and vertices may appear repeatedly in a sequence an inner vertex may also be an initial vertex or a terminal vertex or both.

If the sequence has an initial vertex but no terminal vertex, or, on the other hand, a terminal vertex but no initial vertex, it is called a *one-way infinite* sequence. It is *two-way infinite* when it has neither an initial nor a terminal vertex. The sequence is *non-trivial* if it contains at least one edge; for systematic reasons the *null-sequence*, containing no edges may be introduced.

22

When S has both an initial vertex a_0 and a terminal vertex a_n we can write

(2.1.3) $$S = S(a_0, a_n)$$

and call a_0 and a_n the *endpoints* of S. We also say that S is an *edge sequence of length n connecting* a_0 *and* a_n. If $a_0 = a_n$ the sequence is *cyclic*. When a_i and a_j are two vertices in the sequence the subsequence

$$S(a_i, a_j) = (E_i, E_{i+1}, \cdots, E_{j-1})$$

is called a (finite) *section* of S.

A sequence of edges is a *path* when no edge appears more than once in it; the vertices in a path may possibly be traversed several times. Any section of a path is a path. A non-cyclic path is called a *simple path* or an *arc* if none of its vertices is traversed more than once. A cyclic path with endpoint a_0 is a *circuit* if a_0 appears only as the endpoints and no other vertex appears twice. A section of an arc or a circuit is an arc.

We have assumed G undirected. In a directed graph one may introduce either *undirected sequences, paths* and *arcs* where the direction of the edges are not taken into account, or one may consider *directed sequences* (paths, arcs) in which all edges (2.1.2) are traversed in their prescribed directions.

2.2. **Connected components**. Let G be undirected. Two vertices a and b are called *connected* if there exists an edge sequence (2.1.1) with these two endpoints. If S should pass through some vertex a_i more than once one can evidently leave out a cyclic section such that the remaining edges still form a sequence S' connecting a and b. By repeating such reductions it follows that vertices connected by an edge sequence are also connected by an arc. A graph is said to be *connected* if any pair of vertices is connected.

If in an arbitrary graph G the vertex a is connected to b and b to c then clearly a is connected to c. We conclude that the relation of being connected is an equivalence relation for the vertices. Consequently, there exists a decomposition of the vertex set

(2.2.1) $$V = \sum_i V_i$$

into disjoint sets such that in each V_i all vertices are connected while no vertices belonging to two different blocks are connected. Corresponding to (2.2.1) one has a direct decomposition

(2.2.2) $$G = \sum_i G(V_i)$$

of the graph G_i into disjoint connected subgraphs $G(V_i)$. These graphs we call the *connected components* of G. We have shown:

THEOREM 2.2.1. *An undirected graph decomposes uniquely into a disjoint sum* (2.2.2) *of its connected components.*

This theorem makes it possible to reduce most graph problems to the case of connected graphs. As an example of a decomposition into connected components we recall the decomposition (1.4.6) of an equivalence relation into a direct sum of universal graphs.

The complement $\bar{G}$ of G in the complete graph U on the same vertex set also has a unique decomposition into its connected components. By using the decompositions of G and $\bar{G}$ alternatingly one obtains a further unique decomposition of the vertex set V. In the component decomposition

$$G = \sum G_i$$

of G one takes the complement of each G_i in its vertex set and let

$$\bar{G}_i = \sum G'_j$$

be its component decomposition. To each of these components G'_j one may again take the decomposition of the complement and so on. This leads to a representation of G in which each term is a connected graph whose complement on the same vertex set is also connected.

We shall prove a few facts about connectedness which are required later on.

THEOREM 2.2.2. *Let the finite graph G have exactly two vertices a_0 and b_0 of odd local degrees. Then a_0 and b_0 are connected.*

PROOF. According to Theorem 1.2.1 any finite graph has an even number of vertices of odd degree. Since this holds for the component of G to which a_0 belongs, b_0 must belong to the same component. One sees further that a_0 and b_0 must remain connected in the graph $\bar{H}$ obtained from G by the removal of a subgraph H in which all local degrees are even.

Next we shall show:

THEOREM 2.2.3. *Let G be a connected graph and H a subgraph. Then the complement $\bar{H}$ of H in G cannot have more connected components than there are vertices in H.*

PROOF. Let C be any component of $\bar{H}$. We obtained C by the removal from G of the edges in H, and hence there is at least one vertex a in C incident to edges of H. Since C is a connected component there cannot be edges of any other component of $\bar{H}$ at a. Thus each vertex in H is associated with at most a single component C of $\bar{H}$. If H has a finite number of vertices, then $\bar{H}$ has a finite number of components.

THEOREM 2.2.4. *When G is a graph with single edges and no loops having n vertices and k connected components then the maximal number of edges in G is*

(2.2.3) $$N(n,k) = \tfrac{1}{2}(n-k)(n-k+1).$$

PROOF. Suppose that G is a graph with k components G_i each having n_i vertices. Then the maximal number of edges in G is

$$N = \tfrac{1}{2} \sum_i n_i(n_i-1), \qquad\qquad i = 1, 2, \cdots, k,$$

and this number occurs when all G_i are complete graphs on n_i vertices. Assume that there are two G_i with more than a single vertex, for instance, $n_2 \geqq n_1 > 1$. We construct another graph G' with the same number of vertices and components by replacing G_1 and G_2 by complete graphs G'_1, and G'_2 on n_2+1 and n_1-1 vertices respectively. One readily verifies that this increases the number of edges. Thus the maximal number of edges must occur for the graph which consists of $k-1$ isolated vertices and a single complete graph on $n-k+1$ vertices. Its number of edges is given by (2.2.3).

When Theorem 2.2.4 is applied to $k = 2$ it follows:

THEOREM 2.2.5. *A graph with n vertices and more than*

$$N(n, 2) = \tfrac{1}{2}(n-1)(n-2)$$

edges is connected.

For a directed graph G the components are defined by means of the associated undirected graph G_u. The connected components of G are the section graphs $G(V_i)$ defined on the vertex sets V_i of the connected components of G_u. Thus G is connected if and only if G_u has this property.

PROBLEM

1. In a connected graph with v_v vertices what is the smallest number of edges?

2.3. **One-to-one correspondences.** As a simple illustration of some of the concepts introduced in the preceding section, let us examine the graph defined by a *one-to-one correspondence* or *permutation*

(2.3.1) $$a \to a' = \tau(a), \qquad\qquad a \in V$$

of the elements in a set V. One can interpret (2.3.1) as a binary relation

$$a\, \tau\, a'$$

which holds if and only if a' is the image of a under τ. The converse relation is defined by the *inverse correspondence* τ^{-1}. In the graph G of τ there will be a single outgoing edge $(a, \tau(a))$ and a single incoming edge $(\tau^{-1}(a), a)$ at every vertex a. Thus the local degrees are

$$\rho(a) = \rho^*(a) = 1$$

so that G is regular of degree 1. Conversely, any regular directed graph of degree 1 defines a one-to-one correspondence τ of V to itself, obtained by letting the single outgoing edge (a, a') determine the image a' of a under τ.

For a one-to-one correspondence τ each vertex a defines a unique directed sequence of edges passing through the successive vertices

(2.3.2) $\qquad\qquad\qquad a, \tau(a), \tau^2(a), \cdots.$

Two cases may occur:

1. There exists repeated vertices in (2.3.2), hence integers m and n such that

$$\tau^m(a) = \tau^{m+n}(a).$$

Since each vertex is the image of a single vertex it follows that

(2.3.3) $\qquad\qquad\qquad \tau^n(a) = a.$

The smallest $n > 0$ with this property is the *order of a under* τ. The first vertex which recurs in (2.3.2) is then a and the edge sequence consists of the edges in the circuit or *directed cycle of length n* passing through the vertices

(2.3.4) $\qquad\qquad C_n(a) = (a, \tau(a), \tau^2(a), \cdots, \tau^{n-1}(a)).$

This is evidently one of the connected components of the graph.

2. The vertices (2.3.2) are all different, Since a is the unique image of $\tau^{-1}(a)$ and this in turn of $\tau^{-2}(a)$ and so on, one can prolong (2.3.2) into a two-way infinite sequence of vertices

(2.3.5) $\qquad\qquad C_\infty(a) = (\cdots, \tau^{-2}(a), \tau^{-1}(a), a, \tau(a), \tau^2(a), \cdots)$

of which no two can be equal. We say that a is of *infinite order* with respect to τ and belongs to the infinite cycle (2.3.5). The vertices in (2.3.5) define a two-way infinite directed arc which must also be one of the components of the graph. Thus we can state:

THEOREM 2.3.1. *The one-to-one correspondences of a set V onto itself are defined by the regular directed graphs of degree 1 on V. The connected com-*

ponents of such a graph are either directed circuits (2.3.4) or two-way infinite directed arcs (2.3.5). (See Figure 2.3.1.)

Figure 2.3.1.

A loop can only occur in this graph when $\tau(a) = a$, that is, the vertex a is a *fixpoint* of the correspondence τ. A *transposition* (a,b) of two vertices corresponds to a two circuit consisting of two edges in opposite direction joining a and b, while all other vertices are fixpoints. (See Figure 2.3.2.)

Figure 2.3.2.

2.4. **Distances.** Let G be a connected undirected graph. Since any two vertices a and b are connected there will be arcs $S(a, b)$ with these endpoints. The lengths of these arcs are non-negative integers; consequently there must exist *arcs of shortest length* between a and b. This shortest length we call the *distance* $d(a, b)$ between a and b. By special definition

$$d(a, a) = 0.$$

One readily verifies that this distance function satisfies the *metric axioms*:

1. $d(a, b) \geq 0$,
2. $d(a, b) = 0$ if and only if $a = b$,
3. $d(a, b) = d(b, a)$,
4. The *triangular inequality*

(2.4.1) $$d(a, b) + d(b, c) \geq d(a, c).$$

For a connected directed graph one can define $d(a, b)$ to be the distance between a and b in the associated undirected graph.

Let us select some fixed vertex $a_0 \in V$. For each integer $n \geq 0$ there will exist a set A_n consisting of those vertices x for which

$$d(a_0, x) = n.$$

Correspondingly we have a disjoint decomposition

(2.4.2) $$V = \sum_n A_n$$

of the vertex set. In the graph G there may be edges connecting vertices in A_n with vertices in

$$A_{n-1}, A_n, A_{n+1}$$

but not with vertices in any other such set. If namely there should be an edge from A_n to A_{n+k}, $k \geq 2$, there would be a vertex in A_{n+k} whose distance to a_0 could not exceed $n+1$.

We shall use the representation (2.4.2) to prove the following result:

THEOREM 2.4.1. *Let G be a connected graph whose local degrees are at most countable. Then G has at most a countable number of vertices and edges.*

PROOF. We may assume that G is undirected. To show that the number of vertices is at most countable we rely upon the well-known property of countable sets:

LEMMA. *A sequence B_1, B_2, $\cdots$ of finite or countable sets contains at most a countable number of elements.*

According to this lemma it is sufficient to show that the sets A_n in (2.4.2) are at most countable. This is evident for A_0 and A_1 and may be proved in general by induction. Let A_n be countable. The set A_{n+1} is contained in the set A'_{n+1} consisting of all vertices which can be reached by an edge from a vertex in A_n. Thus by the lemma A'_{n+1} and A_{n+1} are countable, therefore also V. Since the local degrees are at most countable it follows again from the lemma that the number of edges is also at most countable.

We shall leave it to the reader to verify the following facts which extend Theorem 2.4.1:

Let $\mathcal{N}$ be an infinite cardinal number and suppose that none of the local degrees $\rho(a)$ of the connected graph G exceed $\mathcal{N}$. Then G has at most $\mathcal{N}$ vertices and $\mathcal{N}$ edges.

If $\rho(a) = \mathcal{N}$ for some vertex a the total number of edges is $v_e = \mathcal{N}$. If from some such a the edges actually connect a with $\mathcal{N}$ vertices, for instance, when G has no multiple edges at a, then one has

$$v_e = v_v = \mathcal{N}.$$

This means that one can establish a one-to-one correspondence between edges and vertices.

We shall make a further observation on infinite graphs:

THEOREM 2.4.2. *Let G be an infinite, locally finite connected graph. Then from each vertex in G there is an infinite arc.*

PROOF. Since G is infinite and there is only a finite number of edges at each vertex there must be an infinite, hence countable number of vertices a_i in G. Thus at a vertex a_0 there is an infinite number of shortest connecting arcs $P(a_0, a_i)$. At least one edge $E_0 = (a_0, a_1)$ must be the initial edge for an infinite number of the arcs P since there is only a finite number of edges at a_0. At the vertex a_1 the same reasoning applies; there must exist some edge $E_1 = (a_1, a_2)$ which is the second edge for an infinite number of arcs P. By continuing this argument an infinite arc from a_0 is constructed.

For a finite graph or a graph with bounded distances one can define its *diameter* to be the maximal distance between two of its vertices

$$(2.4.3) \qquad\qquad d(G) = \max d(a, b), \qquad\qquad a, b \in V.$$

The corresponding shortest arcs connecting two vertices with maximal distance may be called *diametral arcs*.

Next we take some fixed vertex c and put

$$(2.4.4) \qquad\qquad r(c) = \max d(c, x), \qquad\qquad x \in V$$

for the maximal distance from c to vertices in G. We shall call c_0 a *center* of G if the quantity (2.4.4) takes its minimal value

$$(2.4.5) \qquad\qquad r_0 = r(c_0) = \min r(c), \qquad\qquad c \in V$$

for this vertex. The value (2.4.5) we call the *radius* of G and any shortest arc from c_0 to a vertex of maximal distance from it is a *radial arc*. The center need not be unique. Suppose that G is a finite graph with the upper bound $\rho_0 \geqq 2$ for the local degrees. For an arbitrary vertex a_0 let (2.4.2) be the decomposition of V according to the distances from a_0. From a_0 there are at most ρ_0 edges to vertices in A_1. From each $a_1 \in A_1$ there are at most ρ_0 edges to A_2 and so on. It follows that

$$(2.4.6) \qquad\qquad n < 1 + \rho_0 + \rho_0^2 + \cdots + \rho_0^r \leqq \frac{1}{\rho_0 - 1} (\rho_0^{r+1} - 1)$$

where $r = r(a_0)$ is the maximal distance from a_0. This yields in particular a result somewhat analogous to Theorem 2.4.2.

THEOREM 2.4.3. *In the connected finite graphs with an upper bound ρ_0 for the local degrees the radius tends to infinity with increasing order n.*

There exists a variety of other central concepts which can be defined in a finite connected graph. For a vertex a one can define the mean *vertex deviation*

$$(2.4.7) \qquad\qquad m_1(a) = \frac{1}{v_v} \sum d(a, x), \qquad\qquad x \in V$$

of its distances from the vertices in G. A vertex a_0 for which this sum is a minimum may be called a *vertex median* and the corresponding value of (2.4.7) the *mean vertex deviation*. Similarly, the sum

$$(2.4.8) \qquad\qquad m_2(a) = \frac{1}{v_v} \sum d(a, x)^2, \qquad\qquad x \in V$$

can be studied: a minimizing vertex a_0 is a *center of gravity*, while the minimal value of the sum is the *variance* of G.

For an edge $E = (x, y)$ one can define its distance to a to be

$$d(a, E) = \tfrac{1}{2}(d(a, x) + d(a, y)).$$

For the *mean edge deviation* one then obtains

$$M_1(a) = \frac{1}{v_e} \sum_E d(a, E) = \frac{1}{v_e} \sum_x \rho(x) \cdot d(a, x).$$

Analogous to (2.4.8) one has the sum

$$M_2(a) = \frac{1}{v_e} \sum_x \rho(x) \cdot d(a, x)^2.$$

PROBLEMS

1. Show that a vertex x belongs to a shortest arc between a and b if and only if
    $$d(a, x) + d(x, b) = d(a, b).$$

2. Construct the graphs for which $d_0 = 2, 3$ and similarly those for which
    $$r_0 = 2, 3.$$

3. Prove that $2r_0 \geq d_0$.
4. Determine the radius and diameter for the Platonic graphs.
5. Prove that if G is connected so is its interchange graph $I(G)$.
6. One can define the distance $d(E_1, E_2)$ between two edges in G

    $$E_1 = (a_1, b_1), \quad E_2 = (a_2, b_2)$$

to be the shortest distance between any two of their end vertices. How is this concept related to the distance between E_1 and E_2 in the interchange graph $I(G)$?

2.5. **Elongations.** In the preceding we examined distances and shortest paths in a graph. For finite connected graphs we shall also introduce the *elongation* $e(a, b)$ between two vertices a and b as the length of the longest arc connecting them. Evidently $e(a, b)$ satisfies the metric axioms. There exist *diametral elongation arcs* or *longest arcs*; their length l_0 is the *elongation diameter*. For each vertex v there are longest arcs with v as an endpoint; their length

$$e(v) = \max e(v, x), \qquad\qquad e \in V$$

is the *elongation number* of v. The *elongation centers* are the vertices s_0 with a minimal elongation number

$$e_0 = e(s_0) = \min e(v), \qquad\qquad v \in V.$$

The corresponding longest arcs from these centers may be called *radial elongation arcs* while their length e_0 is the *elongation radius*.

Among the various properties of these concepts we mention first:

THEOREM 2.5.1. *Any two longest arcs have common vertices.*

PROOF. Let $P(a, b)$ and $Q(c, d)$ be the two longest arcs. (See Figure 2.5.1.)

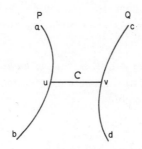

Figure 2.5.1.

If there should be no common vertices there would be some connecting arc $C(u, v)$ having only the endpoints u and v on P and Q. If $P(a, u)$ and $Q(v, c)$ are the longest sections of P and Q defined by the division points u and v then the arc

$$P(a, u) + C(u, v) + Q(v, b)$$

would have a length exceeding l_0.

THEOREM 2.5.2.   *The elongation number satisfies*

$$(2.5.1) \qquad\qquad e(v) \geqq \tfrac{1}{2}l_0, \quad e(v) \geqq \tfrac{1}{2}(l_0 + 1)$$

depending on whether l_0 is even or odd. The equality may hold only when v lies on every longest arc.

PROOF. When P is a diametral arc and v not on P one can construct a connecting arc $C(v, u)$ to P and for the length of the arc

$$C(v, u) + P(u, a)$$

(2.5.1) will be satisfied with equality excluded.

In particular, the elongation radius satisfies (2.5.1). However, we notice explicitly that the elongation centers need not lie on a diametral arc and even if they do the equality in (2.5.1) need not hold for e_0.

The existence of circuits in a graph with single edges is sometimes assured through the following observation:

THEOREM 2.5.3.   *When $P(a, b)$ is an arc from a vertex a which cannot be continued from b then b lies on a circuit of length at least equal to $\rho(b) + 1$.*

PROOF. The $\rho(b)$ edges from b can only go to vertices on P.

When P is a diametral arc both a and b must lie on circuits of lengths at least $\rho(a) + 1$ and $\rho(b) + 1$.

Suppose that L is some arc in the graph G. When one omits from G all vertices on L and all edges from them the remaining graph $G(V - L)$ will have a certain number $i(L)$ of connected components; we call $i(L)$ the *component index* of L. We shall prove:

THEOREM 2.5.4.   *In a finite graph G without loops or multiple edges let l_0 be the length of the longest arc and i_0 the maximal component index for any arc. Then there exists an upper bound*

$$(2.5.2) \qquad\qquad \rho(v) \leqq b(l_0, i_0), \qquad\qquad\qquad v \in V$$

independent of G for the local degrees in G.

PROOF. The endpoints of the diametral elongation arcs cannot have a local degree exceeding l_0 since the arc cannot be continued. We classify the other vertices according to their elongation number and assume that it has already been shown that a bound exists

$$(2.5.3) \qquad\qquad \rho(v) \leqq b_r(l_0, i_0)$$

for all vertices with elongation r or greater. From this we prove that such a bound exists for each vertex v_{r-1} with $e(v_{r-1}) = r - 1$. This means that at v_{r-1} there is a radial elongation arc $P(x_0, v_{r-1})$ of maximal length $r-1$. We denote by Y the set of all vertices not on P which can be reached from x_0 through a continuation of P over v_{r-1}. Then all $y \in Y$ have $e(y) \geq r$. Furthermore, a component of the graph $G(Y)$ must be a component of $G(V-P)$ since an arc from $y \in Y$ can only reach a vertex not in Y through a vertex on L. We conclude that $G(Y)$ has at most i_0 components $G(Y_t)$. By assumption the local degrees in $G(Y_t)$ have the upper bound (2.5.3) so by (2.4.6) the order n_t of $G(Y_t)$ has the upper bound

$$n_t < \frac{1}{b_r-1} \cdot (b_r^{l_0+1} - 1).$$

Since the edges at v_{r-1} either go to vertices on L or to vertices in Y we conclude

$$\rho(v_{r-1}) < l_0 + \frac{i_0}{b_r-1}(b_r^{l_0+1}-1)$$

as desired.

PROBLEMS

1. Determine the elongation diameter and the elongation number for a Platonic graph.

2. Let $P(a_0, b_0)$ be an arc which cannot be prolonged at either end. Show that a_0 and b_0 lie on the same circuit when

$$\rho(a_0) + \rho(b_0) > l(P).$$

3.* Study the intertwining properties of two or more longest arcs.

2.6. **Matrices and paths. Product graphs.** Let H and K be two graphs defined on the same vertex set V. The *product graph*

(2.6.1) $$G = K \cdot H$$

we define as the graph with the G-sets (Section 1.2)

(2.6.2) $$G[a] = H[K[a]].$$

Geometrically this means that the neighboring set to the vertex a under the product graph (2.6.1) consists of all vertices which can be reached from a by an edge sequence of length 2 in which the first edge belongs to K and the second to H. (Figure 2.6.1).

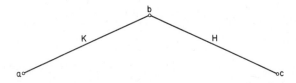

Figure 2.6.1.

Through the definition (2.6.2) of the G-sets of the product graph (2.6.1) the edges of the graph are given. When H and K are graphs with multiple edges it seems natural to introduce a multiplicity also for the product graph as follows. Let

(2.6.3) $$E_K = (a, b), \quad E_H = (b, c)$$

be edges in K and H with multiplicities

$$\rho_K(a, b), \quad \rho_H(b, c).$$

By combining these edges one can form

$$\rho_K(a, b) \cdot \rho_H(b, c)$$

2-sequences from a to c. Thus the total number of such sequences will be the sum

(2.6.4) $$\rho_{KH}(a, c) = \sum_b \rho_K(a, b) \cdot \rho_H(b, c)$$

extended over all b appearing as middle term in some K,H sequence from a to c.

This result can be formulated by means of the vertex incidence matrices of K and H as defined in Section 1.5. If these are M_K and M_H respectively the formula (2.6.4) expresses that

(2.6.5) $$M_{KH} = M_K \cdot M_H.$$

The graph product can be extended to an arbitrary number of graphs. The powers G^n of a graph G appear in the discussion of several questions. One sees that the neighboring sets

$$G^n[a], \quad G^{*n}[a]$$

consist of all vertices which can be reached from a by sequences of length n in G or G^*. The terms in the corresponding matrices

$$M(G^n), \quad M(G^{*n})$$

indicate the number of such sequences connecting the various pairs of vertices. The set of all vertices which can be reached from a by a path in G is

$$G^\infty[a] = \sum G^i[a], \qquad\qquad i = 0,1, \cdots.$$

This is the smallest set A containing a with the property that

$$G[A] \subseteq A.$$

In the multiplication of the matrices (2.6.5) one could disregard the multiplicities of the edges and put

$$\rho(a, c) = 1, \quad \rho(a, c) = 0$$

depending on whether there exists a pair of edges (2.6.3) or not. This corresponds to a Boolean multiplication of the matrices. Then the power matrix $M(G^n)$ has a 1 or 0 at the place (a, b) depending on whether or not there exists an edge sequence of length n between a and b.

Still another way of defining the multiplication of incidence matrices is the following. We suppose that with each edge (a, b) in G there is associated a non-negative measure $\mu(a, b)$ and use the operations

$$\alpha \oplus \beta = \min (\alpha, \beta), \quad \alpha \odot \beta = \alpha + \beta$$

instead of the usual arithmetic sums and products. We associate with G the *measure matrix*

$$M\mu(G) = M(\mu(a, b)).$$

The term at the place (a, c) in the product matrix

$$M\mu(KH) = M\mu(K) \otimes M\mu(H)$$

then becomes

$$\min_b(\mu(a, b) + \mu(b, c)).$$

One verifies that by this definition the (a, b)-term in the power matrix $M\mu(G^n)$ represents the shortest measured distance from a to b in G.

In addition to the previous graph sums and products there exist the so-called Cartesian sums and products. Let

$$H_1, H_2, \cdots, H_k$$

be a family of graphs defined on vertex sets V_i. Their *Cartesian product graph*

$$\pi = H_1 \times H_2 \times \cdots \times H_k$$

has for its vertex set the product set

$$V = V_1 \times V_2 \times \cdots \times V_k$$

consisting of all k-tuples

$$v = (v_1, v_2, \cdots, v_k), \qquad\qquad v_i \in V_i.$$

In π there is an edge (v, w) to a vertex

$$w = (w_1, w_2, \cdots, w_k), \qquad\qquad w_i \in V_i$$

if and only if there exists a family of edges

(2.6.6) $E_1 = (v_1, w_1), \cdots, E_k = (v_k, w_k),$ $E_i \subset H_i.$

The *Cartesian sum graph*

$$\sum = H_1 \oplus H_2 \oplus \cdots \oplus H_k$$

is also defined on the product set V and in this case there is an edge (v, w) in $\sum$ if and only if there exists at least one edge (2.6.6) in one of the graphs H_i. The Cartesian operations can be extended to arbitrary families of graphs.

2.7. **Puzzles.** A number of well-known puzzles can be described in terms of graphs and when put in this form their solution depends on the existence of a path connecting a given vertex with some other vertex. In the puzzle there will be a certain number of permitted positions or states. Each of these can be taken to be a vertex in the graph associated with the puzzle while the edges indicate the possible moves from one position to another. An edge will be undirected or directed depending on whether the move is reversible or not. Usually the puzzle has some initial position and the solution depends on finding a series of moves, i.e., a path in the graph, connecting this first position with a winning one. This is a simple interpretation but it rarely contributes much to the solution.

We shall illustrate the situation on a few extremely ancient puzzles:

The ferryman. A ferryman (m) has been given the task of transporting a sheep (s), a dog (d) and a box full of cabbage (c) across the river. The skiff is so small that, besides the man, it can take only one of the other items. Furthermore, the cabbage cannot be left alone with the sheep, nor the sheep with the dog. How can the transfer be made?

The various situations can be described by the objects left on the first bank. Originally one has the group *mdsc*. The first permissible move can only be the transfer of the sheep, leaving *dc*. The various possible positions are very few in this case. They are described by the graph in Figure 2.7.1.

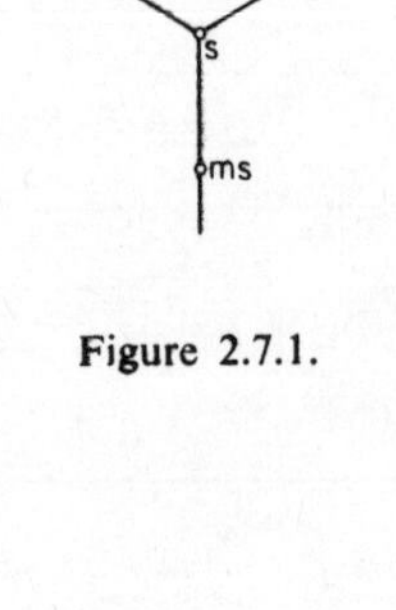

Figure 2.7.1.

The reader may draw the graphs in the following puzzles:

The jealous husbands.   Three jealous husbands and their wives must ferry a river. There is only one small skiff available, capable of taking two persons at a time. How can all six be transported across if no wife is ever left with other men when her husband is not present?

The distribution problem.   Two men have a full eight gallon jug of wine, and also two empty jugs of five and three gallons capacity respectively. How can they divide the wine evenly between them?

The tower of Hanoi.   A board has three pegs. On the first there are m circular discs of tapering size. How can these discs be moved, one at a time, into the same position on another peg, if with each step, no disc may ever be placed on top of a smaller one?

PROBLEMS

1. Draw the graph of the Tower of Hanoi problem when $m = 4$.
2. Examine the possibility of generalizing the puzzles described in this section.

CHAPTER 3

PATH PROBLEMS

3.1. **Euler paths.** As we pointed out in the introduction, the *Königsberg Bridge Problem* initiated the mathematical theory of graphs. Euler's map of the seven bridges in the city of Königsberg is reproduced in Figure 3.1.1.a. The problem is to find a walk which returns to its starting point *C* and passes each bridge just once.

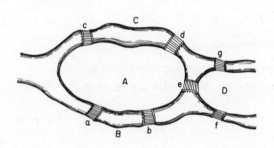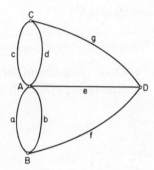

Figure 3.1.1.a.   Figure 3.1.1.b.

Since only the passages over the bridges are of importance, the map may be reduced to a graph diagram in which the bridges correspond to the edges and the various separated sections of the city to the vertices (Figure 3.1.1.b). It is evident that there exists no cyclic route passing through the edges once and only

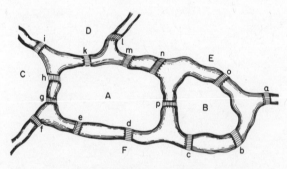

Figure 3.1.2.

38

once. In Figure 3.1.2 one finds the map of an imaginary city used as an illustration by Euler.

The pastime of drawing figures in a continuous trait without repeating lines is probably a very ancient one. The following figure, called *Mohammed's scimitars* is said to have originated with the Arabs (Figure 3.1.3).

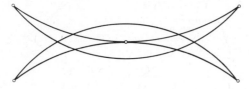

Figure 3.1.3.

Euler turned to the general graph problem: When is it possible in a finite graph to find a cyclic path of edges such that each edge in the graph appears once and only once in the path?

Such a path, when it exists, is called an *Euler path* and a graph which has such a path is called an *Euler graph*. The answer to Euler's query is then as follows:

THEOREM 3.1.1. *A finite graph G is an Euler graph if and only if*:
1. *G is connected.*
2. *All local degrees are even numbers.*

PROOF. Condition 1 is evidently necessary. Furthermore, anytime an Euler path passes through some vertex it must enter through one edge and exit through a different edge; thus condition 2 is also necessary.

Suppose now that these two conditions are fulfilled. We begin a path P at some arbitrary vertex a in G and continue as far as possible, always through new edges. Since at each vertex the number of edges is even, this process can only come to an end by returning to a. If P does not include all edges of G we remove from G the subgraph P consisting of the edges in this path.

Both P and G have even local degrees; the same must be true for the remaining graph $\bar{P}$. Since G is connected there must be some vertex b through which P passes at which there are also edges of $\bar{P}$. From b one can then construct a new path P' including only edges belonging to $\bar{P}$. Again such a path must terminate by returning to b. But P and P' can then be combined to form a new path

$$P_1 = P(a, b) + P' + P(b, a)$$

which returns to a and contains more edges of G than P. If P_1 is not an Euler path the same construction may be repeated and the process can only come to a halt when one has obtained an Euler path (Figure 3.1.4).

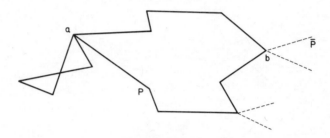

Figure 3.1.4.

As a generalization of Euler's problem one may determine the smallest number of edge disjoint paths P_i which is required to *cover* the arbitrary finite connected graph G; that is, include all edges. The solution can be reduced to that of Euler's problem.

If G is not an Euler graph let there be k vertices with odd local degrees. According to Theorem 1.2.1, k is an even number. Evidently each odd vertex must be the endpoint of at least one of the paths P_i used to cover G. Thus the number of such paths is at least $\frac{1}{2}k$. On the other hand, G can be covered by paths in this number. To verify this we enlarge G to a new graph G' by adjoining to it $\frac{1}{2}k$ edges E', each connecting a different pair of odd vertices. Then G' is an Euler graph and has an Euler path P'. When the edges E' are omitted from P' this graph decomposes into $\frac{1}{2}k$ sections covering G. Thus we have shown:

THEOREM 3.1.2. *Let G be a finite connected graph with k vertices of odd degree. Then the minimal number of edge disjoint paths covering G is $\frac{1}{2}k$.*

In the two preceding theorems one can also include graphs with loops, provided these are counted with the multiplicity 2 in the local degrees.

Analogous problems may be considered for directed graphs. An argument similar to that used in the proof of Theorem 3.1.1 leads to the result:

THEOREM 3.1.3. *Let G be a finite directed and connected graph. A necessary and sufficient condition that there exist a cyclic directed path including all edges of G is that each vertex have the same number of entering and outgoing edges, that is,*

$$\rho(a) = \rho^*(a), \qquad\qquad a \in V.$$

A formula for the number of such paths has been given by *Aardenne-Ehrenfest* and *de Bruijn*.

A graph with an Euler path may, for instance, be considered a suitable pattern for the arrangement of an exposition in which the visitors are to be guided by directional signs through the various passages in such a manner that they see each exhibit once and once only. If there are exhibits on both sides of the passages one may wish to direct the public through each of them twice so that each side may be inspected separately. This, however, places no restriction on the basic plan as the following theorem shows:

THEOREM 3.1.4. *In a finite connected graph it is always possible to construct a cyclic directed path passing through each edge once and only once in each direction.*

PROOF. It is sufficient to duplicate the edges in the given graph G so that each of them is split into a pair of edges with opposite directions. The duplication G_d of G is then a directed graph in which the conditions of Theorem 3.1.3 are satisfied.

A quite simple rule, proposed by *Tarry* (see *Lucas*, Chapter 1) may be used for finding a path of the type required in Theorem 3.1.4. This construction also gives a solution to the so-called *Labyrinth problem* discussed in Section 3.3. Beginning at an arbitrary vertex a_0 one follows a path P, marking each edge as one passes with the direction in which it has been traversed. When one arrives at some vertex g for the first time the entering edge is marked especially. When one reaches a vertex g one always follows next an edge (g, r) which either has not previously been traversed, or, if it has, then only in the opposite direction. However, the entering edge should be followed only as a last resort when there are no other edges available.

One observes that by each passage through a vertex g there will be one incoming edge and one departing edge in the path P; consequently it can only end at a_0. We shall prove that P must cover all edges in G once in each direction. First we verify this fact for all edges with an endpoint at a_0. Since P comes to a halt all edges at a_0 must have been covered in the direction from a_0; but because there are as many outgoing as incoming edges in P at each vertex each edge at a_0 must be covered in both directions.

The corresponding result is then obtained by induction for the other vertices in P. We follow P from a_0 to some vertex a_n and assume that at the preceding vertices a_i all edges have been covered in both directions. The entering edge to a_n is of the form (a_i, a_n) and so by assumption it has been passed in both directions. But the entering edge at a_n should only be used when there are no other exits available, hence all edges at a_n must also be covered in both directions.

The question of the existence of Euler paths appears in various games and puzzles. Usually the various positions are the vertices in the corresponding graph and the edges connecting them are the moves. One may ask when there is some cyclic sequence of successive moves such that all possible moves between two positions are included just once.

PROBLEMS

1. Determine which of the graphs of the five Platonic solids have Euler paths, and when not, how many paths are required to cover all edges.

2. Draw the graph corresponding to Euler's map in Figure 3.1.2 and determine whether there exists an Euler path.

3. The pieces of a domino set carry all pairs of points from 0 to 6. Beginning with $(0,0)$ how many domino configurations including all pieces can be laid?

4. On a chess-board place one of the pieces (king, queen, rook, knight) at some position and determine whether there exists a succession of moves which includes all possible moves just once.

5. Formulate a theorem for directed graphs analogous to Theorem 3.1.2 for undirected graphs.

6.* The complete graph U_n for a vertex set with n elements will have even degrees $n-1$ when n is odd. Give an explicit Euler path and the total number of such paths.

7. When does the interchange graph of a given graph have an Euler path?

3.2. Euler paths in infinite graphs. In an infinite graph G there may be Euler paths covering all edges. For such a path P one can have only two alternatives:

1. P is a one-way infinite path.
2. P is two-way infinite.

Evidently the two following conditions are necessary in either case:

α) G is connected.

β) G has a countable number of edges.

If there is a one-way infinite Euler path the initial vertex must either be odd or P must pass through it an infinite number of times. The other vertices are even or infinite. Thus in addition to the two previous conditions we can add in this case:

γ_1) At most one vertex of G is of odd degree; if there is none there must be at least one of infinite degree.

For two-way infinite paths one must have:

γ_2) There are no vertices of odd degree.

However, these conditions are not sufficient for the existence of infinite Euler paths as the examples in Figure 3.2.1 show.

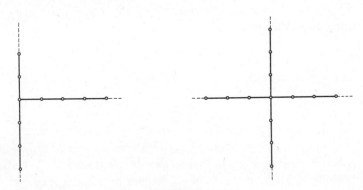

Figure 3.2.1.

Necessary and sufficient conditions for the existence of Euler paths in infinite graphs have been determined by *Erdös, Grünwald* and *Vázsonyi*. (See also Erdös, Grünwald and Weiszfeld.) We shall derive their results in a somewhat simpler manner.

THEOREM 3.2.1. *A necessary and sufficient condition for a graph G to have a one-way Euler path is that it satisfy the conditions* α), β) *and* γ_1) *and in addition*:

δ_1) *Any finite subgraph H of G shall have a complement $\bar{H}$ in which only one connected component is infinite.*

To show that δ_1) is necessary we assume that G has a one-way infinite Euler path P. Then for any finite subgraph H of G there exists a section P_0 of P from the initial vertex a_0 such that P_0 includes all edges in H. We write

$$P = G = P_0 + P_\infty$$

where P_∞ is the remaining infinite section. After P_0 is removed from G the connected infinite graph P_∞ remains. But the graph $\bar{H}$ is obtained from P_∞ by adding a finite number of edges.

For the proof of the sufficiency of the conditions in Theorem 3.2.1, we shall rely upon the auxiliary result:

LEMMA. *Let G be a connected graph satisfying condition* γ_1). *We denote the odd vertex by a_0 if it exists; otherwise a_0 is of infinite degree. If $P(a_0, a_n)$ is a path connecting a_0 with a vertex a_n then there also exists a path $Q(a_0, a_n)$ between the same vertices including all edges in P such that the complement $\bar{Q}$ has no finite components and also satisfies* γ_1).

PROOF. According to Theorem 2.2.3, the graph $\bar{P}$ has a finite number of components. Let F be a finite such component. We shall show that all local degrees in F are even. Since F is a finite graph all its local degrees $\rho_F(v)$ are finite, and because only the edges in P have been removed the degree $\rho_G(v)$ in G is finite. But according to γ_1) all

$$\rho_G(v), \hspace{8cm} v \neq a_0$$

are even and we conclude that

$$\rho_F(v), \hspace{6cm} v \neq a_0, \ v \neq a_n$$

must be even. It remains to consider the vertices $v = a_0$ and $v = a_n$.

Case 1. $a_0 \neq a_n$. If $v = a_0$ then $\rho_G(a_0)$ is finite, hence odd by assumption. There is an odd number of edges in P at a_0 and so $\rho_F(a_0)$ is even. Then also $\rho_F(a_n)$ is even according to Theorem 1.2.1 since F cannot have a single odd vertex.

Case 2. $a_0 = a_n$. Then a_0 cannot be a vertex in a finite component F because $\rho_G(a_0)$ would be finite and therefore odd by assumption. The number of edges of P at a_0 is now even so that a_0 would be the only odd vertex in F, contradicting Theorem 1.2.1.

Next we form the finite connected graph

$$(3.2.1) \hspace{4cm} Q = P + \sum F_i$$

where the sum is extended over all finite components F_i of $\bar{P}$. In Case 1 this is a graph in which all degrees

$$\rho_Q(v), \hspace{6cm} v \neq a_0, \ v \neq a_n$$

are even while for $v = a_0$ and $v = a_n$ the degrees are odd. Thus according to Theorem 3.1.2 there exists a path $Q(a_0, a_n)$ covering all edges in Q. By its construction $\bar{Q}$ has no finite components. When $\rho_G(a_0)$ is infinite it remains infinite in $\bar{Q}$ and this graph can have no odd vertices. When $\rho_G(a_0)$ is finite, hence odd, the vertex a_0 becomes even in $\bar{Q}$ and a_n is the only possible odd vertex in $\bar{Q}$. In Case 2 the graph Q in (3.2.1) is an Euler graph so there is a cyclic path $Q(a_0, a_0)$ covering it. Again $\bar{Q}$ has no finite components while a_0 is odd or infinite in $\bar{Q}$ as in G. All other vertices in $\bar{Q}$ are seen to be even or infinite and so $\bar{Q}$ satisfies the condition γ_1).

We return to the proof that the conditions of Theorem 3.2.1 are sufficient for the existence of a one-way infinite Euler path. The graph G has a countable number of edges according to Theorem 2.4.1 and so we may arrange them in a sequence

$$(3.2.2) \hspace{4cm} E_1, E_2, \cdots, E_n, \cdots .$$

Since G is connected there is a path $P_1(a_0, a_1)$ from a_0 including E_1. The lemma shows that there is some path $Q_1(a_0, a_1)$ including P_1 such that $\bar{Q}_1$ has no finite components. When δ_1) holds this means that $\bar{Q}_1$ is connected. Furthermore $\bar{Q}_1$ satisfied γ_1) with a_1 as the exceptional vertex. Let E_k be the first edge in (3.2.2) not in Q_1. Then in the same way one can construct a path $Q_2(a_1, a_2)$ in $\bar{Q}_1$ which includes E_k and has a connected complement in $\bar{Q}_1$. This construction may be continued indefinitely and

$$Q = Q_1 + Q_2 + \cdots$$

is the desired Euler path.

For two-way infinite Euler paths one has the following criterion:

THEOREM 3.2.2. *A necessary and sufficient condition for a graph to have a two-way infinite Euler path is that in addition to* α), β) *and* γ_2) *it satisfy the two conditions:*

δ_2) *If H is any finite subgraph of G then $\bar{H}$ has at most two infinite connected components.*

δ_3) *If H is a finite subgraph with even degrees then $\bar{H}$ has just one infinite connected component.*

PROOF. We show first that the two conditions are necessary. Suppose that G has a two-way infinite Euler path P. For a given finite subgraph H one can find a finite section

$$P_0 = P(a_0, \ a_n)$$

of P including the edges of H; we write

$$G = P = P_{-\infty} + P_0 + P_\infty.$$

Evidently the graph

(3.2.3) $$\bar{P}_0 = P_{-\infty} + P_\infty$$

has at most two infinite components and the same is therefore true in $\bar{H}$.

Next let H be finite with even degrees. In this case the two terms in the graph (3.2.3) are connected by a path in $\bar{H}$. This is evident when $a_0 = a_n$. When $a_0 \neq a_n$ the graph $P_0 - H$ will have even local degrees at all vertices except at a_0 and a_n where they are odd. From Theorem 2.2.2 we conclude that there is a path in $P_0 - H$ connecting a_0 and a_n. Thus in this case $\bar{H}$ cannot have more than one infinite component.

To show the sufficiency of the conditions δ_2) and δ_3) we order the edges in G as in (3.2.2). Suppose that $P(a_0, a_n)$ is a path including some of these. As in the preceding lemma one shows that the finite graph (3.2.1) has even degrees at all vertices different from a_0 and a_n. When $a_0 \neq a_n$ these vertices have odd local degrees while the degree is even when $a_0 = a_n$. In any case there is a path $Q(a_0, a_n)$ including all edges of P while the graph $\bar{Q}$ has no finite components.

Suppose first that the vertices a_0 and a_n are not connected in $\bar{Q}$. Then by δ_1) $\bar{Q}$ must decompose into two infinite components

$$\bar{Q} = A_1 + A_2.$$

Each of these is seen to satisfy the conditions of Theorem 3.2.1; consequently there exists one-way infinite Euler paths $P_1(a_0)$ and $P_2(a_n)$ within them. When these are joined with $Q(a_0, a_n)$ one obtains a two-way infinite Euler path for G.

Secondly, assume a_0 and a_n are connected in $\bar{Q}$. Then one can combine a path $P_1(a_n, a_0)$ in $\bar{Q}$ with $P(a_0, a_n)$ and obtain a cyclic path $Q_1(a_0, a_0)$ including P and P_1 such that $\bar{Q}_1$ has no finite components. Since Q_1 is a finite Euler graph it follows from δ_3) that $\bar{Q}_1$ is connected.

Let E_k be the first edge in (3.2.2) not included in Q_1. Then from some vertex a_1 in Q_1 there must exist a path $Q_2(a_1, a_1')$ including E_k. As before we can assume that

$$Q_2 = Q_2(a_1, a_1)$$

is cyclic such that its complement in $\bar{Q}_1$ is connected. By continuing this construction one obtains a sequence of Euler graphs

(3.2.4) $Q_1, Q_2, \cdots$

including all edges of G. The graphs (3.2.4) are edge disjoint, but two consecutive ones have at least one vertex in common. One sees that the Euler paths for the graphs (3.2.4) may be combined into a two-way infinite Euler path for G.

As an example one may take the infinite graph consisting of the edges in the unit squares in a plane coordinate system; according to Theorem 3.2.2 it has a two-way infinite Euler path. The construction is indicated in Figure 3.2.2.

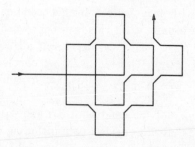

Figure 3.2.2.

For the infinite graph consisting of the edges of the unit cubes in an n-dimensional coordinate system there must exist a two-way infinite Euler path according to Theorem 3.2.2. An explicit construction has been given by *Vázsonyi*. Our previous Theorem 3.1.4 has the following extension to infinite graphs:

THEOREM 3.2.3. *A necessary and sufficient condition that a graph G have an infinite path passing through each edge once in each direction is that G satisfy the conditions α), β) and δ_1).*

The proof is simple and shall be left to the reader.

PROBLEMS

1. Construct a graph satisfying all conditions of Theorem 3.2.2 except δ_3).
2. Determine an Euler path for the infinite network in Figure 3.2.3.

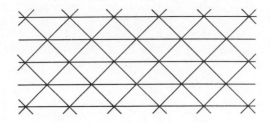

Figure 3.2.3.

3.* Let G be an infinite graph with even or countable degrees. Find the condition that G be the edge direct sum of exactly k and no less two-way infinite paths.

4.* Find the condition that an infinite graph be the edge direct sum of k and no less finite or infinite paths.

3.3. **An excursion into labyrinths.** Ever since Theseus felt his way through the passageways of the labyrinth at Knossos, after having killed the Minotaur, the problem of finding a course through a labyrinth has been a popular puzzle. Many medieval churches have mazes as decorations in the mosaics of their floors. Perhaps a method for finding the opening it came from may be useful for a party lost in a cave. But otherwise the labyrinth problems are now mainly for the amusement of children and for the psychologists when they let loose their rats in intricate mazes.

Briefly described, a labyrinth consists of passages connecting meeting places with other passages. Accordingly it can be described by a graph, with edges corresponding to passages and vertices corresponding to the junctions of these passages. Figure 3.3.1a is the plan of the famous labyrinth from the garden at Hampton Court while Figure 3.3.1b represents the corresponding graph.

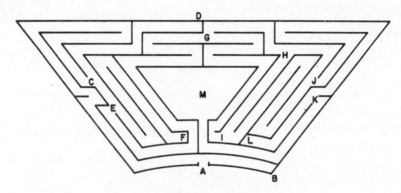

Figure 3.3.1a.

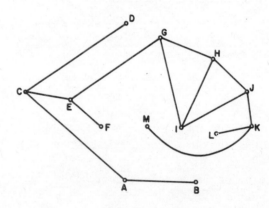

Figure 3.3.1b.

In terms of graphs the *labyrinth problem* may be stated simply as follows: From a given vertex a_0 determine a method to find a sequence of edges in the graph such that one is certain to arrive at some prescribed other vertex a_1, the *exit*. It is evident that to prevent endless wanderings in cyclic sequences it must be possible to remember which vertices or edges one has previously passed; thus one must assume that the errant knight has the means to mark edges or vertices in some fashion.

Most collections of mathematical puzzles contain an account of the labyrinth problem. (See for instance *Rouse Ball, Lucas* and also *König* (Chapter 1), for methods, examples and references.) In all these presentations the labyrinth problem is put in the form that a finite graph G is given and some sequence of edges from a_0 including *all* edges of G shall be found. Eventually the exit a_1 must then also be passed.

The first systematic procedure for finding a way out of a maze seems to have been suggested by *Wiener* (1873). His rule is as follows: From the given vertex a_0 one proceeds along the edges of the graph as far as possible, selecting at each vertex an edge which has not previously been traversed. At a vertex where one can move no further the sequence is retraced until one arrives at some vertex where there is still some unused edge. The last operation will consist in retracing the entire way, returning to a_0. It is clear that such a sequence will cover all edges. However, it will involve many repetitious walks and to retrace the steps requires that one is in the possession of some sort of "Ariadne's thread".

More economical is the method by Tarry which we described in Section 3.1. Here each edge was passed twice, once in each direction. The same result is achieved in a different manner by a method proposed by *Tremaux*, reported by Lucas and discussed in some detail by him and König.

All these methods are concerned with the labyrinth problem in the form that all edges in the graph shall be covered. However, for the actual determination of an exit this does not seem to be the most appropriate point of view. If a wanderer is lost at some point a_0 he must have arrived there by a walk of bounded length and the exit must be within this range. But in this case it is unnecessary to meander through the whole labyrinth to its most distant recesses. What is wanted is rather a method of search insuring that all vertices within a certain distance have been visited; this would apply even if the graph should be infinite.

To touch upon all vertices at the distances 1 is easily done. One passes through the various edges at a_0 to their endpoints, each time returning to a_0. In order to continue systematically it is necessary to mark these edges in some way: Each edge $E = (a_0, a_1)$ is marked once as one leaves a_0 and at a_1 it is marked as the entering edge. If there should happen to be no edges at a_1 except E we mark E as closed when returning to a_0. If some other edge $E' = (a_0, a_1)$ should also lead to a_1 from a_0 we mark it closed at both ends; the same is done by any loop at a_0.

To reach the vertices at a distance 2 from a_0 one selects some open edge $E = (a_0, a_1)$ and marks it again: At a_1 the open edges are traversed and marked, eventually as closed if they lead to vertices already visited. When this is completed one returns to a_0 from a_1 by the entering edge. If there should remain no edges open at a_1 the entering edge to it is closed at a_0. After the return to a_0 the same process is repeated on the other open edges and the operation is continued until all edges at a_0 are marked twice.

After all vertices at a distance n have been visited the situation stands as follows: All open edges at a_0 are marked n times; the open edges at any vertex a_1 are marked $n-1$ times and so on. To visit next the vertices at a distance $n+1$ one moves successively to each vertex a_1 at unit distance and visits all vertices at a distance n from a_1, using only the open edges while marking and closing these according to the rules described.

This procedure of *progressive covering* of the graph is a little complicated to state, but in actual examples this radial method tends to simplify itself a good deal through the rapid closing of many edges. (See Ore.)

Related to the labyrinth problems are the map problems. Here we suppose that the G represents a road map with roads (a, b) connecting the various junctions or vertices a and b. In order to find a path

$$(3.3.1) \qquad\qquad P(a_0, b_0) = (a_0, a_1) \cdots (a_{n-1}, a_n), \qquad\qquad a_n = b_0$$

between two localities a_0 and b_0 one can proceed by the previous progressive covering method used in the labyrinth problem. As one knows a path is usually found without too much guess-work due in part to the special construction of the highway system, in part to the fact that the graph is planar.

However, the essential map problem is usually another, namely the determination of a shortest path in time or distance between two places. Here there is associated a *measure* $\mu(a, b) > 0$ with each edge $E = (a, b)$, $a \neq b$ of the graph and one wishes to find a path (3.3.1) for which the *measured distance*

$$\mu(P) = \sum_i \mu(a_i, a_{i+1}), \qquad\qquad i = 0, 1, \cdots, n-1$$

is a minimum.

There exists an ingenious *index reduction procedure* for this minimal distance problem. (See Ford or Beckman-McGuire-Winsten.) The initial vertex a_0 is marked by the number $M(a_0) = 0$; each of the other vertices b are marked by a number $M(b)$ (or ∞) exceeding all measures $\mu(u, v)$ of the various edges (u, v). A repeated reduction is performed as follows. When a pair of vertices u and v with the numbers $M^{(i)}(u)$ and $M^{(j)}(v)$ exist such that

$$\mu(u, v) < M^{(j)}(v) - M^{(i)}(u)$$

then the number $M^{(j)}(v)$ is replaced by

$$M^{(j+1)}(v) = M^{(i)}(u) + \mu(u, v).$$

At the same time one indicates at v that the last reduction was performed from the vertex u. Since the graph is finite this reduction process eventually comes to a halt. At the vertex a_n there will then be a neighboring vertex a_{n-1} used in the last reduction; similarly at a_{n-1} there is a last reduction vertex a_{n-2} and so on. Correspondingly one has a decreasing sequence of index numbers

$$M(a_n) = M(a_{n-1}) + \mu(a_n, a_{n-1}),$$
$$M(a_{n-1}) = M(a_{n-2}) + \mu(a_{n-1}, a_{n-2}).$$
$$\cdots\cdots\cdots\cdots\cdots\cdots\cdots\cdots\cdots\cdots\cdots\cdots$$

Evidently the correponding path P can only terminate at a_0. By summing one finds

$$M(a_n) = \sum \mu(a_i, a_{i+1}), \qquad\qquad i = 0, 1, \cdots, n-1.$$

To prove that P is a shortest measured path suppose that

$$Q = (a_n, b_1, b_2, \cdots, a_0)$$

is another path passing through the vertices b_i. Since there are no possible reductions we have

$$M(a_n) \leq M(b_1) + \mu(a_n, b_1),$$
$$M(b_1) \leq M(b_2) + \mu(b_1, b_2),$$
$$\cdots\cdots\cdots\cdots\cdots\cdots\cdots\cdots\cdots\cdots\cdots$$

and by summing these inequalities one finds

$$M(a_n) \leq \sum \mu(b_i, b_{i+1})$$

so that Q cannot be shorter than P.

This index reduction, while elegant, is not very practical, suffering from the same weaknesses as those we pointed out in connection with the methods used in the labyrinth problem. In particular, it requires a reduction of the entire graph. The following procedure is more efficient and applies to any locally finite graph.

Beginning at a_0 in G one proceeds to all vertices which can be reached by a single edge and at each vertex one writes the distance from a_0. Next, as in the previous progressive covering method one moves to all vertices which can be connected by 2-edge paths to a_0 and again the measured distances to a_0 are noted. If there are several paths to such a vertex one is interested only in the shortest ones and it is indicated from which vertices they enter. One continues this progressive covering of G from a_0 until some path P_1 of length M_1 reaches b_0. One then discards from consideration all vertices whose distances exceed M_1 and continue the construction on the remaining ones. If b_0 is reached in some other path P_2 of length $M_2 < M_1$ all vertices of greater distance than M_2 are discarded and so on. Since all distances increase, the construction will halt after a certain number of steps.

1. Apply the method on the graphs of the regular polyhedra and compare it to Tarry's method. How many steps are needed in each case to reach all vertices?

2. Apply the method to find the way in the Hampton Court maze.

3.* In the preceding shortest path determination for maps by index reduction only one shortest path is obtained. Can all others be found by a suitable order of the reductions?

4.* A graph has directed and undirected edges, for instance, a city with one-way and two-way streets. Describe procedures to determine paths from one location to another, also methods for finding the shortest such path.

3.4. Hamilton circuits. Euler paths were characterized by the property of being cyclic paths which include every edge just once. *Hamilton circuits* are defined for finite connected graphs in an analogous manner with respect to the vertices: a circuit is called *Hamiltonian* if it passes through every vertex in the graph. In Figure 3.4.1 Hamilton circuits have been drawn for a few simple graphs.

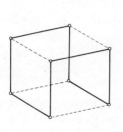 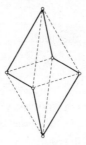 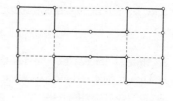

Figure 3.4.1.

A popular way of presenting the problem of Hamilton circuits is the following: A dinner is being served at a circular table. Among the guests some are known to be friends. When is it possible to seat the party in such a manner that each guest has two of his friends next to him?

In the applications of graph to games the vertices correspond to the various positions. Thus the existence of a Hamilton circuit is equivalent to the fact that a cyclic sequence of moves exists which includes each position just once. An instance is the famous *Knight Problem* on the chessboard: Is it possible, beginning at any position on the board, to move a knight in such a sequence of moves that it occupies each of the sixty-four positions once and returns to its initial position? The diagram in Figure 3.4.2 indicates one of several solutions.

```
56  41  58  35  50  39  60  33
47  44  55  40  59  34  51  38
42  57  46  49  36  53  32  61
45  48  43  54  31  62  37  52
20   5  30  63  22  11  16  13
29  64  21   4  17  14  25  10
 6  19   2  27   8  23  12  15
 1  28   7  18   3  26   9  24
```

Figure 3.4.2.

A *Hamilton arc* in a graph is an arc passing through all vertices once. Thus in a graph depicting the moves in a game a Hamilton arc corresponds to a sequence of moves from a given position always leading to new positions and covering all of them. An infinite graph with a Hamilton arc has a countable number of vertices.

Just as in the case of Euler paths the questions concerning Hamilton circuits can be extended in various ways. If no Hamilton circuits exist one may try to determine a disjoint sum of circuits passing through all vertices. In directed graphs one may ask for directed cyclic paths passing through each of the vertices once.

The so-called *Traveling Salesman Problem* is a problem related to the Hamilton paths. A salesman is assigned a certain territory consisting of a number of cities to be visited. Their mutual distances are known and it is desired to determine the shortest possible route covering all localities and returning to the starting point. The problem has a number of applications in operational research, for instance, to the most efficient use of rolling stock or equipment.

One can represent the cities as vertices in a graph G in which a distance $\mu(a, b)$ is assigned to each pair of vertices. If two of them should not be connected one may put $\mu(a, b) = \infty$. The question is then to find a Hamiltonian circuit P such that

$$\mu(P) = \sum \mu(a_i, a_{i+1}), \qquad\qquad i = 0, 1, \cdots, n-1$$

is a minimum. Since usually there is only a finite number of vertices the problem can be solved by trial and error, but no effective algorithm is known in general. A few special devices have been introduced in particular instances. A large scale example has been carried through by Dantzig, Fulkerson and Johnson in determining a shortest air path connecting the various capitals of the states in the U.S.A.

In spite of the similarity of the definitions of Euler paths and Hamilton circuits the theories for the two concepts have little in common. We saw that for Euler paths it was simple to establish a criterion for their existence; for Hamilton circuits no such general rule is known. Indeed, even in a specific graph it may be most difficult to decide whether such a circuit can be found. We observe that for the study of the existence of Hamilton circuits in a connected graph there is no restriction in assuming that the graph has no loops or multiple edges.

We shall derive certain conditions under which it can be ascertained that a Hamilton circuit exists. These investigations are closely connected with the properties of maximal arcs. Denote by

(3.4.1) $$A:(a_0, a_1)(a_1, a_2) \cdots (a_{l-1}, a_l)$$

some arc of length l in the graph G. We say that A is of *circuit type* when the section graph

(3.4.2) $$G_0 = G(a_0, a_1, \cdots, a_l)$$

has a Hamilton circuit. This implies in particular that A is a Hamilton arc in G_0. We denote by $\rho_0^{(0)}$ and $\rho_l^{(0)}$ respectively the local degrees of the vertices a_0 and a_l in the graph (3.4.2). Let (a_0, a_i) be some edge in G_0. If there should exist also some edge (a_l, a_{i-1}) then G_0 has a Hamilton circuit, namely (see Figure 3.4.3)

$$(a_0, a_i) + A(a_i, a_l) + (a_l, a_{i-1}) + A(a_{i-1}, a_0).$$

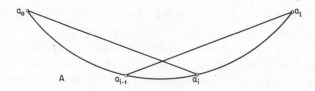

Figure 3.4.3.

However, if one should have

$$\rho_l^{(0)} > l - \rho_0^{(0)}$$

then it is clear that for at least one edge (a_0, a_i) there must exist a corresponding edge (a_l, a_{i-1}). We conclude that when

$$\rho_0^{(0)} + \rho_l^{(0)} \geq l + 1$$

the arc A is of circuit type.

We say that an arc (3.4.1) is *completed* when it cannot be prolonged by adding edges at either end. Then all edges from a_0 and a_l must go to vertices in the graph (3.4.2) so that

$$\rho(a_0) = \rho_0^{(0)}, \quad \rho(a_l) = \rho_l^{(0)}.$$

This gives:

THEOREM 3.4.1.   *A completed arc of length l is of circuit type when*

$$\rho(a_0) + \rho(a_l) \geq l + 1.$$

Next we observe

THEOREM 3.4.2.   *A maximal arc in a connected graph can only be of circuit type when the graph has a Hamilton circuit.*

PROOF. If the graph (3.4.2) has a Hamilton circuit but G_0 is not the whole graph there would due to the connectedness of G exist some edge (a_i, b) where b is not in G_0. But in our case this is impossible since it would lead to an arc larger than A.

From Theorems 3.4.1 and 3.4.2 follows:

THEOREM 3.4.3.   *A connected graph either has a Hamilton circuit or its maximal arcs have a length satisfying*

(3.4.3) $$l \geq \rho(a_0) + \rho(a_l).$$

The condition (3.4.3) implies that

$$l \geq \min(\rho(a_0) + \rho(a_l))$$

for all pairs of vertices a_0 and a_l and one can even restrict the condition to those pairs for which there is no edge (a_0, a_l). Let us state:

THEOREM 3.4.4.   *In a graph without Hamilton circuits the length of the longest arcs satisfy*

$$l \geq \rho_1 + \rho_2$$

where ρ_1 and ρ_2 are the two smallest local degrees.

As special cases of the preceding results one obtains:

THEOREM 3.4.5.   *If in a graph G with n vertices one has*

$$\rho(a_0) + \rho(a_l) \geq n - 1$$

for any pair of vertices then G has a Hamilton arc. When

$$\rho(a_0) + \rho(a_l) \geq n$$

then G has a Hamilton circuit.

This in particular implies a result due to Dirac that a graph has a Hamilton circuit when

$$\rho(a) \geqq \tfrac{1}{2}n$$

for every vertex.

For later use we shall derive a couple of auxilliary results due to Erdös and Gallai:

THEOREM 3.4.6. *Let G have a Hamilton circuit whose vertices in cyclic order are*

(3.4.4) $a_0, a_1, \cdots, a_{n-1}.$

When two vertices, say a_0 and a_j are not connected by a Hamilton arc then

(3.4.5) $\rho(a_1) + \rho(a_{j+1}) \leqq n.$

PROOF. The two vertices a_0 and a_j cannot be adjoining in (3.4.4); thus the vertices a_0, a_1, a_j, a_{j+1} are distinct. If G contains an edge

$$(a_1, a_g), \qquad\qquad\qquad 2 \leqq g \leqq j-1$$

there can be no edge (a_{j+1}, a_{g-1}) because it would lead to a Hamilton arc

$$a_0, a_{n-1}, \cdots, a_{j+1}, a_{g-1}, \cdots, a_1, a_g, \cdots, a_j.$$

Similarly if there is an edge

$$(a_1, a_g), \qquad\qquad\qquad j+2 \leqq g \leqq n-1$$

there can be no edge (a_{j+1}, a_{g+1}); in particular, there is no edge (a_1, a_{j+1}). As in the proof of Theorem 3.4.1 the inequality (3.4.5) follows.

We shall call a vertex a *Hamilton center* if there is a *Hamilton arc* from it to every other vertex.

THEOREM 3.4.7. *Let G be a graph with the Hamilton circuit* (3.4.4). *If one has*

(3.4.6) $\rho(a_1) + \rho(a_i) > n$

for all vertices a_i connected with a_0 by a Hamilton arc then a_0 is a Hamilton center.

PROOF. Clearly there are Hamilton arcs from a_0 to a_1 and a_{n-1} and the proof follows by induction. If there is a Hamilton arc from a_0 to a_i then (3.4.6) holds by assumption and so according to Theorem 3.4.6 there is a Hamilton arc from a_0 to a_{i-1}.

PROBLEMS

1.   Which Platonic graphs have Hamilton arcs and circuits?

2.   Why is it not necessary to assume in Theorem 3.4.4 that the graph is connected?

3.   Divide a square into n^2 squares by parallels to the edges. (Figure 3.4.4 illustrates the case $n = 3$.)

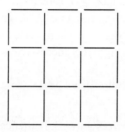

Figure 3.4.4.

Do these graphs have Hamiltonian arcs and circuits?

4.   Find an infinite Hamilton arc for $n = \infty$ in Figure 3.4.4. The same problem for an arbitrary number of dimensions has been solved by Vázsonyi.

5.   Are there solutions to the Knight Problem on a chessboard with n^2 squares? Try $n = 3, 4, 5, 6, 7$.

6.   The graph in Figure 3.4.5 is planar and regular of degree 3. It has been shown by Tutte that it has no Hamilton circuit. Does it have Hamilton arcs?

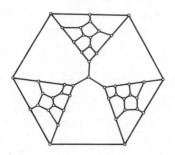

Figure 3.4.5.

CHAPTER 4

TREES

4.1. Properties of trees. A connected undirected graph is called a *tree* when it has no circuits. In particular, a tree has no loops and no multiple edges. A *circuit free graph* is a graph whose connected components are trees; occasionally such a graph has been called a *forest*. Any path in a circuit free graph is an arc; any subgraph is also circuit free.

THEOREM 4.1.1. *In a tree any two vertices are connected by a unique path.*

PROOF. If there were two connecting paths there would also be a circuit; the condition is also sufficient for a tree.

For a graph T which is a tree one obtains a perspicuous form by the following construction. An arbitrary vertex a_0 is selected. From a_0 all edges are drawn to the vertices at the distance 1. From these vertices one draws the edges to the vertices of distance 2 and so on. From a vertex a_n at distance n from a_0 there will be a single edge to a unique preceding vertex a_{n-1} of distance $n-1$ and also a certain family of edges from a_n to vertices a_{n+1} of distance $n+1$. To none of these vertices a_n can there be any edges joining it to vertices of the same or lesser distance except (a_{n-1}, a_n). Thus a tree may be represented in the form indicated in Figure 4.1.1.

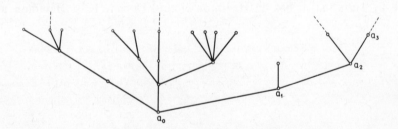

Figure 4.1.1.

In an arbitrary graph G a vertex a is *terminal* when $\rho(a) = 1$, that is, there is a single edge $E = (a, b)$ with the endpoint a; the edge E is called a *terminal edge*. The preceding construction shows:

THEOREM 4.1.2. *Any nontrivial finite tree has at least two terminal vertices and at least one terminal edge.*

58

When a special vertex a_0 has been designated as in Figure 4.1.1 one calls a_0 the *root* of the tree T, while a tree in which a root has been selected is a *rooted tree*.

For certain purposes it is convenient to single out some particular path

$$(4.1.1) \qquad P = \cdots, (a_{-2}, a_{-1}), (a_{-1}, a_0), (a_0, a_1), (a_1, a_2), \cdots$$

in a tree T and call P the *stem* of T. This stem may be finite or one-way or two-way infinite. Each vertex v in T is connected by a unique path to a nearest vertex a_i in P. We say that v *belongs to the branch of T from a_i* (Figure 4.1.2).

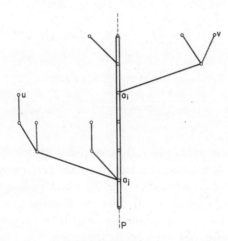

Figure 4.1.2.

The following result on trees is due to *Cayley* who examined these graphs in connection with chemical structure diagrams:

THEOREM 4.1.3. *The number of different trees which can be constructed on n given vertices is*

$$(4.1.2) \qquad t_n = n^{n-2}.$$

The number of m-rooted trees on n vertices should be $\approx \binom{n}{2}$

PROOF. To derive this formula we shall make use of a method due to *Prüfer*. The elements of the given vertex set V we denote in some fixed order by the numbers

$$(4.1.3) \qquad 1, 2, \cdots, n.$$

For any tree T defined on V we shall introduce a symbol which characterizes it uniquely. According to Theorem 4.1.2 there will be some vertices in T which are terminal. We denote by b_1 the first such vertex in the ordered set (4.1.3) and by $E_1 = (a_1, b_1)$ the corresponding terminal edge. We remove E_1 and the vertex b_1 from T to obtain a new tree T_1. For T_1 there is some first vertex b_2 in (4.1.3) which is terminal with the edge $E_2 = (a_2, b_2)$. We repeat the reduction until after the removal of the edge

$$E_{n-2} = (a_{n-2}, b_{n-2})$$

there is a single edge

$$E_{n-1} = (a_{n-1}, b_{n-1})$$

connecting the two remaining vertices. The bracket

(4.1.4) $$\sigma(T) = [a_1, a_2, \cdots, a_{n-2}]$$

is then uniquely defined by T and two different trees T and T' are seen to correspond to different symbols. Each vertex a_i appears

$$\rho(a_i) - 1$$

times in (4.1.4).

But conversely, each symbol (4.1.4) gives rise to a tree T by the reverse construction. When (4.1.4) is given one determines the first vertex b_1 in (4.1.3) which does not appear in it. This defines the edge $E_1 = (a_1, b_1)$ and we remove the vertex a_1 from (4.1.4) and b_1 from (4.1.3). The construction may then be continued on the remaining numbers. The graph resulting from this construction is a tree. This may be established, for instance, by induction. After the removal of E_1 the symbol (4.1.4) is reduced to $n-3$ terms. If it corresponds to a tree T_1 also the graph T obtained by adding E_1 is a tree since the vertex b_1 does not belong to T_1.

In the symbol (4.1.4) one can let the vertices a_i run through all n possible values. Each corresponds to a different tree and so formula (4.1.2) follows.

We mention briefly another formulation which is of some interest. Let G be a graph with n vertices (4.1.3) having no loops and single edges. Each edge can then be represented in the form

(4.1.5) $$E_{ij} = (i, j), \qquad i \neq j.$$

The set of all permutations of the n numbers form the *symmetric group* Σ_n. In this group each pair (i, j) can be considered to be a *transposition* of two elements. A *transposition basis* for Σ_n is a minimal set of transpositions generating Σ_n. One verifies that a family (4.1.5) of transpositions is a transposition basis if and only if it consists of $n-1$ transpositions and the corresponding graph is a tree. Cayley's formula shows immediately that the number of transposition bases in

Σ_n is n^{n-2} (Dziobek; for another proof of Cayley's formula, see Bol; for the use of trees in evaluating determinants see Bott and Mayberry and also the paper by Whitin).

In Cayley's formula all trees with n given vertices are counted. Many of these are isomorphic graphs and the question arises as to the number of non-isomorphic trees among them. This is a more difficult problem but it is of considerable importance in many applications. There exists an extensive literature on this question and on related topics concerning the enumeration of all non-isomorphic graphs of special types. Much of this work is based upon a general principle formulated by Pólya. A complete analysis of these enumeration problems would take too much of the space available in this book; the reader may be referred to the excellent presentation in the book by Riordan.

A popular form of Cayley's problem is the following: One wishes to connect n cities by railroad lines in such a manner that no superfluous connectors are built. In how many ways can the system be constructed? This type of question may be extended and leads to problems of a very practical nature. Suppose that the cost of construction of railroad lines is known and equal to $\mu(a, b)$ for a pair of cities a and b. How can one build a road-net connecting all cities at the smallest possible cost? The same question comes up in the construction of electrical networks. In terms of graphs we can state: In the finite graph G there are measures $\mu(a, b)$ associated with each edge $E = (a, b)$. Construct a connected subgraph T covering the vertices of G in such a manner that its total measure

$$(4.1.6) \qquad\qquad \mu(T) = \sum \mu(E), \qquad\qquad E < T$$

is a minimum. Clearly T is a tree.

This *Minimal Connector Problem* is superficially reminiscent of the Travelling Salesman Problem. However, as we shall see, it is a much simpler problem for which there are effective solution algorisms. The first method for solving the problems seems to be due to Boruvka; a related procedure was given by Kruskal. (See also papers by Choquet and Jarnik-Kossler.)

We begin our construction by selecting a shortest edge $A_1 = E_1$ in G. In each subsequent step one constructs the subgraph A_i from A_{i-1} by adding an edge E_i selected as the shortest edge such that A_i has no circuits. If there should be several edges E_i of the same length available any one of them may be used. Clearly the last graph A_{n-1} must cover the vertices of G and be a tree. We shall prove that A_{n-1} has a minimal total measure (4.1.6).

Suppose that T is a covering tree with

$$\mu(T) < \mu(A_{n-1}).$$

Then there will be a first edge E_i in A_{n-1} which is not in T and the graph $T + E_i$ will have a single circuit C. Since A_{n-1} has no circuits there is an edge E' in C not in A_{n-1}. The graph

$$T_1 = T + E_i - E'$$

is also a covering tree for G and since T has minimal measure one concludes

$$\mu(E_i) \geqq \mu(E').$$

Here the inequality cannot hold because in the construction of A_i one should have selected E' instead of E_i. Thus one must have

$$\mu(E_i) = \mu(E'), \quad \mu(T_1) = \mu(T)$$

so that T_1 is also a tree with minimal measure (4.1.6). But T_1 has more edges in common with A_{n-1} than T and by continuing such reductions it follows that

$$\mu(A_{n-1}) = \mu(T).$$

PROBLEMS

1. Show that the intersection $T_1 \cap T_2$ of two subtrees T_1 and T_2 of a tree T is a tree.

2.* For n given vertices determine the total number of circuit free graphs with m edges.

3.* Determine the condtions for a set of positive integers ρ_i, $i = 1, 2, \cdots, n$ to be the local degrees of a tree with n vertices.

4. In the preceding solution of the Minimal Connector Problem show that one obtains all minimal connectors by a suitable choice of the edges E_i.

5. How must the preceding procedure be modified if one requires that all successive graphs A_i shall be trees?

4.2. **Centers in trees.** We assume that T is a tree in which the distances $d(a, b)$ between any two vertices are bounded. As in Section 2.4, a path $P(a_0, a_\delta)$ is called *diametral* when its length δ is maximal; δ is the *diameter* of T.

We select such a diametral path P as a stem in T. Let v be a vertex belonging to the branch of T from the vertex a_i in P. Then one must have

(4.2.1) $d(v, a_i) \leqq i, \quad d(v, a_i) \leqq \delta - i$

because otherwise one of the paths

$$Q(v, a_i, a_0), \quad Q(v, a_i, a_\delta)$$

would have a greater length than δ.

Suppose on the other hand that the condition (4.2.1) is satisfied for all vertices v. We examine the distance $d(u, v)$ between two vertices u and v in T belonging respectively to the branches from the vertices a_i and a_j (see Figure 4.1.2).

First take $i = j$ so that

$$d(u,v) \leq d(u, a_i) + d(a_i, v) \leq i + \delta - i = \delta.$$

The equality sign will hold only when

$$d(u, a_i) = i = \delta - i = \tfrac{1}{2}\delta,$$

$$d(v, a_i) = \tfrac{1}{2}\delta$$

and the two paths $Q(u, a_i)$ and $Q(v, a_i)$ have no edges in common. The combined path

$$Q(u,v) = Q(u, a_{\delta/2}) + Q(a_{\delta/2}, v)$$

becomes a diametral path and $a_{\delta/2}$ is the only vertex in Q belonging to the stem P. Evidently this case is only possible when the diameter δ is even.

Secondly assume $i \neq j$ and take the notations as in Figure 4.1.2 with $i > j$. Then

$$d(u, v) = d(u, a_j) + i - j + d(a_i, v)$$

and according to (4.2.1)

$$d(u, v) \leq j + i - j + \delta - i = \delta.$$

The equality sign holds only when

(4.2.2) $\qquad\qquad\qquad d(u, a_j) = j, \quad d(v, a_i) = \delta - i$

and then the path

$$Q(u, v) = Q(u, a_j) + P(a_j, a_i) + Q(a_i, v)$$

is a diameter. When (4.2.1) and (4.2.2) are combined it follows that

$$i \geq \tfrac{1}{2}\delta, \quad j \leq \tfrac{1}{2}\delta.$$

This establishes the following facts:

THEOREM 4.2.1. *A necessary and sufficient condition for a path $P(a_0, a_\delta)$ in a tree T to be a diametral path is that the conditions* (4.2.1) *be fulfilled for every vertex v. Every other diametral path either has a section*

$$P(a_i, a_j), \qquad\qquad\qquad i \geq \tfrac{1}{2}\delta \geq j$$

in common with P or possibly a single vertex $a_{\delta/2}$ when the diameter δ is even.

In Section 2.4 we defined the concepts of *radius* and *centers* for an arbitrary graph. In the case of trees their properties are simple. We use the previous notations. When δ is even the maximal distance from

(4.2.3)
$$c_0 = a_{\delta/2}$$

to any other vertex is $\frac{1}{2}\delta$. Furthermore, if

$$d(u, c_0) = \frac{1}{2}\delta$$

then u is the end of a diameter path through c_0. If δ is odd the maximal distance from the two vertices

(4.2.4)
$$c_1 = a_{(\delta-1)/2}, \quad c_2 = a_{(\delta+1)/2}$$

is at most $\frac{1}{2}(\delta + 1)$ and as before if

$$d(u, c_i) = \frac{1}{2}(\delta + 1), \qquad\qquad i = 1 \text{ or } 2$$

then u is the end of a diametral path through c_i. For any other vertices on P or for vertices not on P one sees that the maximal distances exceed these values.

THEOREM 4.2.2. *Let T be a tree of diameter δ and $P(a_0, a_\delta)$ a diametral path. When δ is even T has a single center c_0 defined in (4.2.3) and radius $\rho = \frac{1}{2}\delta$; all diametral paths go through c_0 and are the sum of two radial paths. When δ is odd T has two centers (4.2.4) and the radius $\rho = \frac{1}{2}(\delta + 1)$. All diametral paths pass through the centers and the central edge $E_0 = (c_1, c_2)$; they are the sum of two radial paths, one to each center.*

Another concept, a *mass center* of a tree, is of importance in certain questions. At a vertex v in T we denote by

$$E_i = (v, u_i)$$

the various edges with the endpoint v. All edges which belong to paths from v with the first edge E_i form a subgraph

$$B_i = B(v, E_i)$$

which we call the *branch* defined by E_i and v; we include E_i in B_i. The number of edges in B_i is $v_e(B_i)$ so that

(4.2.5)
$$v_e(T) = \sum_i v_e(B_i), \qquad\qquad i = 1, 2, \cdots, \rho(v).$$

The number

$$w(v) = \max v_e(B_i), \qquad\qquad i = 1, 2, \cdots, \rho(v)$$

is called the *weight* at v and any branch B_i with

$$v_e(B_i) = w(v)$$

is a *weight branch*. A *mass center* m_0 is a vertex of minimal weight while

$$w(m_0) = w(T)$$

is the *weight* of T.

We shall compare the weight $w(v)$ with the weight $w(u_1)$ of a neighboring vertex u_1 connected to v by the edge $E_1 = (v, u_1)$. The branches at u_1 shall be denoted by B_j' with B_1' including E_1. From Figure 4.2.1 one sees immediately the relation

(4.2.6) $$v_e(B_1) + v_e(B_1') = v_e(T) + 1.$$

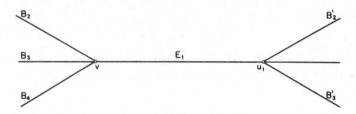

Figure 4.2.1.

Suppose that some B_j', $j \neq 1$ is a weight branch at u_1. From Figure 4.2.1 one verifies that

$$v_e(B_1) = \sum_{j \neq 1} v_e(B_j') + 1$$

and so in this case

$$v_e(B_1) \geq 1 + w(u_1)$$

or $w(v) > w(u_1)$. This inequality shows that if v is a mass center then for each neighboring vertex u_1 the only weight branch is B_1'.

Assume next that B_1 is a weight branch at the mass center v so that

$$v_e(B_1) = w(v) = w(T).$$

Then as we just observed

$$w(u_1) = v_e(B_1') \geqq w(v)$$

and by substitution in (4.2.6) one obtains

(4.2.7) $$w(v) + w(u_1) = v_e(T) + 1.$$

  Case 1. u_1 is not a mass center. Then

$$w(u_1) \geqq w(v) + 1,$$

and one concludes from (4.2.7) that

$$w(T) = w(v) \leqq \tfrac{1}{2} v_e(T).$$

In this case there can only be one mass center in T. For according to Figure 4.2.1
no vertex

$$v' \in \sum B_i, \qquad\qquad\qquad i \neq 1, \ v \neq v'$$

can be a mass center because it will have a branch including B_1 as a proper subgraph. Nor can any vertex

$$v'' \in \ \sum B_j', \qquad\qquad\qquad j \neq 1$$

be a mass center since it has a branch including B_1'.
  Case 2. u_1 is a mass center:

$$w(v) = w(u_1) = w(T).$$

Then from (4.2.7) one concludes:

  THEOREM 4.2.2. *A finite tree T has a single mass center when*

$$w(T) \leqq \tfrac{1}{2} v_e(T)$$

and two neighboring mass centers when

$$w(T) = \tfrac{1}{2}(v_e(T) + 1).$$

  This latter case can only occur when T has an odd number of edges, hence
an even number of vertices.

PROBLEMS

  1.* Study some of the other concepts introduced in Section 2.4 in the case
of trees.

4.3. **The circuit rank.** We notice that when a root a_0 has been selected in a tree T as in Figure 4.1.1 then a one-to-one correspondence is established between an edge $E = (a, b)$ and the endpoint b which has the greatest distance from a_0. Consequently, for any finite tree one has the relation

$$(4.3.1) \qquad\qquad v_v - v_e = 1$$

between the number v_v of vertices and v_e of edges.

Now take G to be an arbitrary finite connected graph. One can construct G from its edges by first selecting an arbitrary one among them and then successively adding one at time such that the new edge has at least one endpoint in common with the edges already selected. For the first edge one has

$$v_e = 1, 1 \leqq v_v \leqq 2. \quad \textit{if } \varrho \textit{ not a loop.}$$

In each successive step is added one edge and at most one vertex and so it follows that for a finite connected graph one has

$$(4.3.2) \qquad\qquad \gamma(G) = v_e - v_v + 1 \geqq 0.$$

The number $\gamma(G)$ defined in this way, we shall call the *circuit rank* of G. The preceding analysis shows that the circuit rank vanishes only when it is possible to perform the construction of G in such a way that no edge is ever added such that both ends are already in the constructed part. This implies that G has no circuits. On the other hand for a tree (4.3.1) holds so that $\gamma(G) = 0$. If G should happen to have a single circuit it becomes a tree by removing one edge, hence $\gamma(G) = 1$. Conversely, when $\gamma(G) = 1$ there is a single edge in the construction of G producing a circuit. We conclude:

THEOREM 4.3.1.   *For any finite connected graph G the circuit rank satisfies*

$$(4.3.3) \qquad\qquad \gamma(G) \geqq 0.$$

One has $\gamma(G) = 0$ if and only if G is a tree, and $\gamma(G) = 1$ if and only if G contains a single circuit.

According to (4.1.2) the graphs with $\gamma(G) = 1$ can also be characterized by the property that the number of edges and vertices are the same.

One can extend the notion of circuit rank to arbitrary finite graphs by putting

$$(4.3.4) \qquad\qquad \gamma(G) = \sum_i \gamma(G_i)$$

where the sum is extended over all connected components G_i of G. One sees that G is circuit free if and only if $\gamma(G) = 0$. From the formula (4.3.2) follows that in general one can write

(4.3.5) $\gamma(G) = v_e - v_v + \tau_G$

where τ_G is the number of connected components.

4.4. Many-to-one correspondences. In Section 2.3 we studied the one-to-one correspondences of a set V to itself from the graph theory point of view. We shall now do the same for a *many-to-one correspondence* τ of V into itself and show how the graph of τ may be described in terms of trees.

The correspondence τ defines a binary relation in V

$$a \rightarrow \tau(a), \qquad\qquad a \in V.$$

Its graph is directed with a single edge

$$E = (a, \tau(a))$$

issuing from each vertex. Thus a correspondence τ of V into itself is defined by a directed graph G with the local degrees

$$\rho(a) = 1, \; \rho^*(a), \; a \in V.$$

The number $\rho^*(a)$ of incoming edges, i.e., the number of elements in V corresponding to a under τ may be 0 or an arbitrary cardinal number.

We extend the terminology of Section 2.3. We shall call the connected components G_k of G the *generalized cycles* of τ.

THEOREM 4.4.1. *A necessary and sufficient condition that two vertices a and b belong to the same generalized cycle is that there exist non-negative integers i and j such that*

(4.4.1) $\tau^i(a) = \tau^j(b).$

PROOF. When (4.4.1) holds there is a directed path of length i to a vertex c and also a directed path from b of length j to the same c. Conversely, let a and b be vertices connected by a sequence of edges, regardless of directions

(4.4.2) $E_0 = (a, a_1), \cdots, E_{n-1} = (a_{n-1}, b).$

When $n = 1$ a relation (4.4.1) hold because either a is the image of b or vice versa. Assume that a relation (4.4.1) holds when the sequence (4.4.2) has n edges. When a further edge $E_n = (b, b')$ is added one has one of the alternatives

$$b = \tau(b'), \quad b' = \tau(b)$$

and from (4.4.1) follows correspondingly

$$\tau^i(a) = \tau^{j+1}(b'), \quad \tau^{i+1}(a) = \tau^j(b').$$

Assume next that some vertex a has *finite order* n under τ, that is, $n > 0$ is a minimal exponent such that

(4.4.3) $$a = \tau^n(a).$$

Then the vertices

(4.4.4) $$C = \{a, \tau(a), \tau^2(a), \cdots, \tau^{n-1}(a)\}$$

are all different and joined by a directed circuit or a *finite cycle* of τ.

THEOREM 4.4.2. *Each generalized cycle contains at most a single finite cycle.*

PROOF. Suppose that there were some vertex b different from the vertices in (4.4.4) such that

$$b = \tau^m(b).$$

Since a and b are connected there exist exponents i and j such that (4.4.1) holds and this leads to

$$b = \tau^m(b) = \tau^{mj}(b) = \tau^{mi}(a)$$

contradicting the assumption on b.

THEOREM 4.4.3. *A finite generalized cycle always contains a finite cycle.*

PROOF. The finiteness implies that for each a there are exponents $m < n$ with

$$\tau^m(a) = \tau^n(a) = \tau^{n-m}(\tau^m(a))$$

and so a finite cycle exists. The cycle may be a loop when

$$\tau(a) = a,$$

that is, a is a *fixpoint* of τ.

We shall now describe the form of the graph G of τ. Assume first that G_k is one of its generalized cycles containing the finite cycle (4.4.4). For each b not in C there is a smallest exponent $h > 0$ such that

$$\tau^h(b) = \tau^i(a) = a_i \in C.$$

We say that b *belongs* to a_i with *height* h. There is a unique directed path of length h from b to a_i. Among the vertices belonging to a_i there will be some b_1 of height 1

$$\tau(b_1) = a_i.$$

Each of them is connected by an entering edge to a_i not belonging to the cycle
defined by the vertices in C. Next, to each b_1 there will be vertices b_2 of height
2 such that

$$\tau(b_2) = b_1$$

for some b_1. Each b_2 is connected by an entering edge to its b_1. By repeating
this construction a finite or possibly countable number of times one obtains
the edges in the directed generalized cycle.

In the case where the generalized cycle contains no finite cycle it follows from
Theorem 4.4.3 that G_k is infinite. For any vertex a there exists an infinite directed path with the vertices

$$a, \, a_1 = \tau(a), \quad a_2 = \tau^2(a) \cdots .$$

For each b not in this sequence there exists a smallest exponent h such that

$$\tau^h(b) = \tau^i(a) = a_i.$$

We say again that b *belongs* to a_i with *height* h. The set of vertices and their
edges may be constructed for each a_i as previously.

We shall now examine the undirected graph $G_k^{(u)}$ defined by a generalized
cycle G_k. If some $G_k^{(u)}$ contains a circuit $C^{(u)}$ it follows from the uniqueness of
the outgoing edge at a vertex in G_k that C must be a directed circuit in G_k with
vertices (4.4.4). Theorem 4.4.2 shows therefore that $G_k^{(u)}$ can have at most a single
circuit. Suppose that such a circuit $C^{(u)}$ exists. At each vertex a_i in $C^{(u)}$ there will
be attached a finite or infinite tree with the root a_i, connecting a_i with all
vertices belonging to a_i. If $G_k^{(u)}$ has no circuit it must be a tree with infinite paths.
(See Figure 4.4.1 and Figure 4.4.2.)

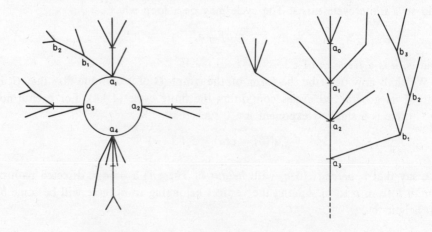

Figure 4.4.1.   Figure 4.4.2.

Conversely if some undirected graph $G^{(u)}$ has components of the two types just described its edges may be directed so that it becomes the graph G of some correspondence τ. Suppose first that there is a single circuit $C^{(u)}$ in $G_k^{(u)}$. To define τ we first construct a directed cycle C from $C^{(u)}$. All other edges are directed by giving them the direction towards the root $a_i \in C$ of the tree to which they belong. If there are no circuits one selects an infinite path P in $G_k^{(u)}$ with the vertices

$$a_0, a_1, a_2, \cdots$$

as the stem of this tree. A direction is assigned to P as indicated. Any other edge E in $G_k^{(u)}$ belongs to a branch from a vertex a_i in P and the single path connecting E with a_i assigns a unique direction to it. We summarize (see Ore):

THEOREM 4.4.4. *A necessary and sufficient condition that an undirected graph $G^{(u)}$ belongs to some correspondence τ of the vertex set V into itself is that each of its connected components either contain a single circuit, possibly a loop or be a tree with an infinite path.*

For a finite graph the condition is simpler:

THEOREM 4.4.5. *A finite graph $G^{(u)}$ is the undirected graph defined by a correspondence if and only if each of its connected components $G_k^{(u)}$ contains a single circuit, or equivalently, its circuit rank is*

$$\gamma(G_k^{(u)}) = 1.$$

The last statement follows from Theorem 4.3.1.

These representations of correspondences by means of graphs are related to the so-called *incidence matchings*. We shall say that an undirected graph G has an *edge-vertex incidence matching* when there is a one-to-one correspondence which associates to each edge E a unique vertex v_E incident to it.

For certain types of graphs one sees immediately that such matchings must exist. In a tree one can select a root a_0 and associate to each edge E that vertex v_E farthest away from a_0. Also when G is the graph of a correspondence τ each edge has the form $E = (v, \tau(v))$ with unique v and one defines $E \to v$.

THEOREM 4.4.6. *A necessary and sufficient condition that a graph G have an edge-vertex incidence matching is that each connected component of G have at most a single circuit.*

PROOF. The preceding observations together with Theorem 4.4.5 show that the condition is sufficient. To verify the necessity we shall prove that no connected graph with more than one circuit can have an edge-vertex incidence matching. Suppose G has a circuit C with the edges

$$(4.4.4) \qquad E_0 = (a_0, a_1), \ E_1 = (a_1, a_2), \ \cdots, \ E_{n-1} = (a_{n-1}, a_0)$$

and that in an incidence matching the edge E_0 corresponds to a_1. Then each E_i must be matched upon a_{i+1} with E_{n-1} corresponding to a_0. As a consequence all edges outside of C must be matched upon vertices outside of C. This shows that if G should have another circuit C_1 there cannot be any common vertices to C and C_1. Assume therefore that there exists an arc

$$P(c, c_1), \qquad\qquad c \in C, \ c_1 \in C_1$$

such that c and c_1 are the only vertices which P has in common with C and C_1. Since c is already the image of an edge in C the first edge in P must be matched upon its other endpoint. The argument can be repeated for each subsequent edge in P until the last edge is matched upon c_1. This contradicts the fact that all vertices in C_1 are the images of edges in C_1.

A *vertex-edge incidence matching* is a one-to-one correspondence of the vertex set V into the set of edges $v \to E_v$ such that E_v and v are incident.

THEOREM 4.4.7. *A graph has a vertex-edge incidence matching if and only if each of its connected components contain at least one circuit or an infinite arc.*

PROOF. To prove the necessity we observe that every tree with vertex-edge matching must have infinite arcs. Such an arc is obtained by forming a path $P(a_0)$ from any vertex a_0 by letting each vertex a_i in P be followed by its image edge E_i. Since there are no circuits it is evident that P cannot terminate.

The proof of the sufficiency of the conditions in Theorem 4.4.7 we divide up into three steps:

LEMMA 1. *In a connected graph one can always incidence match all but one given vertex a_0 upon edges.*

PROOF. We decompose the vertex set

$$V = a_0 + A_1 + A_2 + \cdots$$

where each A_i consists of all vertices having the same distance i from a_0. Each $a_i \in A_i$ is connected by a family of edges to vertices in A_{i-1} and for a_i we select a single one among them.

LEMMA 2. *A connected graph with at least one circuit has a vertex-edge incidence matching.*

PROOF. Let C be an arbitrary circuit in G with the edges (4.4.4). We match each vertex a_i in C upon the edge $E_i = (a_i, a_{i+1})$. Next we remove from G all edges and vertices in C as well as all edges incident to its vertices a_i. The remaining graph G' will decompose into a number of connected components

$$(4.4.5) \qquad\qquad G' = \sum G'_k$$

where G'_k possibly may be a single vertex. Since G is connected each G'_k must be connected to at least one of the vertices a_i in C by an edge. For each G'_k we select a single such edge

$$(4.4.6) \qquad\qquad E_k = (v_k, a_i)$$

and write

$$(4.4.7) \qquad\qquad G''_k = E_k + G'_k.$$

By Lemma 1 one can find a matching for G''_k such that all vertices except a_i are incidence matched upon edges of G''_k. When these matchings are combined with the vertex-edge matching selected for C the lemma follows.

LEMMA 3. *A connected graph with an infinite arc has a vertex-edge incidence matching.*

PROOF. Let P be an infinite arc with the edges

$$E_0 = (a_0, a_1), \ E_1 = (a_1, a_2), \cdots.$$

We associate a_i with E_i. As in the preceding proof we remove from G all edges and vertices in P and all edges incident to the vertices a_i. The remaining graph G' has a decomposition (4.4.5) into connected components G'_k. For each G'_k we select a single edge (4.4.6) connecting it with a vertex a_i in P. For the connected graph (4.4.7) one has a vertex-edge incidence matching for all vertices except a_i according to Lemma 1. When these are combined with the matching in P our Lemma 3 follows. The proof of Theorem 4.4.7 is completed by combining Lemmas 1 and 2.

The preceding results can be expressed in a more popular form. A city has streets, and squares at their intersections. One may ask if it is possible to name the squares and streets in such a way that at each square there is an adjoining street with the same name; say at Eisenhower square there is always an Eisenhower street running into it. This is usually possible according to Theorem 4.4.7, provided only that the town is so large that there is at least one street circuit. However, if one requires that each street shall have a square of the same name attached to it this is not possible according to Theorem 4.4.6, except in a village in which there is none or at most one street circuit.

PROBLEMS

1. Determine the number of graphs with n vertices which are the undirected graphs of correspondences.

2. Determine the number of non-isomorphic such graphs.

4.5. Arbitrarily traceable graphs. We shall examine a special path problem in graphs. Suppose that some finite Euler graph G is given; according to Section 3.1, G is connected and has even local degrees. In the process of constructing an Euler path it is usually necessary to piece it together from several cyclic sections. As a very simple example one may take the figure 8 shaped graph in Figure 4.5.1. When starting at the vertex a one may first proceed in the circuit $a\ b\ c\ d\ a$; in order to trace all edges it is necessary afterwards to insert the circuit $c\ e\ f\ g\ c$. This leads us to consider the following problem regarding Euler graphs.

When does an Euler graph have the property that an Euler path is always obtained when one follows any path from a vertex a according to the single rule that at each vertex one selects one of the edges not previously traversed?

A graph with this property shall be called *arbitrarily traceable* from the vertex a. Such a graph may be suitable as a layout for an exposition where all exhibits are automatically visited once if one always proceeds along lanes not previously traversed.

Various cases may occur. In Figure 4.5.2 one has a graph which is arbitrarily traceable from a and no other vertex while the graph in Figure 4.5.3 is arbitrarily traceable both from a and b. Such a graph which consists of edge disjoint circuits intersecting only in two vertices a and b we call a *skein*.

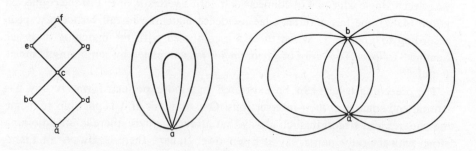

Figure 4.5.1.   Figure 4.5.2.   Figure 4.5.3.

To determine the general form of an arbitrarily traceable graph it is necessary first to derive some auxiliary facts.

THEOREM 4.5.1. *Let* G *be a graph which is arbitrarily traceable from the vertex* a *and* H *some Euler subgraph including* a. *Then* H *and its complement* $\bar{H}$ *are both arbitrarily traceable from* a.

PROOF. The graph H has an Euler path returning to a and since G is arbitrarily traceable from a the remaining graph $\bar{H}$ must also be so traceable from a. The same argument applies to H as complement of $\bar{H}$.

THEOREM 4.5.2. *When* G *is arbitrarily traceable from the vertex* a *with the local degree*

$$\rho(a) = 2n$$

then G *is the edge direct sum*

(4.5.1) $$G = \sum C_i$$

of n *circuits* C_i *through* a.

PROOF. An Euler path through G from a returns to a, hence there is also a returning circuit C_1 to a. Since C_1 is an Euler graph Theorem 4.5.1 shows that the remaining graph $\bar{C}_1$ is arbitrarily traceable from a. By repeated reductions of this kind, (4.5.1) follows.

The circuits in (4.5.1) have the property:

THEOREM 4.5.3. *Any two circuits* C_1 *and* C_2 *in* (4.5.1) *intersect in at most one vertex different from* a.

PROOF. The graph $C_1 + C_2$ is arbitrarily traceable according to Theorem 4.5.1. In proceeding on C_1 from a in the two possible directions let b and c denote the two first vertices lying on C_2. (See Figure 4.5.4.)

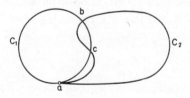

Figure 4.5.4.

In tracing $C_1 + C_2$ one may begin by following the path C_1 to b in the direction not passing c and then proceed back to a on that section of C_2 which does not include c. From a we continue on C_1 to c on the section not passing b and then back to a on that section of C_2 which does not include b. When this path has been completed there are no further edges from a on which it may be continued. Thus by assumption the whole graph $C_1 + C_2$ must have been covered. But if $b \neq c$ the section $C_1(b, c)$ has not been traversed; hence $b = c$.

We are now ready to show:

THEOREM 4.5.4.   *A necessary and sufficient condition that an Euler graph G be arbitrarily traceable from a vertex a is that all circuits in G include a.*

PROOF.   Suppose that there exists some circuit C in G not passing through a. The graph $\bar{C}$ has even local degrees; it may not be connected but it will have some connected component K including a. K is an Euler graph and so arbitrarily traceable from a according to Theorem 4.5.1. The same must be true for the connected graph $G_1 = K + C$. But this gives rise to a contradiction since there is an Euler path from a through K back to a. There are then no further edges of G_1 at a and yet the edges in C have not been traversed.

Suppose conversely that every circuit in G passes through a. If G were not arbitrarily traceable there would be a cyclic path P from a and exhausting all edges at this vertex. The complement $\bar{P}$ is also an Euler graph and since every Euler graph has a circuit we are led to a contradiction.

Theorem 4.5.4 gives a simple criterion for graphs which are arbitrarily traceable from more than one vertex.

THEOREM 4.5.5.   *A graph which is arbitrarily traceable from more than one vertex is a skein.*

PROOF.   Let a and b be two vertices from which the graph G is arbitrarily traceable. According to Theorem 4.5.4 every circuit in G passes through a and b. In the representation (4.5.1) the circuits can only have the vertices a and b in common, hence they form a skein.

Theorem 4.5.4 gives a simple construction of all graphs which are arbitrarily traceable. We denote by S_a the star at a consisting of all edges with an endpoint at this vertex; S_a includes the loops at a. We write

$$G = S_a + G_1.$$

Theorem 4.5.4 shows that G is arbitrarily traceable from q if and only if it is an Euler graph and G_1 a graph without circuits.

Assume conversely that some circuit free graph G_1 is given; thus G_1 is the direct sum of trees. We select a vertex a outside of G_1 and draw edges from a to the vertices in G_1 such that these vertices have even local degrees in the new graph G. This may be achieved by drawing a single edge from a to the odd vertices in G_1 and none to the even ones. More general, one can draw an arbitrary odd

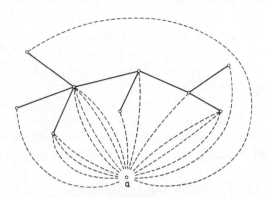

Figure 4.5.5.

number in the first case and an even number in the second. To these edges one may add loops at a. The resulting graph is an Euler graph since $\rho(a)$ is also even according to Theorem 1.2.1. We state:

THEOREM 4.5.6. *All arbitrarily traceable graphs are obtainable from circuit free graphs G_1 by joining the vertices in G_1 by edges to a new vertex a such that the resulting graph has even degrees; loops may be added at a.*

The preceding results are taken from a paper by the author (Ore). Further studies on arbitrarily traceable graphs have been made by Baebler and Harary.

CHAPTER 5

LEAVES AND LOBES

5.1. **Edges and vertices of attachment.** We denote by A some subset of the vertex set V of a graph G and by

$$\bar{A} = V - A$$

its complement. Such a set defines a division of the edges of G into three disjoint categories (see Figure 5.1.1).

1. *Interior edges*
   $E_1 = (a_1, a_2)$, $a_1 \in A$, $a_2 \in A$ lying in A, that is,
   E_1 is an edge in the section graph $G(A)$.
2. *Edges of attachment (connecting edges, or edges touching A)*
   $E_2 = (a, \bar{a})$, $a \in A$, $\bar{a} \in \bar{A}$
   with one vertex in A and the other in $\bar{A}$.
3. *Exterior edges*
   $E_3 = (\bar{a}_1, \bar{a}_2)$, $\bar{a}_1 \in \bar{A}$, $\bar{a}_2 \in \bar{A}$
   which are interior edges to $\bar{A}$.

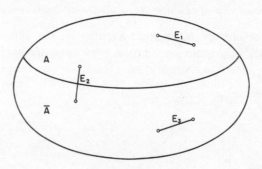

Figure 5.1.1.

The number of edges of attachment of a set A shall be denoted by

(5.1.1) $$k = \rho(A, \bar{A})$$

and called the *edge attachment number* of A and $\bar{A}$. One also says that A is *k-edge attached* or that A is a *peninsula of rank k*. A *peninsula* is a set A with $k = 1$.

The sum

(5.1.2)
$$\rho(A) = \sum_a \rho(a), \qquad\qquad a \in A$$

of the local degrees for the vertices in A represents the total number of edges issuing from them, counting twice the edges lying in A (including the loops) while the edges of attachment are counted singly. Thus when the edge attachment number (5.1.1) is subtracted from (5.1.2) one obtains twice the number of edges lying in A. Consequently the number of edges in each of the three categories introduced above is given by the expressions

(5.1.3)
$$\tfrac{1}{2}(\rho(A) - \rho(A,\bar{A})), \quad \rho(A,\bar{A}), \quad \tfrac{1}{2}(\rho(\bar{A}) - \rho(A,\bar{A})).$$

An immediate consequence is:

THEOREM 5.1.1. *The edge attachment number of a finite set A satisfies the condition*

(5.1.4)
$$k = \rho(A,\bar{A}) \equiv \rho(A)\,(\mathrm{mod}\,2).$$

In particular when the local degrees $\rho(a)$ in A are even then k is even. A finite graph with even local degrees can have no peninsulas.

The graph G is *k-edge connected* when no set $A \neq \emptyset$ and $A \neq V$ has an edge attachment number less than k. The maximal number k_0 of this kind is the *edge connectivity* of G. A graph is connected if and only if $k_0 \geqq 1$. Evidently

(5.1.5)
$$k_0 \leqq \min \rho(v), \qquad\qquad v \in V.$$

Analogous concepts to these can be introduced for the vertices. Any subgraph H and its complement

$$\bar{H} = G - H$$

define a division of the vertices into three classes:
1. *Interior vertices* of H incident to no edges of $\bar{H}$.
2. *Vertices of attachment* incident both to edges in H and $\bar{H}$.
3. *Exterior vertices*, that is, interior vertices of $\bar{H}$.

These concepts shall be used principally with respect to a section graph $H = G(A)$. We denote by $C(A)$ the set of vertices of attachment of H (or A). It consists of those end points of the edges of attachment which lie in A. Similarly $C'(A)$ consists of the remaining end points of the edges of attachment. One has

$$C'(A) \cdot C(A) = \emptyset, \quad C(\bar{A}) = C'(A),$$
$$C(A) \subset A, \quad C'(A) \subset \bar{A}.$$

The attachment graph $G(A,\bar{A})$ is the bipartite graph whose edges are the edges of attachment end having the vertex sets $C(A)$ and $C'(A)$. One sees that

$$G = G(A) + G(\bar{A}) + G(A,\bar{A}).$$

The *vertex attachment number* $l(H)$ of a subgraph H is the number of its vertices of attachment; we say that H (and $\bar{H}$) is $l(H)$-*vertex attached*. Thus a single edge is at most 2-vertex attached. These concepts apply also to sets of vertices when one takes $H = G(A)$ to be the section graph of the given set A. According to this definition a single non-isolated vertex is 1-vertex attached; a set of l vertices is at most l-vertex attached.

Suppose now that A is a set such that the graphs

(5.1.6) $G(A),\ \overline{G(A)} = G(\bar{A}) + G(A,\bar{A})$

both have inner vertices. If for every such set A one has

$$l(G(A)) = v(C(A)) \geqq l$$

then we say that G is l-*vertex connected*. The largest l_0 such that G is l_0-vertex connected is the *vertex connectivity* of the graph.

One verifies that G is connected in the usual sense if and only if $l_0 \geqq 1$.

According to this definition one should say formally that a graph has arbitrarily high vertex connectivity when there are no sets A such that both graphs (5.1.6) have inner vertices. We point out:

THEOREM 5.1.2. *In order that a graph G have the property that for no set A both subgraphs (5.1.6) have inner vertices it is necessary and sufficient that G contain a complete subgraph U covering the vertex set V; in other words, G shall have the diameter $d_0 = 1$.*

PROOF. When a subgraph U exists every vertex in A is connected by an edge to every vertex in $\bar{A}$ so that $G(A)$ can have no inner vertices. Suppose conversely that for no set A do both graphs (5.1.6) have inner vertices. We take an arbitrary vertex v_0 with its incident edges

$$E_i = (v_0, v_i), \qquad\qquad\qquad i = 1, 2, \cdots.$$

Then v_0 is an inner vertex of the graph

(5.1.7) $G(A),\ A = \{v_0, v_1, \cdots\}.$

Since all vertices in $\bar{A}$ must be incident to an edge in $G(A)$ we have $A = V$.

This situation makes it desirable at times to limit the definition of vertex connectivity to graphs with $d_0 \geq 2$. For such a graph G the number of vertices must be at least $l_0 + 2$. As an analogue to (5.1.5) one has

$$(5.1.8) \qquad\qquad l_0 \leq \rho(v_0)$$

for all vertices v_0 for which there are vertices v having distances at least 2. To see this one need only consider the graph (5.1.7) constructed for the proof of Theorem 5.1.2.

The concepts of separating vertices and edges have been extended to separating graphs. A study of separation by means of shortest paths has been made by MacLane; a number of other generalisations have been introduced by Nettleton, Goldberg and Green.

Problems

1. Determine the edge and vertex connectivities for the Platonic graphs.

2.* Examine the relations between the edge and vertex connectivities for a graph and its interchange graph.

3. Prove that the maximal number of edges in a graph with $n \geq 3$ vertices and edge connectivity k_0 is

$$v_e = \tfrac{1}{2}(n-1)(n-2) + k_0$$

and determine the corresponding graphs with the maximal number of edges.

4. The same problem for the vertex connectivity.

5.2. Leaves. An edge $E = (a, b)$ in a graph G is called a *circuit edge* when it belongs to some circuit. A loop is a circuit edge. No terminal edge can be a circuit edge. A tree has no circuit edges and conversely a connected graph without circuit edges is a tree.

An edge $E = (a, b)$ is called a *separating edge* or a *bridge* or a *cut edge* in G if in the graph G_1 obtained from G by the removal of E the vertices a and b are disconnected. Thus we can write

$$(5.2.1) \qquad\qquad G_1 = H_1 + H_2$$

where H_1 and H_2 are disjoint and H_1 contains a and H_2 contains b. We agree to consider E to be a separating edge also when it is a terminal edge; in this special case H_1 or H_2 in (5.1.2) will reduce to a single vertex. A connected graph has a separating edge if and only if its edge connectivity is $k_0 = 1$. From Theorem 5.1.1 we conclude immediately:

THEOREM 5.2.1. *A finite graph with even local degrees can have no separating edges.*

We observe also:

THEOREM 5.2.2. *An edge E is a separating edge if and only if it is not a circuit edge.*

PROOF. If E is a circuit edge the two endpoints a and b remain connected after the removal of E so that no decomposition (5.2.1) can occur. Conversely, if E is not a circuit edge there can be no paths joining a and b not containing E.

We shall say that two vertices a_0 and b_0 are *circuit edge connected* if there exists a sequence P of circuit edges

$$(5.2.2) \qquad\qquad P = (a_0, a_1)(a_1, a_2) \cdots (a_{n-1}, b_0)$$

having a_0 and b_0 for its endpoints. Evidently we can suppose that P is a path or even an arc. An equivalent definition is the following: The vertices a_0 and b_0 are circuit edge connected if there exists a sequence of circuits

$$(5.2.3) \qquad\qquad\qquad C_1, C_2, \cdots, C_k$$

with a_0 on C_1 and b_0 on C_k such that each consecutive pair of circuits in (5.2.3) has at least one vertex in common.

The circuit edge connectedness defines an equivalence relation for the vertex set V of G. The totality of vertices v which are circuit edge connected to a given vertex a_0 we call the *leaf* $L(a_0)$ to which a_0 belongs. Possibly the leaf consists of a_0 alone; then a_0 is a *singular* leaf. This can happen only when all edges at a_0 are loops or separating edges.

The section graph $G(L)$ is the *graph of the leaf* L. The edges in $G(L)$ are all circuit edges. If namely a and b in L are connected by the edge $E = (a, b)$ there is an arc $P(a, b)$ of circuit edges all belonging to $G(L)$ connecting a and b. If P does not include E this edge may be added to P to give a circuit C including E.

The graph $G(L)$ is *circuit closed*, that is, if a circuit C in G has a vertex in common with L then the whole circuit belongs to $G(L)$. Thus every attachment edge of L must be a separating edge. We observe also that there can at most be a single such edge connecting two leaves L_1 and L_2 because if there were more they would necessarily become circuit edges. These observations lead to:

THEOREM 5.2.3. *For a leaf L all edges of attachment are separation edges. The leaf graphs G(L) are 2-edge connected and they are maximal subgraphs of G with this property.*

PROOF. It remains only to verify the last statement. A subgraph which is 2-edge connected is connected and any edge in H is a circuit edge. Thus H is included in some leaf graph $G(L)$.

PROBLEMS

1. Is Theorem 5.2.1 true for infinite graphs?

2. Prove that for a finite graph with separating edges there are at least two leaves with a single edge of attachment.

3. Define $\gamma(E) = 1$ or $\gamma(E) = 0$ depending on whether E is a separating edge or not. Prove that the number of leaves in G is

$$(5.2.4) \qquad\qquad \lambda(G) = 1 + \sum_E \gamma(E), \qquad\qquad E \in G.$$

5.3. Homomorphic graph images. For a graph G with the vertex set V let τ be a correspondence, generally many-to-one, of V into another set V_1. Suppose that a graph G_1 is defined in V_1. We define τ to be a *homomorphism* of G into G_1 when to any edge $E = (a, b)$ in G there exists a corresponding edge

$$(5.3.1) \qquad\qquad E_1 = \tau(E) = (\tau(a), \tau(b)) = (a_1, b_1)$$

in G_1. The graph in V_1 consisting of all edges $\tau(E)$ we call the *homomorphic image $\tau(G)$* of G in V_1.

Under the homomorphism τ of G the vertex set V will decompose into disjoint *inverse image sets*

$$V = \sum \tau^{-1}(a_1), \qquad\qquad a_1 \in V_1$$

where $\tau^{-1}(a_1)$ consists of all vertices in G having the same image a_1 in $\tau(G)$. Then under τ all vertices in the section graph $G(\tau^{-1}(a_1))$ will correspond to the vertex a_1. Thus there will be an edge (5.3.1) in $\tau(G)$ if and only if there exists some edge

$$(5.3.2) \qquad\qquad E = (a, b), \qquad\qquad a \in \tau^{-1}(a_1), \quad b \in \tau^{-1}(b_1)$$

in G.

It should be pointed out that this definition of a graph homomorphism is still somewhat ambiguous. Usually there will be several edges in G connecting the same two inverse image sets in (5.3.2). One can then either join the corresponding vertices a_1 and b_1 in (5.3.1) by a single edge, or one can preserve the multiplicity by making E_1 a multiple edge, repeating it as many times as there are connecting edges (5.3.2). To distinguish the two types of correspondence one may call the single edge correspondence a *(simple) homomorphism* and the multiple edge correspondence a *multiplicity homomorphism*. If

$$(5.3.3) \qquad\qquad a_1 = \tau(a) = \tau(b)$$

we shall in the case of a simple homomorphism let the edge E in (5.3.2) correspond to the vertex a_1. In a multiplicity homomorphism one should include a loop at a_1 for each edge (5.3.2) for which (5.3.3) holds.

In the case of a relation R in a set V this ambiguity does not arise. When the correspondence τ is given one defines the image relation R_1 of R in V_1 as the relation

$$a_1 \, R_1 \, b_1$$

which holds if and only if in V some relation

$$a R b, \quad a_1 = \tau(a), \quad b_1 = \tau(b)$$

is satisfied.

Now let G be an arbitrary graph. We define a correspondence from its vertex set V to a new set

$$V_1 = V_1(L_1)$$

whose elements $\{L_1\}$ are in one-to-one correspondence with the family $\{L\}$ of all leaves of G. The homomorphic image graph $G_1 = \tau(G)$ will have V_1 for its vertex set and there will be an edge (L_1, L_1') in G_1 if and only if the two corresponding leaves L and L' are connected by an edge in G. We call G_1 the *leaf composition graph* of G. We noted in Section 5.2 that there is at most one edge in G connecting two leaves. Furthermore, the graph G_1 can have no circuits because any such circuit would arise from a circuit in G passing through several leaves. We can state (see Figure 5.3.1):

THEOREM 5.3.1. *Any graph G is homomorphic to its leaf composition graph G_1 such that the inverse image sets are the leaves of G. The graph G_1 is circuit free.*

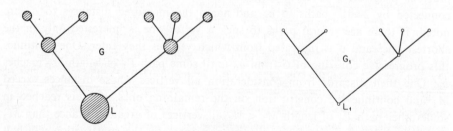

Figure 5.3.1.

There are certain special types of graph homomorphisms. A homomorphism is *independent* or *disjoint* when no two vertices belonging to the same inverse image set are connected by an edge. Any independent homomorphism is obtainable as a succession of *elementary independent homomorphisms* consisting of the identification of a single pair of vertices not connected by an edge.

A homomorphism is *connected* when the section graphs of the inverse image sets are connected. A connected homomorphism is constructible as a series of *elementary connected homomorphisms* in which the endpoints of a single edge are identified. The homomorphism of Theorem 5.3.1 is evidently connected.

In general the section graphs of the inverse image sets consist of a number of connected components. Then the homomorphism may be performed in two steps, first contracting the components to a single vertex and then identifying these independent vertices in each set. This shows:

THEOREM 5.3.2.   *Any homomorphism is the product of a connected and an independent homomorphism.*

When $V = \sum C_i$ is the decomposition of V into disjoint blocks C_i it is often suitable to denote the corresponding homomorphic graph by

$$G_1 = G/C.$$

5.4. **Lobes.** In Section 5.2 we introduced an equivalence relation in the vertex set V by means of the concept of circuit edge connectedness. We shall now define an analogous equivalence in the family of edges in the graph G. Two edges E_1 and E_2 shall be called *strongly circuit connected* when there exists a sequence of circuits (5.2.3) such that E_1 lies on C_1 and E_2 on C_k while any pair of consecutive circuits C_i and C_{i+1} have at least one edge in common. We prove:

THEOREM 5.4.1.   *Two edges are strongly circuit connected if and only if there exists a circuit including them both.*

It is sufficient to show:

THEOREM 5.4.2.   *When E_1 is an edge in a circuit C_1 and E_2 an edge in a circuit C_2 while C_1 and C_2 have at least two vertices in common, then there is a circuit including both E_1 and E_2.*

PROOF. We can assume that E_1 does not lie on C_2. Then by following C_1 in both directions from E_1 let a_1 and a_2 be the two first vertices on C_1 lying also on C_2. We denote by

$$C_1(a_1, E_1, a_2), \quad C_2(a_1, E_2, a_2)$$

the sections of C_1 and C_2 containing E_1 and E_2 respectively. Their sum

$$C = C_1(a_1, E_1, a_2) + C_2(a_2, E_2, a_1)$$

is a circuit including both edges.

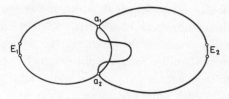

Figure 5.4.1.

One can also say that two vertices a_1 and a_2 are *strongly circuit connected* if there is a pair of strongly circuit connected edges E_1 and E_2 incident to a_1 and a_2 respectively, in other words, a_1 and a_2 lie on the same circuit. It should be noted in contradistinction to the edges that this does not define an equivalence relation for the vertices; for instance, in Figure 5.4.2 the edges in C_1 are strongly connected and so are the edges in C_2. Thus a_1 and a_2 are strongly connected and so are a_2 and a_3 while a_1 and a_3 are not so related.

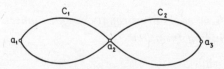

Figure 5.4.2.

The set of all edges which are strongly circuit connected with an edge E form a subgraph, the *lobe graph* of E. The vertex set L^* of this graph is the *lobe* defined by E. The lobe graph is connected. It may consist of a single edge.

LEMMA. *When $P(a_0, b_0)$ is an arc connecting two different vertices in the lobe L^* then all edges in P belong to the lobe graph.*

PROOF. By dividing P into sections we can assume, in case the lemma should not hold, that in $P(a_0, b_0)$ no edge belongs to the lobe graph. But this leads to a contradiction because in the lobe graph there is a path $Q(b_0, a_0)$; consequently

$$P(a_0, b_0) + Q(b_0, a_0)$$

is a circuit whose edges are strongly circuit connected to E.

From the lemma we conclude that the lobe graph is the section graph $G(L^*)$. It is circuit closed in the sense that when a circuit C has at least two vertices in common with L^* then all edges in C belong to $G(L^*)$. Two different lobes can therefore at most have one vertex in common. Evidently all vertices in L^* are circuit edge connected and so each leaf graph $G(L)$ will have an edge disjoint decomposition

$$(5.4.1) \qquad\qquad G(L) = \sum G(L_i^*)$$

into a family of lobe graphs.

In a graph G we define a vertex a to be a *separating vertex* (*cut vertex*) if there is a proper, non-void subgraph H with a as its only vertex of attachment. Since at any vertex $b \neq a$ in H all edges must go to vertices in H it follows that $H = G(A)$ is a section graph. Similarly $\bar{H} = G(B)$ is a section graph having only the vertex a in common with H. Thus when a is a separating vertex one has the edge direct decomposition

$$(5.4.2) \qquad\quad G = G(A) + G(B), \quad V = A + B, \quad A \cdot B = a.$$

Conversely, the decomposition (5.4.2) may be used to define a separating vertex. According to this definition a vertex with a loop is separating.

THEOREM 5.4.3. *The following graph properties are equivalent*:
1. *G is connected and has no separating vertices.*
2. *Any pair of edges lie on a circuit.*
3. *Any pair of vertices lie on a circuit.*
4. *When a, b, c are three different vertices there exists an arc $P(a, b, c)$.*
5. *The vertex connectivity is $l_0 \geqq 2$.*

PROOF. When G is connected and has a separating vertex the decomposition (5.4.2) shows that not all pairs of edges can lie on a circuit. Suppose on the other hand that G has no separating vertex. We form the lobe graph $H = G(L^*)$ defined by some edge E. If H should not be the whole graph it has some vertex of attachment a at which there are edges of the complementary graph $\bar{H}$. We construct the subgraph H_1 of $\bar{H}$ consisting of all edges in paths within $\bar{H}$ from a. This graph H_1 is a component of $\bar{H}$ so that its vertices of attachment must belong to H. But H is connected and so we conclude from the lemma that a is the only vertex of attachment for H_1. Since G has no separating vertices it follows that $H = G$. Then G is strongly circuit connected and according to Theorem 5.4.1 any pair of its edges lie on a circuit. This proves the equivalence of 1. and 2.

Evidently 2. implies 3. On the other hand when 3. holds G is connected and it can have no separating vertices for if $x \in A$, $y \in B$ in (5.4.2) are vertices different from a they cannot lie on the same circuit. Thus 3. and 1. are equivalent.

When 4. holds G is connected, there can be no separating vertex since three vertices x, y, a defined as above for (5.4.2) cannot lie on an arc $P(x, y, a)$ in this order. Conversely, when 1. holds each pair of vertices a, b and b, c lies on a circuit and from these one readily obtains an arc $P(a, b, c)$. Finally it is evident from the definitions that 1. and 5. are equivalent conditions.

THEOREM 5.4.4. *A lobe graph $G(L^*)$ has no separating vertices; all its vertices of attachment are separating vertices for G.*

We noted that any leaf graph $G(L)$ has an edge disjoint decomposition (5.4.1) into edge disjoint lobe graphs $G(L^*)$. According to Theorem 5.4.4 the composition of $G(L)$ from the $G(L^*)$ may be described by a cactus-like figure where the various lobes touch at their vertices of attachment (Figure 5.4.3).

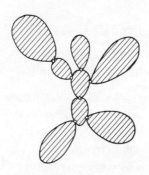

Figure 5.4.3.

We shall need the following observation:

THEOREM 5.4.5. *Let G be a connected graph with a finite number $n \geqq 2$ of lobe graphs. Then at least two of these graphs are 1-vertex attached.*

PROOF. From a vertex v_0 we construct an arc M passing through as many lobe graphs as possible. Since no pair of lobe graphs can have edges belonging to the same circuit it follows that M must finally arrive at a lobe L_0 which is

1-vertex attached. By selecting $v_0 \in L_0$ and proceeding as before, one must reach another lobe graph L_1 which is 1-vertex attached.

Take G as a connected graph without loops and a finite number $\lambda^*(G)$ of lobes. When a vertex v and all incident edges are removed from G the remaining graph $G(V-v)$ will decompose into $i(v)$ connected components. We shall call $i(v)$ the *connective index* of v. One sees that $i(v) = 1$ if and only if v is not a separating vertex for G. When v is a separating vertex $i(v)$ denotes the number of lobes for which it is a vertex of attachment. For the connective indices there exists a relation due to Harary of the same type as the relation (5.2.4):

THEOREM 5.4.6. *When $\lambda^*(G)$ is the number of lobes of the connected graph G without loops, then*

(5.4.3) $$\lambda^*(G) = 1 + \sum_v (i(v) - 1), \qquad v \in V.$$

PROOF. One can prove (5.4.3) by induction with respect to the number $\lambda^*(G)$ of lobes. It is evident for $\lambda^*(G) = 1$. According to Theorem 5.4.5 the graph G can be constructed by successive additions of lobe graphs with a single vertex of attachment. Such an adjunction increases $\lambda^*(G)$ by one unit and a single $i(v)$ by the same amount.

The special graphs in which each lobe graph is a single circuit have been called *Husimi trees*. They may be characterized also by the property that they are graphs in which no edge can belong to more than a single circuit. (See, for instance, the papers by Harary and Norman and by Harary and Uhlenbeck.)

PROBLEMS

1. Prove that a graph is a Husimi tree when all its circuits have odd length.
2. (Dirac). If a graph without separation vertices has an odd circuit then each vertex lies on an odd circuit.

5.5. **Maximal circuits.** We shall examine the circuits of maximal length in a finite graph G. Since a circuit lies wholly within the lobe graph it defines, there is no restriction in assuming that G has no separating vertices.

The vertices in an arc $P(a_0, a_l)$ of maximal length l shall be denoted by

$$a_0, \cdots, a_l.$$

Clearly all edges from a_l must go to vertices lying on P. Let a_m be the vertex nearest to a_0 on P such that there exists an edge (a_l, a_m) (Figure 5.5.1).

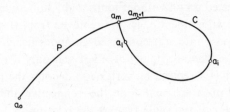

Figure 5.5.1.

The circuit

(5.5.1) $$C = (a_m, a_{m+1}, \cdots, a_l, a_m)$$

we call the *end circuit* of P at a_l. We select P such that in addition the length of its end circuit is maximal. Consider the section graph

$$G(C) = G(a_m, a_{m+1}, \cdots, a_l)$$

defined on the vertex set (5.5.1) of C. Suppose that in $G(C)$ there is a Hamilton arc $H_i(a_m, a_i)$ from a_m to some vertex a_i with

$$m + 1 \leq i \leq l.$$

Then all edges in G at a_i must belong to the graph $G(C)$. This is a consequence of the observation that an edge (a_i, a_j) to a vertex on $P(a_0, a_{m-1})$ would result in a maximal arc

$$P' = P(a_0, a_m) + H_i(a_m, a_i)$$

with a larger end circuit while an edge (a_i, b), b not on P, would give an arc

$$P(a_0, a_m) + H_i(a_m, a_i) + (a_i, b)$$

of length $l + 1$.

Suppose now that

$$\rho(a_{m+1}) + \rho(a_i) > k, \qquad\qquad i = m + 2, \cdots, l$$

where $k = l - m + 1$ is the length of the end circuit. From Theorem 3.4.7 we conclude that all these a_i are the end-points of Hamilton arcs $H_i(a_m, a_i)$, hence all $\rho(a_i)$ edges at a_i belong to $G(C)$. But this in turn makes a_m a separating vertex for $G(C)$ so that the only possibility is that $G = G(C)$ is the whole graph. Thus if we exclude the case where G has a Hamilton circuit one must have

$$\rho(a_{m+1}) + \rho(a_i) \leqq k$$

for some i, hence the result:

THEOREM 5.5.1. *When the connected graph G has no separating vertices then it either has a Hamilton circuit or the length k of a maximal circuit satisfies*

$$k \geqq \rho_0 + \rho_1$$

where $\rho_0 \leqq \rho_1$ are the two smallest local degrees in G.

This theorem implies another due to Dirac: When G is a graph without separating vertices the length of the maximal circuits satisfy $k \geq 2\rho_0$ or else the graph has a Hamilton circuit. Another proof for Dirac's theorem was given by Erdös and Gallai; our argument is a slightly sharper form of their method.

CHAPTER 6

THE AXIOM OF CHOICE

6.1. **Well-ordering.** A set V is said to be *well-ordered* when it is ordered in such a way that every subset has a first element. Any finite set can be well-ordered by numbering its elements. Similarly, any countable set can be well-ordered since its elements are in a one-to-one correspondence to the set of integers.

The importance of the well-ordering lies in the

PRINCIPLE OF TRANSFINITE INDUCTION. *Let V be a well-ordered set with v_0 as its first element. If a property P holds for v_0 and also for an element a_0 whenever it holds for all $x < a_0$, then P holds for every element in V.*

PROOF. If this were not true there would be a smallest element b_0 for which P does not hold. But then P holds for all $y < b_0$, hence for b_0 contrary to assumption.

Any element a_0 in a well-ordered set defines a dichotomy of V into an upper section $U(a_0)$ consisting of all $x \geqq a_0$ and a lower section $L(a_0)$ consisting of all $y < a_0$.

Next let $F\{A\}$ be a family of subsets $A \neq \emptyset$ in a set V. A correspondence

$$(6.1.1) \qquad\qquad A \to f(A) \in A$$

from A to an element $f(A)$ in A is called a *choice function* for F. The *axiom of choice* states:

Every family of sets has a choice function.

It is clear that a well-ordered set V has a choice function for the family of all its subsets, obtained by letting each A correspond to its smallest element in the well-ordering. We shall now prove the converse.

THEOREM OF ZERMELO. *Any set with a choice function for its subsets can be well-ordered.*

We shall follow the lines of one of the proofs given by Zermelo. Let (6.1.1) be a choice function for the family F of all subsets of V. For any set $A \neq \emptyset$ we write

$$A' = A - f(A).$$

Next we define a family Γ of subsets of V to be a *chain* when it has the three properties:

1. The set V belongs to Γ.

2. When $A \neq \emptyset$ belongs to Γ then A' belongs to Γ.

3. Γ is closed with respect to intersection, i.e., the intersection of any number of sets in Γ belongs to Γ.

The family of all subsets form a chain. The common sets of any family of chains is a chain. Thus there exists a unique minimal chain Γ_0 contained in all others and consisting of the sets common to all chains.

In the chain Γ_0 there will be *dividing sets* A_0 characterized by the property that when $B \neq A_0$ is any other set in Γ_0 then one of the cases

$$(6.1.2) \qquad\qquad B \supset A_0, \ B \subset A_0$$

holds. In particular, V is such a set. For a dividing set one has a separation of the family $\Gamma_0 - A_0$ into two disjoint families

$$U(A_0), \ L(A_0)$$

according to the alternatives in (6.1.2).

We denote by $L'(A_0)$ the family of all sets B in Γ_0 with $B \subseteq A_0'$. For no set B in $U(A_0)$ can one have $A_0 \supset B'$ because the relation

$$B \supset A_0 \supset B'$$

would imply that there were at least two elements in B not in B'. It follows in particular that the two families $U(A_0)$ and $L'(A_0)$ have no common sets.

Next we prove:

The family

$$(6.1.3) \qquad\qquad \Gamma_1 = U(A_0) + A_0 + L'(A_0)$$

is a chain.

PROOF. We check the properties of a chain.

1. Either $V = A_0$ or V belongs to $U(A_0)$.

2. We have seen that for every $B \supset A_0$ either $B' \supset A_0$ or $B' = A_0$. The set A_0' is in $L'(A_0)$. The same is true for every B' with B in $L'(A_0)$.

3. The intersection of sets in $U(A_0)$ or such sets with A_0 is either A_0 or a set in $U(A_0)$. An intersection of sets in (6.1.3), some of which belong to $L'(A_0)$, must belong to $L'(A_0)$.

Since Γ_0 is a minimal chain and Γ_1 a subchain one must have $\Gamma_0 = \Gamma_1$ or

$$\Gamma_0 = U(A_0) + A_0 + L'(A_0).$$

This representation shows that also A_0' is a dividing set.

The dividing sets in Γ_0 form a chain.

PROOF. 1) V is a dividing set. 2) For any dividing set A_0 also A_0' is a dividing set. 3) Let $D = \Pi A_i$ be the intersection of dividing sets A_i. For any $B \neq D$ in Γ_0 one either has $B \supseteq A_i$ for some i, hence $B \supset D$ or $B \subset A_i$ for all i, hence $B \subset D$.

From the minimality of Γ_0 we conclude further:

Every set in Γ_0 is a dividing set, i.e., the sets in Γ_0 are ordered by inclusion.

From this fact we shall derive an ordering of the elements in V. For an arbitrary subset $B \neq \emptyset$ in V let B_0 be the intersection of all sets in Γ_0 containing B. Then

$$(6.1.4) \qquad\qquad f(B_0) \in B, \ B_0 \supseteq B$$

because otherwise B_0' would be a smaller set in Γ_0 containing B. We show further:

B_0 is the only set in Γ_0 satisfying (6.1.4).

PROOF. Let B_1 be another set in Γ_0 containing B so that $B_1 \supset B_0 \supseteq B$. We have already seen that this implies $B_1' \supseteq B_0$ so that $f(B_1)$ cannot belong to B.

We apply this result to a single element $B = (b)$. It follows that there exists a unique set $B_0(b)$ in Γ_0 such that

$$b \in B_0(b), \quad f(B_0) = b.$$

This defines a one-to-one correspondence between the elements $b \in V$ and the sets B_0 in Γ_0. Since the latter are ordered by inclusion a corresponding order is defined for the elements in V.

Finally take an arbitrary set B in V. It corresponds to a unique smallest set B_0 in (6.1.4). Every element $b \neq f(B_0)$ is contained in B_0' and so it follows that

$$B_0(b) \subset B_0(f(B_0)).$$

This shows that in the ordering which has been defined, $f(B_0)$ is the largest element in B. By reversing the order in V a well-ordering is established.

6.2. **The maximal principles.** The method of transfinite induction is often rather cumbersome to apply. However, it may be replaced by various types of so-called *maximal principles* which are equivalent to it. The proofs of these principles must involve well-ordering or the axiom of choice. They may be formulated in terms of inclusion of sets or in terms of a partial order according to preference (see Section 1.4). A family of sets which is ordered by inclusion shall be referred to as a *chain*.

The *Hausdorff* or *Kuratowski* maximal principle has the form:

Any ordered subset of a partially ordered set P is contained in a maximal ordered set.

Here a maximal ordered set is an ordered subset O of P such that no element can be added to O without destroying its property of being ordered.

We shall make use of the following observation: Let $\{O_k\}$ be a chain of sets, each ordered, in the partially ordered set P. Then the sum set

$$O = \sum O_k$$

is ordered. If namely a and b are any two elements in O then there exists some O_k to which they both belong and so $a > b$ or $b > a$ in P since O_k is ordered.

To prove the Hausdorff-Kuratowski maximal principle we shall use the process of *transfinite construction* to obtain the maximal ordered set. We suppose that the elements in P have been well-ordered and that O_0 is some given ordered subset of P. Let $a \in P - O_0$. We assume that for every element x preceding a in the well-ordering an ordered set O_x including O_0 has been defined such that $O_x \supseteq O_y$ whenever y precedes x. We observed that

$$O_a' = \sum O_x$$

is an ordered subset of P and write

$$O_a = O_a' + a, \text{ or } O_a = O_a'$$

depending on whether the adjunction of a to O_a' gives an ordered set or not.

The set O_a is defined for every $a \in P$ because otherwise there would be a smallest a for which O_a were undefined, contrary to the construction rule. For the same reason O_a is uniquely defined by a and the well-ordering. The sum set

$$O = \sum O_a, \qquad\qquad a \in P$$

is the desired maximal ordered subset of P. First, it is an ordered set and includes O_0. Secondly, let b be an element in P not in O. Then b cannot belong to O_b, hence the adjunction of b to O_b' does not produce an ordered set. We conclude that O is a maximal ordered set.

The Hausdorff-Kuratowski principle is equivalent to *Zorn's maximal principle*, commonly called *Zorn's lemma*:

Let P be a partially ordered set in which for every ordered set O there is an upper bound $m(O)$ for its elements. Then P contains maximal elements contained in no others.

To prove this principle we take a maximal ordered set O in P; then one must have $m(O) \in O$. But $m(O)$ is also a maximal element in P because if $x > m(O)$ then x could be included in O.

Conversely, to prove the Hausdorff-Kuratowski principle from that of Zorn, we consider the family Q of all those ordered subsets in P which include a given ordered set O. The sets in Q form a partial order by inclusion. Any chain C in Q has an upper bound, namely the sum of the sets in C. Thus Zorn's lemma implies that Q has maximal elements, that is, maximal ordered subsets of P including O.

Finally we establish that the two principles are equivalent to the axiom of choice by deducing it from Zorn's lemma. To certain families F of subsets of a set V there will exist choice functions $f(F)$. We define a partial order for these functions by putting

$$f_1(F_1) \supset f_2(F_2)$$

whenever f_1 is an extension of f_2, that is, $F_1 \supset F_2$ and the two functions coincide on F_2. Then any ordered set $\{f_i\}$ of such functions has an upper bound, namely the function $f(F)$ defined on the sum family

$$F = \sum F_i$$

in such a manner that for any set A_k in F one has

$$f(A_k) = f_i(A_k)$$

where F_i is one of the families to which A_k belongs. We conclude that there exists a maximal choice function for the subsets of V. But then f must be defined for every subset because if it were not defined for some set A one could select some element $a \in A$ and put $f(A) = a$, contrary to the fact that f is maximally defined.

6.3. **Chain sum properties.** There are other formulations of the maximal principles which for many purposes are still more directly applicable. Let V be a set and Γ a property defined for subsets of V. We call Γ a *chain sum property* when it satisfies the condition: If

(6.3.1) $C = \{V_i\}$

is a chain of subsets each having the property Γ then the sum set

(6.3.2) $V_0 = \sum V_i$

has this property.

Let $\{\Gamma\}$ be a collection of set properties. We call a set A a $\{\Gamma\}$-*set* if it possesses all properties in $\{\Gamma\}$. We then have the

CHAIN SUM PRINCIPLE. *Let* $\{\Gamma\}$ *be a collection of chain sum properties and* $\Psi = \{V_i\}$ *the family of* $\{\Gamma\}$-*subsets of a set* V. *Then* Ψ *contains maximal* $\{\Gamma\}$-*sets* $M\{\Gamma\}$.

To bring the chain sum principle in closer contact with applications in algebra and graph theory we shall specify two particular types of properties:

Inclusion property. We denote by F some fixed subset of V and by $\Gamma(F)$ a set uniquely defined by F. We say that a set A has the *inclusion property* Γ when $A \supseteq F$ implies

$$A \supseteq \Gamma(F).$$

Exclusion property. The set A has the *exclusion property* Γ when $A \supseteq F$ implies

$$A \cdot \Gamma(F) = \emptyset.$$

When A does not contain F we consider either relation to be trivially satisfied. The special case $F = \emptyset$ is also permitted. Then $G = \Gamma(\emptyset)$ is some fixed set and the inclusion, resp. exclusion, property Γ means that A contains G, resp. A, is disjoint from G.

The inclusion or exclusion property Γ is of *finite type* when F is a finite set, possibly $F = \emptyset$. We prove:

Inclusion and exclusion properties of finite type are chain sum properties.

PROOF. This is evident when $F = \emptyset$. When this is not the case we denote the finite number of elements in F by

$$f_1, f_2, \cdots, f_k.$$

Suppose that for the chain of Γ-sets (6.3.1) the sum set V_0 in (6.3.2) contains F. Then for each $f_t \in F$ there will be some set $V(f_t)$ in (6.3.1) including it, consequently a set V_l containing all f_t, hence

$$V_m \supset F, \quad m \geq l.$$

For an inclusion property this gives

$$V_m \supset \Gamma(F), \quad V_0 \supset \Gamma(F)$$

while for an exclusion property one concludes

$$V_m \cdot \Gamma(F) = \emptyset, \quad V_0 \cdot \Gamma(F) = \emptyset.$$

Thus we can state the

INCLUSION-EXCLUSION PRINCIPLE. *When* $\{\Gamma\}$ *is a collection of inclusion and exclusion properties of finite type in a set* V *then the family of all* $\{\Gamma\}$-*subsets has maximal sets.*

To illustrate the application in a simple case let G be a group. To show that there exist maximal Abelian subgroups we notice first that the property of being a subgroup H is an inclusion property: when $a, b \in H$ then also the product $a \cdot b$ shall be in H. Secondly, to be Abelian is an exclusion property: when $a \in H$ then H shall contain no element from the set A_a of elements which do not commute with a.

Let us add a few remarks which sometimes facilitate the applications of the Inclusion-Exclusion Principle. Both inclusion and exclusion properties of finite type can be formulated in terms of inclusion and exclusion of finite sets. An inclusion property Γ is satisfied for a set A only when $A \supset F$ implies that A contains all sets

$$(6.3.3) \qquad\qquad\qquad F + g, \qquad\qquad\qquad g \in \Gamma(F).$$

An exclusion property Γ holds when $A \supset F$ implies that A contains none of the sets (6.3.3).

One often desires to establish the existence of maximal subsets in which the elements satisfy certain conditions

$$Q(t_1, t_2, \cdots, t_k),$$

each involving only a finite number of elements. This is achieved by excluding for each Q all finite sets $T = \{t_i\}$ for which Q is not satisfied. On the other hand one may want maximal sets for which no conditions Q hold. These are obtained by excluding all finite sets $T' = \{t_i'\}$ for which they are satisfied.

To show finally that the Inclusion-Exclusion Principle is equivalent to the preceding let us deduce the Hausdorff Principle as a consequence. We take our $\{\Gamma\}$-sets to be ordered subsets in a partial order P. Such a set A is characterized by the property that for any a, $b \in A$ one of the relations $a > b$ or $b > a$ must hold. Thus as exclusion sets one may take all pairs (a, b) for which none of these relations are satisfied.

As an illustration of the use of the preceding principles let us show:

THEOREM 6.3.1. *For each $i \in I$ in an index set I let there be defined a finite family of subsets*

$$(6.3.4) \qquad\qquad \Phi_i = (F_{i,1}, \ldots, F_{i,n_i})$$

of a set V. Then there exists minimal subsets H such that for each $i \in I$ the set H contains at least one set F_{ij} and for every $h \in H$ there is an i such that all F_{ij} contain h.

PROOF. When $\{H^{(k)}\}$ is an inclusion ordered family of subsets containing at least one F_{ij} for each i also the intersection of the $H^{(k)}$ has the same property. If not for a fixed i there would be some set $H^{(k)}$ not containing a given F_{ij}; since there is only a finite number of sets F_{ij} there would be some $H^{(k)}$ containing none of them, contrary to assumption. This establishes the existence of a minimal H and since H is minimal there must be some i for each $h \in H$ such that no set F_{ij} is in $H - v$. This implies that all F_{ij} in Φ_i include h.

The following theorem has a number of applications:

THEOREM 6.3.2.   Let $F = \{A\}$ be a family of finite subsets of a set V with the property that for sets A_1 and A_2 there is also a set $A_0 \supseteq A_1 + A_2$ in F. To every A there is associated a set M_A in V. Then there exists a subset H of V such that for each A

(6.3.5) $$M_C \cdot A \supseteq H \cdot A \supseteq M_B \cdot A$$

for suitable sets $A \subset B \subset C$ in F.

PROOF.   According to Theorem 6.3.1 there is a minimal subset H of V containing at least one of the sets

$$M_B \cdot A, \qquad\qquad\qquad B \supset A$$

for each A. We observed that for every $h \in H \cdot A$ there is a set A_h satisfying

$$h \in M_C \cdot A_h \qquad\qquad \text{for all } C \supset A_h.$$

We select

$$C \supset B + \sum_h A_h, \qquad\qquad h \in H \cdot A$$

in F; then M_C contains $H \cdot A$.

Under certain conditions the inclusion

$$M_C \cdot A \supset M_B \cdot A$$

implies

(6.3.6) $$M_C \cdot A = M_B \cdot A.$$

Then (6.3.5) reduces to

(6.3.7) $$M_C \cdot A = H \cdot A$$

for a suitable $C \supset A$.

As an illustration we may select $F_1 = \{G(A)\}$ to be a family of finite section graphs in a graph G defined over a family of sets $F = \{A\}$ satisfying the conditions of Theorem 6.3.2. To each A or $G(A)$ we associate a subgraph M_A. Then there exists a subgraph H of G with

$$M_C \cdot G(A) \supseteq H \cdot G(A) \supseteq M_B \cdot G(A)$$

for each A and suitable $A \subset B \subset C$ in F. If for instance a graph $M_B \cdot G(A)$ should have local degrees independent of B it is clear that the condition

$$M_C \cdot G(A) = M_B \cdot G(A)$$

is satisfied and so also

$$M_C \cdot G(A) = H \cdot G(A).$$

6.4. Maximal exclusion graphs. A common application of the axiom of choice in graph theory consists in establishing that a given graph G has maximal subgraphs with certain properties. The conditions are often so formulated that one seeks a maximal subgraph H such that a family of special subgraphs

(6.4.1) $\{F_i\}$

shall be *excluded* or *forbidden* in H. We assume usually that the void graph is not a member of (6.4.1). A subgraph H is an *exclusion graph* for the family (6.4.1) when it has none of these graphs as a subgraph; it is a *maximal exclusion graph* if it is not a proper subgraph of another exclusion graph.

When all graphs in (6.4.1) are finite we have a *finite type exclusion*. As examples one may take (6.4.1) to consist of all circuits or all circuits with special properties. The Inclusion-Exclusion Principle gives immediately:

THEOREM 6.4.1. *Let G be an arbitrary graph and* (6.4.1) *a family of finite subgraphs. Then there exist maximal exclusion graphs in G containing any given exclusion graph H_0.*

As an example let us take (6.4.1) to consist of all circuits in G. We conclude from Theorem 6.4.1:

THEOREM 6.4.2. *Every graph contains maximal circuit free subgraphs.*

To give another example we suppose that in the graph G there is assigned a non-negative integer $\kappa(v)$, the *multiplicity*, to each vertex v. Then there exist maximal subgraphs H of G whose local degrees are bounded by these multiplicities

$$\rho_H(v) \leq \kappa(v), \qquad\qquad v \in V.$$

It is sufficient to let the excluded family (6.4.1) be all star subgraphs $S(v)$ of G consisting of $\kappa(v) + 1$ edges with the endpoint v.

It is of interest that from the properties of the excluded subgraphs (6.4.1) one can draw various conclusions in regard to the corresponding maximal exclusion graphs. We prove first:

THEOREM 6.4.3. *When none of the finite subgraphs in* (6.4.1) *have terminal edges then the maximal exclusion graphs H cover the vertices of G.*

PROOF. We shall show that there is at least one edge of H at every non-isolated vertex v in G. If in some H there should be no edges at v then any edge in G with the endpoint v could be added to H without producing any forbidden subgraph in it.

The result in Theorem 6.4.3 can be extended as follows: Let $\mu \geq 1$ be the minimum of the local degrees at any vertex in the excluded subgraphs. Then at a vertex v a maximal exclusion graph H must have at least

$$\min (\mu - 1, \rho(v))$$

edges.

When G is a connected graph one may ask for conditions under which the maximal exclusion graphs H are connected.

THEOREM 6.4.4. *Let G be a connected graph and (6.4.1) a family of finite 2-edge connected subgraphs. Then the maximal ecxlusion graphs must be connected and cover the vertices of G.*

PROOF. When none of the excluded graphs (6.4.1) have separation edges it follows from Theorem 6.4.3 that a maximal exclusion graph H must cover the vertices of G. Suppose that H has some connected component H_1. Since G is connected there exists an edge $E = (a_1, a_2)$ connecting H_1 with some other component H_2. But then E could be added to H without producing any forbidden subgraphs (6.4.1) for they have no separation edges.

When the excluded graphs (6.4.1) are circuits the conditions of Theorem 6.4.4 are fulfilled. One can generalize this theorem as follows: When the graph G is t-edge connected and each excluded graph in (6.4.1) is $(t+1)$-edge connected, then a maximal exclusion graph H is t-edge connected. In particular, when $t = 2$, H has no separating edges.

PROBLEMS

1. Prove analogous theorems when the excluded graphs are t-vertex connected.

2. Find conditions when the maximal exclusion graphs have no separation vertices.

6.5. **Maximal trees.** We shall apply the preceding discussion to the case where the family (6.4.1) of excluded subgraphs consists of all circuits in the graph G. From Theorem 6.4.3 and 6.4.4 follows immediately:

THEOREM 6.5.1. *A connected graph contains maximal trees and these cover the vertices of the graph.*

These maximal tree subgraphs have been given various names, among them *skeletons* or *scaffoldings* of G; we shall refer to them simply as *maximal trees*.

Let $T(G)$ be a maximal tree in a finite connected graph G. One may then obtain $T(G)$ from G by the successive removal of a series of edges

$$(6.5.1) \qquad\qquad E_1, E_2, \cdots, E_k$$

each selected from a circuit in the preceding graph. Evidently all these graphs are connected. The number of vertices in $T(G)$ is v_v, the same as in G. Then by Theorem 4.1.3 the number of edges in the tree $T(G)$ is

$$v_e(T) = v_v - 1.$$

The number k of edges in (6.5.1) required to reduce G to $T(G)$ is therefore

$$(6.5.2) \qquad\qquad \gamma(G) = v_e - v_v + 1$$

where v_e is the number of edges in G.

THEOREM 6.5.2. *The number of edges which must be removed from a finite connected graph to obtain a maximal tree is the circuit rank (6.5.2).*

In Figure 6.5.1 and Figure 6.5.2 a maximal tree is indicated for the graphs of the cube and the octahedron.

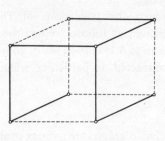
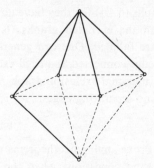

Figure 6.5.1.   Figure 6.5.2.

The existence of maximal trees was established by means of the maximal principle. One can also give a construction based directly upon the axiom of choice. As in Section 2.4 we select a fixed vertex a_0 and write

$$V = a_0 + A_1 + A_2 + \cdots$$

where A_i consists of all vertices a_i with the distance

$$d(a_0, a_i) = i$$

from a_0. At a vertex a_i there are edges connecting it with A_{i-1}. We select a single such edge (a_{i-1}, a_i) for each a_i and eliminate all other edges. One sees that the remaining graph T is connected, and has no circuits; furthermore, the addition of any single edge to T will produce a circuit. This gives the result:

THEOREM 6.5.3. *In a connected graph G let a_0 be some fixed vertex. Then there exists maximal trees T in G such that the distance from a_0 to any vertex v is the same in T as in G.*

PROBLEMS

1. Construct a maximal tree for the graphs of the dodecahedron and the icosahedron.

2. For the infinite graph consisting of the edges of the unit squares in the plane.

3. Show by an example that not all maximal trees are obtainable by the construction in Theorem 6.5.3.

4.* Determine all graphs for which this is the case.

6.6. **Interrelations between maximal graphs.** We shall return to the general case of maximal exclusion graphs H for a family (6.4.1) of forbidden finite graphs. Under certain conditions one can state simple rules for deriving any such graph H_1 from another maximal graph H. The adjunction of a set of edges

$$E = \sum E_i$$

will produce certain forbidden subgraphs F_j in the graph $H+E$. The sum graph

$$F(E) = \sum F_j$$

we may call the *forbidden component of* E in regard to H. Each F_j contains at least one of the edges E_i.

A set of edges

$$R = \sum R_k$$

in $F(E)$ shall be called a *reduction set* for $F(E)$ if the graph $F(E) - R$ has no forbidden subgraphs while no proper subset of R possesses this property. Then the graph

(6.6.1) $$H_1 = H + E - R$$

is an exclusion graph for the family (6.4.1). It is maximal if and only if the adjunction of any single edge E_0 to E produces forbidden subgraphs in the graph (6.6.1), i.e., R cannot be a reduction set for any larger set than E.

The maximal graph H shall be called *singular* if the adjunction of a single edge E to H produces only a single excluded subgraph $F(E)$ in $H + E$. Any edge R in $F(E)$ is then a reduction edge and the graph H_1 in (6.6.1) is an exclusion graph which we say has been obtained from H by a *singular edge exchange*.

We define further: A singular maximal graph is *strongly singular* when it has the property that no forbidden component $F(E_1, E_2)$ defined by two edges can be reduced by a single edge. The preceding discussion shows:

THEOREM 6.6.1. *When H is a strongly singular maximal graph then any singular edge exchange gives another maximal graph.*

Now take H_1 and H_2 to be two different strongly singular maximal graphs and E_2 an edge in H_2 not in H_1. The adjunction of E_2 to H_1 produces a single excluded graph $F(E_2)$ in $H_1 + E_2$. The graph $F(E_2)$ cannot be entirely in H_2 so it contains an edge E_1 in H_1 but not in H_2. The interchange of E_1 and E_2 gives a new maximal graph H_1' differing from H_2 in one pair of edges less than H_1 and H_2. Let us use the terminology that two graphs are *singularly related* when one can be transformed into the other by a series of singular interchanges. Our discussion shows:

THEOREM 6.6.2. *When the maximal exclusion graphs are finite and strongly singular then they are all singularly related, hence have the same number of edges.*

Suppose that G is finite and H an exclusion graph with a maximal number of edges. Then a singular edge exchange must give another such graph without assuming that H is strongly singular. Thus we can also state:

THEOREM 6.6.3. *In a finite graph let all exclusion graphs with a maximal number of edges be singular. Then they are all singularly related.*

Let us apply these observations to the case of maximal trees $T(G)$ in a graph G. When an edge E_1 is added to $T(G)$ the graph

$$T(G) + E_1$$

has a single circuit C_1 since in $T(G)$ there is a single path connecting the end points of E_1. The removal of an edge E_0 from C_1 again gives a tree $T_1(G)$ which we say has been obtained from $T(G)$ by a *singular cyclic interchange*. If one adds two edges E_1 and E_2

$$T(G) + E_1 + E_2$$

will contain at least two different circuits. One readily verifies that then the removal of a single edge E_0 from this graph cannot produce a circuit free graph. Thus we conclude from the preceding:

THEOREM 6.6.4. *When T_1 and T_2 are maximal trees in a finite connected graph then one can be derived from the other by singular cylic interchanges.*

PROBLEMS

1.* One may define the distance between two maximal trees in a finite graph G to be the smallest number of cyclic interchanges required to transfer one into the other. Determine the maximal distance between two such trees.

2.* In the finite graph G let each edge have a measure $\mu(a, b)$, hence each subgraph H a total measure

$$\mu(H) = \sum \mu(E), \qquad\qquad E \subset H.$$

Let $\{H\}$ be a family of strongly singular maximal graphs. Show how one can construct a graph H_0 in $\{H\}$ with minimal total measure by a method analogous to the one used in the Minimal Connector Problem in Section 4.1. Consider the same problem for arbitrary classes of maximal subgraphs.

3.* In a tree there is a unique shortest arc between any two vertices, but there are also other connected graphs with the same property. Try to characterize these "geodetic" graphs in other ways.

CHAPTER 7

MATCHING THEOREMS

7.1. Bipartite graphs. A *bipartite graph* $G = G(V,V')$ is a graph in which the vertex set

$$(7.1.1) \qquad S = V + V', \quad V = \{v\}, \quad V' = \{v'\}$$

decomposes into two disjoint sets V and V' such that each edge $E = (v, v')$ connects a vertex $v \in V$ with a vertex $v' \in V'$. This special type of graphs plays a considerable role in various applications.

A subgraph of a bipartite graph is bipartite. If G is connected each vertex $v \in V$ has an even distance from vertices in V and an odd distance from those in V'. One may ask when a given graph can be represented as a bipartite graph:

THEOREM 7.1.1. *A graph is bipartite if and only if all circuits in G have even lengths.*

PROOF. Clearly, in a bipartite graph the condition is fulfilled. Suppose conversely that G has this property. We select a vertex a_0 in a connected component G_0 of G. The vertex set S of G_0 decomposes as in (7.1.1) where V consists of the vertices at even distances from a_0 and V' of those with an odd distance. To show, for instance that no two vertices v_1 and v_2 in V can be joined by an edge $E = (v_1, v_2)$ we take

$$P(a_0, v_1), \ Q(a_0, v_2)$$

as shortest arcs from a_0. Both have even lengths. When b is the last common vertex in P and Q the distances $d(b, v_1)$ and $d(b, v_2)$ are either both even or both odd. If there existed an edge E between v_1 and v_2 the path

$$P(b, v_1) + E + Q(v_2, b)$$

would be an odd circuit contrary to assumption. In the same way one shows that no two vertices in V' are connected by an edge. Thus all components G_0 and so G itself is bipartite.

Since a bipartite subgraph G of an arbitrary given graph G is characterized by the fact that B shall contain no odd circuits, it follows from the general results in Chapter 6:

THEOREM 7.1.2. *Every graph G contains maximal bipartite subgraphs B_0. When G is connected, these graphs B_0 are also connected and cover the vertices of G.*

A direct method for the construction of a maximal bipartite subgraph of the connected graph G is the following. One selects a vertex a_0 and decomposes the vertex set S of G

$$S = a_0 + A_1 + A_2 + \cdots$$

where A_i consists of the vertices at the distance i from a_0. In each A_i one eliminates all edges connecting two of its vertices. Then the remaining graph is seen to be a maximal bipartite subgraph.

We state next a theorem due to Rado:

THEOREM 7.1.3. *Let $G(V, V')$ be a bipartite graph which is locally finite in V. For each finite set $A \subset V$ let there be defined a choice function*

$$f_A(a), \qquad\qquad\qquad a \in A$$

associating with the unique edge $(a, f_A(a))$ from it. Then there exists a choice function $f_V(v)$ for V with the property that for each A there exists a set $C \supset A$ such that

$$f_V(a) = f_C(a), \qquad\qquad\qquad a \in A.$$

The theorem may be considered a special case of Theorem 6.3.2. We denote by $G\{A\}$ the finite graphs consisting of all edges with an endpoint in A. To each we associate the subgraph M_A defined by the edges $(a, f_A(a))$ of its choice function. As in (6.3.5) we obtain for each A

$$M_C \cdot G\{A\} \supseteq H \cdot G\{A\} \supseteq M_B \cdot G\{A\},$$

$$A \subset B \subset C$$

for a suitable graph H. This implies

$$M_C \cdot G\{A\} = M_B \cdot G\{A\}$$

so that

$$M_C \cdot G\{A\} = H \cdot G\{A\}.$$

This is equivalent to the fact that H defines a choice function which coincides with f_C on A.

PROBLEMS

1. Prove that G is bipartite if and only if for a fixed a_0 there is no edge $E = (b, c)$ such that

$$d(a_0, b) = d(a_0, c).$$

2. Determine a maximal bipartite subgraph for each of the Platonic graphs.
3. Are the maximal bipartite subgraphs singular in the sense of Section 6.6?

7.2. **Deficiencies.** A number of important applications of graph theory are consequences of the so-called *matching theorems* for bipartite graphs. To prove these theorems we make use of the *deficiency functions* which we shall now introduce. We assume that in the bipartite graph G under consideration the vertices $v \in V$ in the vertex set (7.1.1) have finite local degrees $\rho(v)$.

Take A to be a finite subset of V. The number of vertices in A we denote by $v(A)$ and the number of edges from A by $\rho(A)$. For two such sets A_1 and A_2 one has evidently

(7.2.1) $$v(A_1 + A_2) + v(A_1 \cdot A_2) = v(A_1) + v(A_2)$$

and

(7.2.2) $$\rho(A_1 + A_2) + \rho(A_1 \cdot A_2) = \rho(A_1) + \rho(A_2).$$

To each subset A of V there exists an associated subset $V'(A)$ of V' consisting of all those vertices in V' which are joined by an edge to at least one vertex in A. When A is finite also $V'(A)$ is finite due to the local finiteness condition on V. For the sets $V'(A)$ one has the relation

(7.2.3) $$v(V'(A_1 + A_2)) + v(V'(A_1 \cdot A_2)) \leqq v(V'(A_1)) + v(V'(A_2)).$$

To verify this we notice that the vertices in $V'(A_1 + A_2)$ are those which are connected with A_1 or A_2 or both so we can write

$$v(V'(A_1 + A_2)) = v(V'(A_1)) + v(V'(A_2)) - \Delta$$

where Δ is the number of vertices counted in both $V'(A_1)$ and $V'(A_2)$. These consist of the $v(V'(A_1 \cdot A_2))$ vertices of $V'(A_1 \cdot A_2)$ and in addition those vertices which are connected both to A_1 and A_2 but not to $A_1 \cdot A_2$. If there are no such vertices we have

(7.2.4) $$V'(A_1 \cdot A_2) = V'(A_1) \cdot V'(A_2)$$

and the equality holds in (7.2.3).

For any finite subset A of V the difference

$$\delta(A) = v(A) - v(V'(A))$$

shall be called its *deficiency*.

THEOREM 7.2.1. *For the deficiencies of two sets A_1 and A_2 one has*

(7.2.5) $$\delta(A_1 + A_2) + \delta(A_1 \cdot A_2) \geq \delta(A_1) + \delta(A_2).$$

PROOF. This relation follows by subtracting (7.2.3) from (7.2.1). It holds also when the intersection of the two sets is void provided one puts

(7.2.6) $$\delta(\emptyset) = 0$$

a convention we shall adopt in the following. The equality holds in (7.2.5) if and only if (7.2.4) holds. We notice that the deficiencies are integers.

We shall from now on introduce a further limitation on our graph:

Bounded deficiencies. For the finite subsets of V there shall exist an upper bound for the deficiencies.

There will then exist some *maximal deficiency* δ_0 and correspondingly some sets of maximal deficiency or *critical sets* such that

(7.2.7) $$\delta(A) = \delta_0.$$

According to the convention (7.2.6) one always has $\delta_0 \geq 0$. If $\delta_0 \neq 0$ the sets satisfying (7.2.7) are non-void.

THEOREM 7.2.2. *When A_1 and A_2 are critical sets then both their sum and intersection have the same property; furthermore they satisfy (7.2.4).*

PROOF. From

$$\delta(A_1) = \delta(A_2) = \delta_0$$

and Theorem 7.2.1 it follows that

$$\delta(A_1 + A_2) + \delta(A_1 \cdot A_2) \geq 2\delta_0.$$

Since δ_0 was the maximal deficiency this is only possible when

$$\delta(A_1 + A_2) = \delta(A_1 \cdot A_2) = \delta_0.$$

Theorem 7.2.2 yields immediately:

THEOREM 7.2.3. *There exists a unique minimal critical set N contained in all other critical sets. When V is finite there is a unique maximal critical set containing all others.*

One has $N = \emptyset$ if and only if $\delta_0 = 0$.

Let us say that a subset A of V is *without deficiency* if no subset of A has positive deficiency. The entire set V is without deficiency if and only if $\delta_0 = 0$.

Denote by A_1 some critical set and A_2 a finite set disjoint from A_1. By Theorem 7.2.1 one has

$$\delta(A_1 + A_2) \geqq \delta(A_1) + \delta(A_2)$$

and consequently $\delta(A_2) \leqq 0$. When this remark is applied to $A_1 = N$ we conclude:

THEOREM 7.2.4.   *The vertex set V can be decomposed uniquely*

(7.2.8) $$V = N + \bar{N}$$

where N is the minimal critical set and its complement $\bar{N}$ is a set without deficiency.

We mention the further fact:

THEOREM 7.2.5.   *In the set $V'(N)$ defined by a minimal critical set N there must be at least two edges from N at every vertex.*

PROOF.   Suppose that for some $a' \in V'(N)$ there were only a single edge (a, a') from N. Then the set $N - a$ cannot have a deficiency less than δ_0 and this would make $N - a$ critical contrary to the definition of N.

7.3. **The matching theorems.** We shall now examine the effect upon the maximal deficiency of removing a vertex $a_1 \in V$ and all its edges from G. When A is a subset of V not containing a_1 the removal of a_1 and its edges cannot have any effect upon the deficiency of A. Thus if there is some critical set not containing a_1 its deficiency remains δ_0. On the other hand, if a_1 is contained in every critical set hence in N there is no longer any set of deficiency δ_0 in V. From Theorem 7.2.5 follows readily that

$$\delta(N - a_1) = \delta_0 - 1$$

and the new minimal critical set N_1 is contained in $N - a_1$. We state:

THEOREM 7.3.1.   *The removal of a vertex a_1 and all its edges from V will only change the maximal deficiency when $a_1 \in N$ and then the new maximal deficiency is*

$$\delta_0' = \delta_0 - 1.$$

By repetition of this reduction it follows:

THEOREM 7.3.2.   *When the maximal deficiency of the vertex set V is $\delta_0 > 0$ and N the minimal critical set then V can be reduced to a set without deficiency through the removal of δ_0 suitably chosen vertices in N and the edges from them.*

Suppose next that V is a set without deficiency. We shall examine the possibility of removing from the graph G a connected pair of vertices (a, a') and all edges with these endpoints in such a way that in the resulting graph G_1 the vertex set $V_1 = V - a$ remains without deficiency.

Assume first that V has no non-void set of zero deficiency. We can then remove an arbitrary edge (a, a') and the corresponding edges. If namely A_1 is an arbitrary finite subset of V_1 then it is also a subset of V and according to assumption the associated set $V'(A_1)$ in G must contain at least one more vertex than A_1. The removal of a' from V' can at most result in one vertex less in the associated set in G_1 so that one must still have $\delta_1(A_1) \leqq 0$.

Secondly, let there exist non-void subsets of zero deficiency in V. Among these we select a minimal one A. We have $a \in A$ and a' as the endpoint of some edge (a, a'). Again let A_1 run through the finite subsets of $V_1 = V - a$.

In case $\delta(A_1) < 0$ the previous argument shows that one still has $\delta_1(A_1) \leqq 0$ in G_1. Thus there remains the case $\delta(A_1) = 0$. Since $A \neq \emptyset$ was minimal among those with zero deficiency we conclude from Theorem 7.2.2 that either A_1 contains A or the two sets are disjoint. The first alternative is excluded since A_1 does not contain a. Consequently A_1 has zero deficiency and is disjoint from A. But then according to Theorem 7.2.2 the condition (7.2.4) is fulfilled so that the sets $V'(A)$ and $V'(A_1)$ are also disjoint. As a consequence the removal of the edges from the vertices

$$a \in A, \quad a' \in V'(a)$$

cannot influence the deficiency of A_1 so that it remains $\delta_1(A_1) = 0$ in G_1.

We define: a subset A of V is *matched* to a subset A' of V' if there exists a one-to-one correspondence between A and A' such that corresponding vertices are connected by an edge. We shall also call such a matching a *partial matching* of V upon V' and denote it by $\{A, M_A\}$ where M_A is used to indicate the various matchings which may be selected. The set of all partial matchings form a partially ordered set if one defines

$$\{A, M_A\} \supset \{B, M_B\}$$

when $A \supset B$ and M_A is an extension of M_B.

We return to the case where V has no deficiency. A partial matching $\{A, M_A\}$ shall be called *proper* if after the removal of all vertices in V and V' involved in M_A as well as the edges issuing from these vertices, the remaining set $V - A$ is without deficiency in the reduced graph.

LEMMA.   *Every proper partial matching is contained in a maximal matching which is a matching of the whole set V.*

PROOF.   This lemma is evident when V is a finite set according to the preceding. When V is infinite we use the maximal principle and consider an ordered set of proper partial matchings $\{A, M_A\}$. The sum set $\sum A$ is then also matched in a proper matching. If namely $V - \sum A$ should contain any finite subset B which had positive deficiency then this would have been produced by the removal of certain edges issuing from B. But originally there was only a finite number of such edges, hence B would obtain a positive deficiency already by the removal of the edges in one of the matchings $\{A, M_A\}$, contrary to the fact that these were proper. Furthermore, if A_0 is a maximal set with a proper matching then $A_0 = V$ because otherwise A_0 could be increased by the mapping of a further vertex as we have shown.

The preceding discussion leads to the *main matching theorem*:

THEOREM 7.3.3.   *Let the vertex set V be locally finite and have the maximal deficiency δ_0. Then one can find a subset D of V with δ_0 vertices such that $V - D$ is matched upon a subset of V' and δ_0 is the smallest number with this property. A necessary and sufficient condition that V can be matched upon a subset of V' is that V have no deficiency.*

PROOF.   If V contains a subset A with positive deficiency the vertices in A cannot be matched upon $V'(A)$ because the latter set contains too few vertices. We have seen that δ_0 is the smallest number of vertices which must be removed from V in order to obtain a set without deficiency. The rest of the theorem follows from the lemma. The proof could have been simplified through the use of Theorem 7.1.3.

In case V is a finite set it is not necessary to impose the restriction that its vertices be locally finite, because by eliminating edges one can obtain a subgraph G' of G with finite local degrees and the same maximal deficiency. Let V contain n vertices. No subset A of V containing at least one vertex a of infinite degree $\rho(a)$ can have a positive deficiency. This remains true if one eliminates from a all but n edges. The remaining graph G' is locally finite and has the same sets of positive deficiency as G. Theorem 7.3.3 gives:

THEOREM 7.3.4.   *When the vertex set V is finite with n vertices and maximal deficiency δ_0 then the maximal number of vertices which can be matched upon V' is*

$$\mu = n - \delta_0.$$

The last part of Theorem 7.3.3 is equivalent to the theorem of P. Hall on *set representatives*:

THEOREM 7.3.5. *Let* $F(A_i)$ *be a family of finite subsets of a set* V'. *If any* k *of the sets* A_i *contain at least* k *elements then one can find distinct elements* $a_i' \in V'$ *such that for each* i

$$a_i' \in A_i.$$

The proof is immediate by letting the sets A_i be the vertices in V and joining any A_i by edges to the elements a_j' in V' which belong to A_i. One also has the more general result from Theorem 7.3.3:

THEOREM 7.3.6. *If in Theorem 7.3.5 there exists a fixed number* δ_0 *such that any* k *of the sets* A_i *contain at least* $k - \delta_0$ *elements then one can find distinct representatives* a_i *for all but* δ_0 *sets in the family* $F(A_i)$.

We observe finally by means of Theorem 7.3.4 that when the family $F(A_i)$ has only a finite number of sets it is unnecessary to assume that the A_i be finite sets in Theorems 7.3.5 and 7.3.6.

7.4. **Mutual matchings.** Until now we have studied the matchings of the set V into V'. Next we shall investigate the mutual matchings of V into V' and V' into V. We prove first:

THEOREM 7.4.1. *Let* M *be a matching of a subset* A *of* V *into* V' *and* M' *a matching of a subset* A' *of* V' *into* V. *Then from the edges in* M *and* M' *one can construct a partial matching between* V *and* V' *in which all vertices in* A *and* A' *are included.*

PROOF. From each vertex $a \in A$ there is a unique edge $E = (a, v')$ in M and for each vertex $a' \in V'$ a unique edge $E' = (a', v)$ in M'. Thus the graph $M + M'$ has at most two edges at each vertex in $A + A'$ and at most one edge at other vertices in $V + V'$. Suppose that two vertices a_0 and a_0' are connected by the same edge $E = (a_0, a_1')$ in M and M'. Then we leave a_0 and a_0' matched. Suppose next that $E_0 = (a_0, a_0')$ is in M and there is a different edge $E_0' = (a_0', a_1)$ in M' at a_0'. We may continue from a_1 in some edge $E_1 = (a_1, a_1')$ in M and repeat this process as far as possible. As a result one obtains a path

(7.4.1) $(a_0, a_0')\ (a_0', a_1)\ (a_1, a_1')\ (a_1', a_2)$

whose edges belong alternatingly to M and M'. The path (7.4.1) can only be finite when it returns to $a_0 = a_n$. Then a one-to-one matching between the vertices a_i and a_i' is defined by the edges $E_i = (a_i, a_i')$ (see Figure 7.4.1).

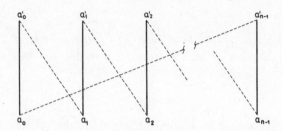

Figure 7.4.1

Let the path (7.4.1) be infinite. Then there may be some incoming edge E'_{-1} $= (a'_{-1}, a_0)$ in M' to a_0 and at a'_{-1} some incoming edge $E_{-1} = (a_{-1}, a'_{-1})$ in M and so on. In this manner the path (7.4.1) may be continued also in the opposite direction. If the construction should come to a halt at some vertex a_{-n} the edges E_i may be used to establish a one-to-one matching between the two vertex sets in the path. If the path should end at some vertex a'_{-n} the edges E'_i may be used. Finally when (7.4.1) can be continued indefinitely in both directions one can use either family of edges (see Figure 7.4.2).

Figure 7.4.2.

When in Theorem 7.4.1 one has $A = V$ and $A' = V'$ the so-called *Bernstein Theorem* follows:

THEOREM 7.4.2. *Let M be a matching of V into V' and M' a matching of V' into V. Then from the edges in M and M' one can construct a one-to-one matching of V onto V'.*

Originally this theorem was introduced to prove the following result from the theory of sets: When a set A is in a one-to-one correspondence with a subset of a set B and also B in a one-to-one correspondence with a subset of A then there exists a one-to-one correspondence between A and B.

From now on we shall suppose that the graph G is locally finite at all vertices in V and V'. Then a deficiency function $\delta'(A')$ can also be introduced for the finite subsets A' of V'. By combining Theorem 7.4.2 with Theorem 7.3.3 one obtains:

THEOREM 7.4.3. *Let G be a locally finite bipartite graph. A necessary and sufficient condition that its two vertex sets V and V' can be one-to-one matched upon each other is that the two maximal deficiencies for V and V' be*

$$(7.4.2) \qquad\qquad\qquad \delta_0 = \delta'_0 = 0.$$

A matching can be defined as a subgraph M of G such that M has exactly one edge at each vertex of G, that is, M is a *regular subgraph of first degree*. Thus Theorem 7.4.3 expresses a necessary and sufficient condition for G to have such a subgraph.

Among the popular versions of this theory is its interpretation as the so-called *marriage* or *dancing problem*. In a group there is an equal number of maidens and swains. Each man is acquainted with a certain number of girls and each girl knows a certain number of men. Under what conditions is it possible to find an arrangement such that each individual can have an acquaintance as a partner?

The so-called assignment problem is an interpretation of a more practical nature: A group of individuals are available for certain jobs. Each individual is qualified only for some of the jobs. When is it possible to fill the positions with qualified men? There are many other versions which may be formulated in terms of fittings, matchings or splicings.

Theorem 7.4.3 can also be formulated as a theorem on sets:

THEOREM 7.4.4. *Let*

$$(7.4.3) \qquad\qquad\qquad F(A_i), \; F'(A'_i)$$

be two families of subsets of a set S. We suppose that each A_i overlaps only a finite number of the sets A'_j and conversely. In order that one can match the sets in the two families (7.4.3) in such a manner that corresponding sets A'_i and A_i have a non-void intersection it is necessary and sufficient that any k sets $(k = 1, 2, \cdots)$ A_i always overlap at least k sets A'_i and vice versa.

To prove Theorem 7.4.4 from Theorem 7.4.3 one lets the sets A_i be the vertices in V and A'_j the vertices in V' and there is an edge (A_i, A'_j) in G if and only if the two sets overlap.

We observe explicitly that Theorem 7.4.4 does not imply that one can find a set of *distinct common representatives* for the sets in the two families (7.4.4), that is, a set of elements a_i such that

$$a_i \in A_i, \quad a_i \in A'_i, \qquad\qquad a_i \neq a_j.$$

To establish conditions for such representatives seems to be a problem of considerable difficulty. However, when one of the families (7.4.3) consists of disjoint sets one obtains such a set of representatives from the matching simply by selecting $a'_i \in A_i \cdot A'_i$ arbitrarily.

Let us make a few observations on the actual construction of a matching M. One may begin by selecting some edge $E = (a, a')$ to belong to M and then remove from G all edges with the endpoints a and a'. The remaining graph can be matched if and only if it has no subsets with positive deficiencies. Let A_1 be a set in $V-a$ with the deficiency $\delta(A_1)$ in G. The removal of the vertex a' will only change the deficiency of A_1 when $a' \in V'(A_1)$ and then it is increased to

$$\delta_1(A_1) = \delta(A) + 1$$

in G_1. Thus in the set $V-a$ the maximal deficiency in G_1 is $\delta_1 = 0$ except when $a' \in V'(A_1)$ for some critical set A_1 in G. This cannot occur when one selects $a \in A_0$ for some minimal critical set $A_0 \neq \emptyset$ in V. In that case any other critical set A_1 in G would either contain A_0 or be disjoint from A_0. The first alternative is excluded since $a \notin A_1$. In the second no vertex a' in an edge $E = (a, a')$ can belong to $V'(A_1)$ because, as one readily sees, one would have

$$\delta(A_0 + A_1) > 0,$$

contrary to assumption. We conclude that $\delta_1 = 0$ in G_1. In the finite case one sees from Theorem 7.4.3 that also $\delta'_1 = 0$ in the set $V'-a'$. (In the infinite case the same conclusion may be drawn as the reader may verify from the considerations in Section 7.6.) Our discussion shows that one obtains a matching by successive selections of edges $E_i = (a, a')$ in the various reduced graphs where each a can be taken as an arbitrary vertex in any minimal critical set.

In the first step one has $\rho(a)$ choices for the edges from a. When the edges from the corresponding vertex a' are removed the local degrees in the set $V-a$ are at most reduced by one unit, provided they are single. Thus at the next vertex one has at least $\rho(b)-1$ choices and so on. This leads to an observation by M. Hall: *Let G be a bipartite graph with single edges for which there exists at least one matching. Then G has at least $\rho_0!$ matchings where*

$$\rho_0 = \min[\rho(a)], \qquad\qquad a \in V.$$

The number of contributions to the matching problem is considerable. The preceding discussion follows in the main a paper by the author. The bibliography includes papers giving different proofs as well as other results on matchings.

1. Try to improve on the lower bound for the number of matchings given above.

2. Try to find upper bounds for the same number.

7.5. **Matchings in special graphs.** There exist various special bipartite graphs for which one can establish fairly easily that a matching exists by showing directly that no finite vertex set can have positive deficiency.

Let G be a regular graph of degree m so that

$$(7.5.1) \qquad\qquad m = \rho(a) = \rho(a')$$

for all vertices $a \in V$ and $a' \in V'$. Then we have:

THEOREM 7.5.1. *A regular graph has no deficiency.*

PROOF. For any finite set $A \subset V$ with $v(A)$ vertices there are

$$\rho(A) = m \cdot v(A)$$

edges having an endpoint in A. These edges all have their other end in $V'(A)$. The total number of edges with an end in $V'(A)$ is

$$m \cdot v(V'(A))$$

and so

$$m \cdot v(V'(A)) \geqq m \cdot v(A).$$

This gives

$$\delta(A) = v(A) - v(V'(A)) \leqq 0$$

as desired.

The graph M_1 consisting of the edges in a matching is a regular graph of degree 1. When the edges of M_1 are eliminated from G the remaining graph

$$G_1 = G - M_1$$

is regular of degree $m-1$. Thus it also has a regular subgraph M_2 of degree 1 whose edges may be eliminated. This reduction can be continued until the graph is exhausted. This leads to:

THEOREM 7.5.2. *A regular bipartite graph of degree m is the edge direct sum*

$$G = \sum_i M_i$$

of m regular subgraphs M_i of degree 1.

This theorem on regular graphs may be applied to the case where one has two decompositions of the same set

(7.5.2) $$S = \sum B_i = \sum B'_j$$

into disjoint blocks B_i and B'_j each containing m elements. We conclude that there exists a set of common representatives for the two families of blocks.

These observations can be used to establish certain properties of coset expansions in groups. Let S be an arbitrary group and A and B finite subgroups of the same order m. Then the coset expansions of S with respect to A and B are disjoint decompositions of the type (7.5.2). We conclude that there exists a set $\{g\}$ of common representatives such that

(7.5.3) $$S = \sum gA = \sum Bg.$$

Similarly there will exist decompositions

(7.5.4) $$S = \sum Ag' = \sum g'B$$

with the same right and left representatives. This result is due to Scorza. In particular, when $A = B$ one obtains an expansion

(7.5.5) $$S = \sum g'A = \sum Ag'$$

with the same representatives for the right and left cosets, a fact first established by Miller and Chapman.

We remark in this connection that due to the special properties of groups it can be shown that expansions (7.5.5) will exist also for general types of infinite subgroups (see Ore). However, the theorem is not always true as shown by an example given by Shü.

We shall investigate next certain graphs which we shall call *nearly regular*. This means that the local degrees of the bipartite graph G have the form

(7.5.6) $$\rho(a) = m - d(a), \quad \rho(a') = m - d(a')$$

where the deviations $d(a)$ and $d(a')$ are positive or negative integers, but only a finite number of them different from zero. We write

(7.5.7) $$\sum d(a) = P + N, \quad \sum d(a') = P' + N'$$

where P is the sum of the positive and N the sum of negative deviations in V while P' and N' have the same meaning for V'. These quantities shall be bounded as follows:

(7.5.8) $$P + |N'| < m, \quad P' + |N| < m.$$

Then we can show:

THEOREM 7.5.3.   *A nearly regular graph G in which the deviations defined by (7.5.6) satisfy the conditions (7.5.8) has a regular subgraph of first degree.*

PROOF.   According to (7.5.6) there are

$$\rho(A) = m \cdot v(A) - \sum d(a), \qquad\qquad a \epsilon A$$

edges having an endpoint in a finite set A. These edges connect A with $V'(A)$. The number of edges from this set is

$$\rho(V'(A)) = m \cdot v(V'(A)) - \sum d(a'), \qquad a' \epsilon V'(A).$$

This number is not less than $\rho(A)$, so by subtraction one obtains

$$m \cdot \delta(A) + \sum d(a') - \sum d(a) \leq 0.$$

From this follows

$$m \cdot \delta(A) \leq P + |N'| < m,$$

and since $\delta(A)$ is an integer we conclude that $\delta(A) \leq 0$ as desired.

Theorem 7.5.3 is an extension of Theorem 7.5.1. Theorem 7.5.2 has a generalization which runs as follows:

THEOREM 7.5.4.   *If in a nearly regular graph G there is a positive integer $t \leq m$ such that in (7.5.7) one has*

$$P + |N'| \leq m - t, \quad P' + |N| \leq m - t$$

then G has a subgraph

$$G_0 = \sum M_i \qquad\qquad (i = 1, 2, \cdots, t)$$

which is the edge direct sum of t regular graphs of first degree.

The proof shall be left to the reader (see Ore). As an application of Theorem 7.5.3 we find:

THEOREM 7.5.5.   *When G is a regular graph of degree m then G has a matching in which $m-1$ arbitrarily prescribed edges do not appear.*

PROOF. When $m-1$ edges are removed from G there remains a nearly regular graph in which all deviations (7.5.6) are positive and

$$\sum d(a) = \sum d(a') = m - 1.$$

Next we shall prove the following generalization of Theorem 7.5.2.

THEOREM 7.5.6. *In the bipartite graph G let there exist a least upper bound m for the local degrees. Then G is the sum of m edge disjoint partial matchings.*

PROOF. We denote by A_m and A'_m respectively the subsets of V and V' consisting of the vertices with the local degree m. By the argument used in the proof of Theorem 7.5.1 one shows that no subsets of A_m and A'_m can have positive deficiencies, hence there exists partial matchings for the vertices in each set. According to Theorem 7.4.1 two such matchings can be combined into a single partial matching M_m for G including all vertices in A_m and A'_m. When M_m is subtracted from G one obtains a new graph in which the maximal local degree is $m - 1$.

By successive reductions of this kind the theorem follows.

A matching theorem of a somewhat different kind is the following:

THEOREM 7.5.7. *Let G be a graph with n vertices in each vertex set and satisfying the two conditions:*

1. No subset of V or V' with less than l vertices has positive deficiency.

2. Any l vertices in V are connected by edges to at least $n/2$ vertices in V' and conversely.

Then G has a matching.

PROOF. When $A \subset V$ has at least l vertices it follows from condition 2

$$v(V'(A)) \geqq n/2.$$

If such a set should have positive deficiency one would have

$$v(A) > n/2.$$

For the minimal critical set N' in V' one would obtain similarly, if it exists,

$$v(V(N')) \geqq n/2.$$

But in the following Theorem 7.6.1 we establish that when A is a critical set the sets A and $V(N')$ are disjoint, hence

$$v(A + V(N')) > n$$

contrary to the fact that V has only n vertices. Thus G can have no sets with positive deficiency.

According to Theorem 7.5.7 matchings exist in the following cases:

1. Each vertex in V is connected by edges to at least $n/2$ vertices in V' and conversely.

2. G has no terminal edges and any two vertices in V are connected to at least $n/2$ vertices in V' and conversely.

Some of the preceding results for locally finite graphs hold also when the degrees are at most countable. Theorem 7.5.2 has the extension:

THEOREM 7.5.8. *Let G be a connected bipartite graph in which the vertex sets*

$$(7.5.9) \qquad\qquad V = (a_1, a_2, \cdots), \quad V' = (a_1', a_2', \cdots)$$

are countable and each vertex in one set connected with a countable number of vertices in the other. Then

$$(7.5.10) \qquad\qquad G = \sum M_i, \qquad\qquad i = 1, 2, \cdots$$

is the edge direct sum of a sequence of complete matchings.

PROOF. Under the given conditions also the number of edges in G is countable

$$(7.5.11) \qquad\qquad E_1, E_2, \cdots .$$

We establish first that G has a complete matching M_1 which includes a given edge E_1. For this purpose we construct a matching M of V into V' by first selecting E_1 and then successively some edge F_i at each of the other vertices a_i in (7.5.9). This is always possible since at each stage the number of edges already selected is finite. Similarly a matching M' of V' into V including E_1 is obtained. As in Section 7.4 M and M' may be combined by the Bernstein theorem to yield a complete matching M_1 of G including E_1. The remaining graph $G-M_1$ is of the same type as G, hence a matching M_2 may be constructed in it which includes the first edge in the sequence (7.5.11) not belonging to M_1. The repetition of this process yields the formula (7.5.10).

7.6. **Bipartite graphs with positive deficiencies.** In the preceding matching theorems we were concerned mainly with graphs in which the conditions (7.4.2) were fulfilled so that there were no sets with positive deficiencies. We shall examine next in some detail the case where the two vertex sets V and V' have positive maximal deficiencies δ_0 and δ_0'. We derive first some auxilliary facts about the interrelations between the deficiencies of subsets of V and V'.

LEMMA 1. *When A and A' are subsets of V and V' respectively then in each of the intersections*

$$(7.6.1) \qquad\qquad D = A \cdot V(A'), \quad D' = A' \cdot V'(A)$$

each vertex is always connected to a vertex in the other.

PROOF. When $a' \in D'$ then $a' \in V'(A)$ and so there is an edge (a, a') with $a \in A$. But all edges from a' must go to $V(A')$ by the definition of this set and so $a \in D$ (Figure 7.6.1).

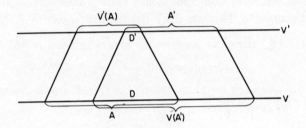

Figure 7.6.1.

An immediate consequence of Lemma 1 is:

LEMMA 2. *One of the relations*

$$D = \emptyset, \quad D' = \emptyset$$

implies the other.

Next we shall show:

LEMMA 3. *One has*

(7.6.2) $$\delta(A) - \delta(A - D) \leqq v(D) - v(D').$$

PROOF. According to the definition of the deficiency function

$$\delta(A) = v(A) - v(V'(A)),$$

$$\delta(A - D) = v(A - D) - v(V'(A - D))$$

and so by subtraction

(7.6.3) $$\delta(A) - \delta(A - D) = v(D) - v(V'(A)) + v(V'(A - D)).$$

No edge (a_1, a_1') from a vertex $a_1 \in A - D$ can go to a vertex $a_1' \in A'$ since a_1 is not in the set $V(A')$. We conclude that

$$V'(A - D) \subseteq V'(A) - D'$$

and so (7.6.2) follows from (7.6.3).

LEMMA 4.

(7.6.4) $$\delta(A) + \delta'(A') \leqq \delta(A-D) + \delta(A'-D').$$

PROOF.   For A' one has the inequality corresponding to (7.6.2)

$$\delta'(A') - \delta'(A'-D') \leqq v(D') - v(D)$$

and when this is added to (7.6.2) the inequality (7.6.4) is obtained.

A consequence of Lemma 4 is:

LEMMA 5.   *When A and A' are critical sets then $A-D$ and $A'-D'$ are critical.*

Finally we have

LEMMA 6.   *When A is a critical set in V and N' the minimal critical set in V' then*

(7.6.5) $$N' \cdot V'(A) = A \cdot V(N') = \emptyset.$$

PROOF.   According to Lemma 5 the set

$$N' - D' = N' - V'(A) \cdot N'$$

is critical. Since N' is a minimal such set this is only possible when

$$V'(A) \cdot N' = \emptyset$$

and the second relation (7.6.5) follows from Lemma 2.

From the preceding lemmas we shall deduce the following facts about the structure of the graph G:

THEOREM 7.6.1.   *Each of the vertex sets of a bipartite graph can be decomposed into three disjoint subsets*

(7.6.6)
$$V = N + V(N') + R,$$
$$V' = N' + V'(N) + R'$$

where N and N' are the minimal critical sets in V and V'. The section graph $G(R, R')$ consisting of the edges joining R and R' has no deficiency. Any critical set in V has the form $N + A$ where A is a subset of R with zero deficiency in $G(R, R')$.

When the vertex sets V and V' are finite with n and n' vertices, then

(7.6.7) $$v(R) = v(R')$$

and

(7.6.8) $$n - \delta_0 = n' - \delta_0'.$$

Proof. The situation is indicated schematically in Figure 7.6.2.

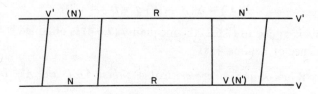

Figure 7.6.2.

According to Lemma 6 the sets N and $V(N')$ are disjoint so one can write V in the form (7.6.6) where R denotes the set of remaining vertices. Since R is disjoint from $V(N')$ the vertices in R can only be joined by edges to vertices in the set

$$V'(N) + R'.$$

The deficiency of a set $A \subset R$ in the graph $G(R, R')$ is

$$\delta_1(A) = v(A) - v(R'(A))$$

and one verifies that in G

(7.6.9) $$\delta(N + A) = \delta_0 - \delta_1(A).$$

Thus $\delta_1(A)$ cannot be positive.

If $\delta_1(A) = 0$ then (7.6.9) shows that

$$\delta(N + A) = \delta_0$$

and $N + A$ is critical. On the other hand, if N_1 is a critical set in V it is disjoint from $V(N')$ according to Lemma 6 and we can write $N_1 = N + A$ and find $\delta_1(A) = 0$.

When V and V' are finite one must have the relation (7.6.7) since $G(R, R')$ has no deficiency. From (7.6.6) follows

$$n = v(N) + v(V(N')) + v(R),$$

$$n' = v(N') + v(V'(N)) + v(R')$$

and by subtraction one obtains (7.5.8).

From Theorem 7.6.1 we derive an extension of the previous matching theorem:

THEOREM 7.6.2. *Let G be a bipartite graph with the maximal deficiencies δ_0 and δ_0'. Then one can find a subset D of N with δ_0 vertices and a subset D' of N' with δ_0' vertices such that the sets*

$$V - D, \quad V' - D'$$

can be matched upon each other and δ_0 and δ_0' are the smallest numbers with this property.

PROOF. We saw in Theorem 7.3.2 that in order to reduce V to a set without deficiency one had to remove a set D of δ_0 vertices and the edges from them from the set N. But this operation can have no effect upon the deficiency of the set V' since according to Theorem 7.6.1 there are no edges from N' to N. Therefore one must in addition remove a set D' of δ_0' vertices from N' to obtain that $V' - D'$ has no deficiency. This proves Theorem 7.6.2.

Theorem 7.6.2 may also be used to give the matching theorem for sets a more general form: Let (7.4.3) denote two families of sets satisfying the conditions of Theorem 7.4.4. If there exist numbers $\delta_0 \geqq 0$ and $\delta_0' \geqq 0$ such that any k sets A_i overlap at least $k - \delta_0$ sets A_j' and any k sets A_j' overlap at least $k - \delta_0'$ sets A_i then one can match all but δ_0 of the sets A_i upon all but δ_0' of the sets A_j' such that corresponding sets have a non-void intersection.

We shall add the following observation which is an immediate consequence of the relation (7.6.8):

THEOREM 7.6.3. *When the two vertex sets of a bipartite graph G are finite and have the same number of vertices then*

(7.6.10) $$\delta_0 = \delta_0'.$$

PROBLEMS

1. What is the maximal deficiency for a family of sets consisting of all subsets of a set V with n elements?

2. The same question for the family of all subsets with m elements.

3. Construct an example of an infinite graph in which Theorem 7.6.3 does not hold.

7.7. **Applications to matrices.** Let us consider some arbitrary finite matrix

7.7.1) $$M = (a_{ij}), \qquad i = 1, 2, \cdots, n; \quad j = 1, 2, \cdots, n'.$$

Its terms a_{ij} may be zero or different from zero. The properties of M in this regard may be described by means of its bipartite *term graph* $G(M)$. The vertex sets V and V' are numbered from 1 to n and from 1 to n' respectively and there is an edge (i,j) in $G(M)$ whenever $a_{ij} \neq 0$.

The graph G has an incidence matrix

$$(7.7.2) \qquad\qquad M_0(G) = (g_{ij}), \qquad i = 1, \cdots, n, \quad j = 1, \cdots, n'$$

where $g_{ij} = 1$ or $g_{ij} = 0$ depending on whether there exists an edge (i,j) or not in G, i.e.,

$$g_{ij} = 1 \qquad\qquad \text{when } a_{ij} \neq 0,$$
$$g_{ij} = 0 \qquad\qquad \text{when } a_{ij} = 0.$$

Suppose first that in (7.7.1) $n = n'$ so that M is a square matrix with the determinant

$$(7.7.3) \qquad\qquad D = |M| = \sum \pm a_{1j_1} a_{2j_2} \cdots a_{nj_n}.$$

In a non-vanishing term in the expansion (7.7.3) all elements a_{ij} must be different from zero, consequently the edges

$$(1,j_1)(2,j_2) \cdots (n,j_n)$$

in G represents a matching of V upon V'. Conversely, if there exists a matching of the two vertex sets V and V' in G the corresponding product occurs in (7.7.3) and is non-vanishing. Thus we conclude from the general matching Theorem 7.4.2.

THEOREM 7.7.1. *The expansion (7.7.3) of a determinant contains non-vanishing terms if and only if any k lines in D include non-vanishing elements a_{ij} from at least k columns $(k = 1, 2, \cdots, n)$.*

We return to the general matrix (7.7.1). Its *term rank* shall be defined as the order of the greatest minor containing a non-vanishing term in its expansion. We define the deficiency of a set A of k lines to be

$$\delta(A) = k - k'(A)$$

where $k'(A)$ is the number of columns in M having at least one non-vanishing element in common with one of the lines in A. The maximal deficiency we denote by δ_0 as before and δ_0' has the analogous meaning for the columns. From Theorem 7.6.2 we conclude:

THEOREM 7.7.2. *The term rank of a matrix of dimension $n \times n'$ is*

$$\rho = n - \delta_0 = n' - \delta_0'$$

where δ_0 and δ_0' are the maximal deficiencies of the sets of lines and columns.

By interchanging the numbering of two vertices in V the corresponding lines in the matrix are interchanged and correspondingly for the columns. By the process of renumbering the vertex sets V and V' one can rearrange the lines and columns of the matrix in any order. This may be used to bring the matrix into a certain normal form. We saw in Theorem 7.6.2 that there exists sets

$$D \subset N, \quad D' \subset N'$$

with δ_0 and δ_0' elements respectively such that the sets

$$V - D, \quad V' - D'$$

are matched upon each other. From (7.6.6) one obtains corresponding decompositions of V and V' into four sets

$$V = V(N') + R + (N - D) + D,$$
$$V' = V'(N) + R' + (N' - D') + D'.$$

When the vertices are arranged in this order and one takes into account which vertex sets are connected by edges it follows that the matrix takes the form:

(7.7.4)

	$V'(N)$	R'	$N'-D'$	D'
$V(N')$	M_{11}	M_{12}	M_{13}	M_{14}
R	M_{21}	M_{22}	0	0
$N - D$	M_{31}	0	0	0
D	M_{41}	0	0	0

Here the matrices M_{31}, M_{22} and M_{13} are square. For further details see Ore; a still more detailed study of these normal forms have been made by Dulmage and Mendelsohn.

Let us mention another problem concerning matchings for bipartite graphs. When such matchings exist one may ask for the number of distinct ones. It is assumed, of course, that the vertex sets V and V' of G are finite with the same number of vertices

(7.7.5) $$n = v(V) = v(V').$$

In the determinant formulation we saw that each matching corresponded to a unique non-vanishing term in the expansion (7.7.3).Similarly each graph matching is associated with a unique term

$$g_{1_{j_1}} g_{2_{j_2}} \cdots g_{n_{j_n}} = 1$$

in the determinant of the incidence matrix (7.7.2). We recall that to a square matrix (7.7.1) there exists in addition to the determinant D in (7.7.3) also another, less used quantity, the *permanent P*. This permanent is defined as the sum

$$P = \sum a_{1j_1} a_{2j_2} \cdots a_{nj_n}$$

of the same terms as in D but all taken with positive signs. Thus we see:

THEOREM 7.7.3. *Let G be a bipartite graph with single edges and finite vertex sets V and V' having the same number (7.7.5) of vertices. Then the number of matchings between V and V' is equal to the value of the permanent of the incidence matrix of G.*

The result in Theorem 7.7.1 can be expressed in a slightly different form. Suppose that the matrix M in (7.7.1) contains a zero matrix O of dimensions $r \times r'$. Then there is a set C of r lines in M which contains non-void elements from at most $n' - r'$ columns so that

$$\delta(C) \geqq r - (n' - r') = r + r' - n'.$$

On the other hand the zero matrix formed by lines 3, 4 and columns 2, 3, 4 in (7.7.4) has the dimensions

$$r = v(N) = v(V'(N)) + \delta_0,$$

$$r' = v(R' + N') = n' - v(V'(N))$$

so that

$$r + r' - n' = \delta_0.$$

Thus we may state:

THEOREM 7.7.4. *The maximal deficiencies of a matrix (7.7.1) are*

(7.7.6) $\delta_0 = \max(0, r + r' - n'), \quad \delta_0' = \max(0, r + r' - n)$

where $r \times r'$ are the dimensions of the zero submatrices of N.

When $n = n'$ the term rank is obtained from Theorem 7.7.2.

(7.7.7) $\rho = 2n - \max(n, r + r').$

This shows:

THEOREM 7.7.5. *The term rank of a square matrix of dimensions $n \times n$ is less than n if and only if there exists a zero submatrix O of dimensions $r \times r'$ with*

$$r + r' > n.$$

We shall apply this result to deduce some properties of matrices with non-negative terms $a_{ij} \geq 0$. The expressions

$$s_i = \sum_{j=1}^{n} a_{ij}, \quad s_j' = \sum_{i=1}^{n} a_{ij}$$

are the *marginal sums* of M while

$$\sigma_0 = \sum_{ij} a_{ij} = \sum s_i = \sum s_j'$$

is its *total*. When

$$s_j' = 1, \qquad\qquad j = 1, 2, \cdots, n$$

the matrix is *stochastic* and one has $\sigma_0 = n$. The matrix is *doubly stochastic* when

$$s_i = s_j' = 1 \qquad\qquad (i, j = 1, 2, \cdots, n).$$

Suppose now that M has a zero submatrix O of dimensions $r \times r'$ with $r + r' > n$. We can write

$$M = \begin{vmatrix} A & B \\ C & O \end{vmatrix}.$$

The sum of the terms in B is then

$$\sum_{B}^{n} a_{ij} = \sum_{j=n-r'+1}^{n} s_j'$$

while for the sum of the terms in A we find

$$\sum_{A} a_{ij} = \sum_{i=1}^{n-r} s_i - \sum_{B} a_{ij} = \sigma_0 - \sum_{C} a_{ij} - \sum_{B} a_{ij} \geq 0.$$

This condition can also be written

$$\sigma_0 \geq \sum_{i=n-r+1}^{n} s_i + \sum_{j=n-r'+1}^{n} s_j'.$$

We see that if one has

$$\sum_{r} s_i + \sum_{r'} s_j' > \sigma_0$$

for any sum of r and r' marginal sums s_i and s_j' then M can have no zero submatrix O with the dimensions $r \times r'$; hence its term rank exceeds (7.7.7). We conclude:

THEOREM 7.7.6. *Let M be a square matrix with non-negative terms, the total term sum σ_0 and the marginal sums*

$$s_1 \leqq \cdots \leqq s_n, \quad s_1' \leqq \cdots \leqq s_n'.$$

If for some fixed $k > n$

(7.7.8) $s_1 + \cdots + s_r + s_1' + \cdots + s_{k-r}' > \sigma_0,$ $r = 1, \cdots, n-1$

then the term rank ρ of M satisfies

(7.7.9) $\rho \geqq 2n - k + 1.$

When $k = n + 1$ the term rank is $\rho = n$. For a stochastic matrix the criterion reduces to:

THEOREM 7.7.7. *When in a stochastic matrix M the conditions*

$$s_1 + \cdots + s_r > n - k + r, \quad k > n, \qquad r = 1, \cdots, n-1$$

are satisfied then the term rank ρ has the lower bound (7.7.9). One has $\rho = n$ when

$$s_1 + \cdots + s_r > r - 1$$

hence in particular for a doubly stochastic matrix.

The condition (7.7.8) can be rewritten

$$s_n + \cdots + s_{r+1} + s_n' + \cdots + s_{k-r+1}' < \sigma_0.$$

If one puts

$$\mu_0 = \max(s_i, s_j'), \qquad\qquad i, j = 1, \cdots, n-1$$

it is certainly fulfilled when

$$(2n - k)\mu_0 < \sigma_0$$

or

$$k > 2n - \frac{\sigma_0}{\mu_0}.$$

This leads to a result by Dulmage and Mendelsohn: *The term rank is at most equal to*

$$\frac{\sigma_0}{\mu_0}.$$

We shall conclude this section with a few observations on a related topic, the *Latin squares.* A Latin square is an $n \times n$ matrix L whose terms are n symbols

(7.7.10) $M_1, M_2, \cdots, M_n$

distributed such that each symbol appears just once in each line and column. The name stems from the fact that Euler used Latin capitals A, B, C, to denote the terms. A Latin square can be considered the multiplication table for an algebraic system S with n elements. Each line in L is associated with a unique element $a \in S$ and similarly for each column and each symbol (7.7.10). If then at the place (a, b) in the table the symbol M_c appears one writes $a \cdot b = c$. The system S is a *quasi-group*, that is, each of the relations

$$xa = xb, \quad ay = by$$

implies $a = b$. The multiplication table of any finite group defines a special Latin square.

A Latin square can also be represented as a complete bipartite graph G in which each vertex set has n elements and each vertex in V is connected by edges to all vertices in V' and conversely. According to Theorem 7.5.2 such a graph is the edge direct sum of n disjoint matchings M_i; conversely in a Latin square each symbol (7.7.10) can be considered to indicate to which matching a particular edge of G belongs in a given decomposition. In a matching M_1 one can select the first edge in n ways, the second in $n-1$ ways, and so on. Thus the total number of matchings is $n!$. The remaining graph $G - M$ is regular of degree $n - 1$, hence according to Section 7.4 it has at least $(n - 1)!$ matchings M_2. When this process is continued it follows (M. Hall) that for a given n there exist at least

$$n!(n - 1)! \cdots 2!\,1!$$

Latin squares.

A matrix K of dimensions

$$k \times l, \qquad\qquad\qquad k \leqq n, l \leqq n$$

containing symbols (7.7.10) shall be called a *partial Latin square* when it has at most one of these symbols in each line and column. One can show:

THEOREM 7.7.8. *A necessary and sufficient condition in order that it shall be possible to complete a partial Latin square to a Latin square is that*

$$\mu(i) \geqq k + l - n, \qquad\qquad i = 1, 2, \cdots, n$$

where $\mu(i)$ is the number of times the ith symbol appears in K.

The proof is a simple consequence of the previous matching theorems.

PROBLEM

1. A partial Latin square is maximal when no line or column can be added without destroying this property. State a necessary and sufficient condition for a partial Latin square to be maximal.

7.8. **Alternating paths and maximal matchings.** An effective tool for many graph problems is the *alternating path method* introduced by Petersen (1891) in his investigations on the existence of subgraphs. Here we shall apply it to bipartite graphs and matchings. Let

(7.8.1) $$M = \{E_i\}, \quad E_i = (a_i, a_i'), \qquad A = \{a_i\}, A' = \{a_i'\}$$

be a partial matching of G having the *matching sets* A and A'. An *alternating path* with respect to M is a path P in which the edges belong alternately to M and $\bar{M}$, usually beginning in an edge not in M. No edge can be repeated.

Denote by

$$F_1 = (v, a_1'), \qquad\qquad v \in V - A, a_1' \in A'$$

some edge from an unmatched vertex v. We construct all alternating paths

(7.8.2) $$P = (F_1, E_1, F_2, E_2, \cdots).$$

Suppose that one can reach some other unmatched vertex v_n' by such a path; then the last edge

$$F_n = (a_{n-1}, v_n'), \qquad\qquad a_{n-1} \in A, v_n' \in V' - A'$$

cannot belong to M. Such a path P can be used to derive a new matching M_1 by replacing all edges E in P and M by the edges F. One sees that in M_1 all vertices in A and A' remain in the matching sets; furthermore, the vertices v and v_n' have matchings. A similar increased matching M_1 can be obtained when the path P in (7.8.2) is infinite, but then only v is added to the matching sets. In either case we shall say that M_1 has been obtained from M by an *alternating augmentation* with respect to P.

From now on we call a matching M *maximal* when there exists no matching M_1 with larger matching sets.

THEOREM 7.8.1. *A matching is maximal if and only if the matching sets cannot be alternatingly augmented.*

PROOF. It suffices to show that a matching M which cannot be augmented is maximal. Suppose there exists a matching M_1 with a larger matching set A_1 and take

$$F_1 = (v, a_1'), \qquad\qquad v \in A_1 - A$$

to be an edge in M_1 but not in M. Then $a'_1 \in A'$ because otherwise M could be augmented. We construct a path (7.8.2) consisting alternately of edges in M_1 not in M and edges in M not in M_1, starting in F_1. The vertex a_1' is matched with v in M_1 so the second edge $E_1 = (a_1', a_1)$ in M leads to a vertex a_1 at which there is a different edge $F_2 = (a_1, a_2')$ in M_1 and so on. Thus P is either infinite or ends at a vertex in V' which is unmatched in M. In either case M can be augmented.

An alternating path P with respect to a matching M is called *cyclic* when it begins in an edge F_1 not in M and returns to the initial vertex in an edge in M. It is *infinite cyclic* when it can be continued indefinitely in both directions. By interchanging the edges of M in P with those not in M one obtains another matching $M(P)$ with the same matching sets. We say that $M(P)$ is obtained from M by a *cyclic deformation*. Next let $\{P\}$ be a family of edge disjoint alternating cyclic paths. The *cyclic deformation* with respect to $\{P\}$ is then the matching $M\{P\}$ obtained by performing all deformations for the paths in $\{P\}$. The new graph has the same matching sets as M.

THEOREM 7.8.2. *When M and M_1 are two complete matchings of the vertex sets V and V' of G then one is obtainable from the other by cyclic deformations.*

PROOF. As above one sees that to an edge E in M not in M_1 there is a finite or infinite cyclic path P including E consisting alternately of edges in M not in M_1 and edges in M_1 not in M. Clearly there exist maximal families $\{P\}$ of edge disjoint paths P. In the remaining graph $G - \{P\}$ there can be no edges of M not in M_1 or vice versa because then one could construct another cyclic alternating path Q in $G - \{P\}$ and Q could be added to $\{P\}$. We conclude that by deforming M with respect to $\{P\}$ one obtains M_1.

Theorem 7.8.2 is valid also for any two matchings with the same matching sets. We shall extend the analysis to two maximal matchings M and M_1 with matching sets $A + A'$ and $A_1 + A_1'$. At an unmatched or *deficient vertex* $v \in V - A$ in M let there be an edge $F_1 = (v, a_1')$ in M_1. We construct an alternating path Q from v beginning in F_1 consisting of edges in M and M_1. Since M is maximal this path is finite and can only end in an M-edge

$$E_n = (a_n', v_1), \qquad\qquad v_1 \in V - A_1$$

at a deficient vertex v_1 in M_1. We call Q a *deficiency path* in V for M and M_1. When M_1 is deformed with respect to Q one sees that in the matching $M_1(Q)$ the vertex v is deficient and v_2 not deficient, as in M. More general, suppose that $\{Q\}$ is a family of edge disjoint deficiency paths for M and M_1. By deforming M_1 with respect to $\{Q\}$ the deficiency character of the matching $M_1\{Q\}$ becomes the same as in M for all endpoints of paths Q. One verifies that there exists maximal families $\{Q\}$ of edge disjoint deficiency paths. After a deformation with respect to $\{Q\}$ the deficient vertices in V for M and $M_1\{Q\}$ must be the same. If namely $v \in V$ should be a vertex deficient in M and not in $M_1\{Q\}$ one could construct a deficiency path Q_1 from v edge disjoint from the paths in the maximal family $\{Q\}$. After deficiency path deformations also for V' one arrives at a new matching M_2

with the same deficient vertices as M. Finally M and M_2 can be deformed into one another by cyclic deformations.

THEOREM 7.8.3. *Any maximal matching M can be transformed into any other M_1 by deformations with respect to deficiency paths and cyclic deformations. There exists a one-to-one correspondence between the deficient vertices in M and M_1 such that corresponding vertices are connected by edge disjoint alternating paths.*

We note also the converse result:

THEOREM 7.8.4. *Let M be a maximal matching and $\{Q\}$ a family of disjoint alternating paths of even lengths from the deficient vertices in M. When M is deformed with respect to $\{Q\}$ the new matching is also maximal.*

The proof shall be left to the reader.

As before, let M be a maximal matching with the matching set $A + A'$. We construct all even alternating paths $Q_0(v)$ from the vertices $v \in V - A$. The set N of all endpoints of these paths are the vertices in V which are deficient in some maximal matching of G. Thus N is independent of the choice of M; we call it the *deficient set* in V. The endpoints of the odd length alternating paths $Q_1(v)$ form the set $V'(N)$. Similarly V' has a deficient set N' consisting of the endpoints of the even alternating paths $Q_0'(v')$ from $v' \in V' - A'$.

THEOREM 7.8.5. *One has*

(7.8.3) $$N \cdot V(N') = N' \cdot V'(N) = \emptyset.$$

PROOF. The formulas (7.8.3) are consequences of the observation: No two alternating paths $Q(v)$ and $Q'(v')$ can have a vertex in common. Suppose that $c \in V$ is the first vertex on $Q(v)$ also on $Q'(v')$. Since $Q(v)$ ends in an M-edge at c the path

$$P = Q(v, c) + Q'(c, v')$$

is an odd alternating path from v to v'. But then M can be augmented with respect to P contrary to the maximality of M.

According to (7.8.3) there exists direct decompositions

$$V = N + R + V(N'),$$
(7.8.4)
$$V' = N' + R' + V'(N)$$

for the vertex sets. We notice that in (7.8.4) each term is independent of the choice of the maximal matching M. Here N and N' consist of the vertices deficient for some M; $V'(N)$ and $V(N')$ are uniquely defined by N and N', hence also the remaining sets R and R'.

Corresponding to (7.8.4) one can define a decomposition of the maximal matching M. At each $v' \in V'(N)$ there is an edge E from M since v' cannot be deficient. Thus the alternating paths from $V - A$ to v' can be continued through E. We conclude that all M-edges from $V'(N)$ have their other endpoint in N, hence in the section graph

$$G(N, V'(N))$$

the set $V'(N)$ has a complete matching M_1 into N. Similarly in

$$G(N', V(N'))$$

the set $V(N')$ has a matching M_2 into N'. Finally at each $r \in R$ there is an M-edge which can only go to some $r' \in R'$ and analogously for every $r' \in R'$. Consequently M defines a complete matching M_3 in the graph $G(R, R')$. Thus we have a decomposition

$$M = M_1 + M_2 + M_3.$$

Here M_1 and M_2 may be called the *deficient components* and M_3 the *complete component*. We notice also that for any subset F of the matching sets of M there is a unique *M-image set* $\mu(F)$ consisting of the endpoints of the M-edges from F. One sees that

$$\mu(R) = R', \quad \mu(R') = R,$$
$$\mu(V'(N)) \subset N, \quad \mu(V(N')) \subset N'.$$

There are certain conditions under which one can establish the existence of maximal matchings. The following case is of importance:

THEOREM 7.8.6.   *A locally finite graph has a maximal matching.*

The proof of this theorem requires some further properties of the deficiency function. A finite subset A of V shall be called a *minimal δ-set* when

$$\delta(A) = \delta > 0, \quad \delta(B) < \delta \quad \text{when } B \subset A.$$

LEMMA.   *When A_1 and A_2 are minimal δ_1 and δ_2-sets, one not containing the other, then $A_3 = A_1 + A_2$ is a minimal δ_3-set with*

(7.8.5) $$\delta_3 > \max(\delta_1, \delta_2).$$

PROOF.   According   to   Theorem   7.2.1

$$\delta(A_1 + A_2) + \delta(A_1 \cdot A_2) \geqq \delta_1 + \delta_2$$

and since $A_1 \cdot A_2$ is a proper subset of A_1 and A_2 one obtains (7.8.5). To show that A_3 is a minimal δ_3-set let

$$B_3 = B_1 + B_2, \qquad\qquad B_1 \subseteq A_1, \quad B_2 \subseteq A_2$$

be a proper subset of A_3. We may suppose that B_3 does not include A_2. From Theorem 7.2.1 follows again

$$\delta(B_1 + A_2) = \delta(B_1 + B_2 + A_2)$$
$$\geq \delta(B_1 + B_2) + \delta(A_2) - \delta(A_2 \cdot B_3).$$

Since A_2 is minimal we conclude

$$\delta(B_1 + A_2) > \delta(B_1 + B_2).$$

By a similar argument one finds

$$\delta(A_1 + A_2) \geq \delta(B_1 + A_2)$$

and so as desired

$$\delta(B_1 + B_2) < \delta_3.$$

We denote by

(7.8.6) $$N_0 = \sum A_\delta, \qquad\qquad \delta = 1, 2, \cdots$$

the sum of all minimal δ-sets; it shall be called the *minimal critical* set in V. We deduce the facts:

　　1. The set $V'(N_0)$ can be matched upon N_0.

　　2. The set $V - N_0$ can be matched upon $V' - V'(N_0)$.

　　1. It suffices to show that no subset A' of $V'(N_0)$ has positive deficiency in the graph

$$G_1 = G(N_0, V'(N_0)).$$

If in G_1 there should be some A' with $\delta'(A') > 0$ we may assume that A' is a minimal δ'-set. The endpoints of the edges in G_1 from A' form the set $B \subset N_0$. By the definition (7.8.6) of N_0 each vertex in B belongs to some minimal δ-set in V. We conclude from the lemma that there is a minimal δ-set A containing B. But when the deficiency relation (7.6.4) is applied to A' and A a contradiction results.

　　2. To prove this property we show that no subset C of $V - N_0$ has a positive deficiency in the graph

$$G_2 = G(V - N_0, \quad V' - V'(N_0)).$$

We write

$$V'(C) = A' + A_1', \qquad A' \subset V'(N_0), \qquad A_1' \subset V' - V'(N_0)$$

and assume that in G_2

$$\delta_2(C) = v(C) - v(A_1') > 0.$$

As before let B be the set of all endpoints of edges from A' to N_0 and A a minimal δ-set containing B. Then for the deficiency of $A + C$ in G one finds

$$\delta(A + C) = \delta + \delta_2(C) = \delta_2 > \delta.$$

Then $A + C$ contains some minimal δ_2-set A_2 with $\delta_2 > \delta$, hence A_2 belongs to N_0. But this contradicts the fact that A_2 must contain vertices from C.

The matching M_1 of $V'(N_0)$ in G_1 can be combined with the matching M_2 of $V - N_0$ in G_2 to the matching

$$M = M_1 + M_2$$

in G. To see finally that M is maximal we notice that the deficient vertices under M must belong to the sets N_0 and $V' - V'(N_0)$. If M could be augmented there would be some alternating path P from N_0 to $V' - V'(N_0)$. But P would have to pass from N_0 in some edge not in M contrary to the fact that all edges from N_0 go to $V'(N_0)$.

We shall make a few further observations on maximal matchings. Suppose that v_0 is a deficient vertex in a maximal matching M and construct an alternating path P from v_0. At the end of any M-edge $E_{n-1} = (v_{n-1}, v_n)$ in P there can be no edge $E_n = (v_n, v_{n+1})$ to a deficient vertex v_{n+1} because M could be augmented. If v_n has infinite local degree one can always continue P by selecting v_{n+1} as a vertex different from the previous v_i. Since P cannot be infinite one must eventually arrive at a vertex v_n of finite degree. When M is deformed with respect to P the deficient vertex v_0 is replaced by v_n. By repeated applications of this procedure one concludes:

THEOREM 7.8.7. *In a bipartite graph G with a maximal matching M let F and I be the sets of vertices of finite and infinite local degrees respectively. Then M can be deformed by even alternating paths into another maximal matching M_1 whose deficient vertices all belong to F.*

It is assumed that each vertex with infinite local degree is connected by edges to an infinite number of vertices. A consequence of Theorem 7.8.7 is.

THEOREM 7.8.8. *If G is a bipartite graph without vertices of finite degrees then any maximal matching is a complete matching.*

PROBLEM

1. Prove that when G is a locally finite graph the deficient sets N and N' for a maximal matching are identical with the minimal critical sets N_0 and N_0' in (7.8.6).

7.9. **Separating sets.** In a bipartite graph G a set

(7.9.1) $$S = T + T',   T \subset V,   T' \subset V'$$

is called a *separating set* when every edge has at least one endpoint in S. Any separating set contains minimal separating sets. Suppose that G has a maximal matching M with the matching set $A + A'$. An *M-set* is a minimal separating set for the graph M, that is, a set $U + U'$ such that each M-edge has exactly one vertex in it, hence, in the previous notation

$$A = U + \mu(U'),   A' = \mu(U) + U'.$$

A separating set (7.9.1) is *conformal with M* when it is an M-set. Finally, a separation set is *conformal* when it is conformal with all maximal matchings.

THEOREM 7.9.1. *Any graph with maximal matchings has conformal separating sets.*

PROOF. In the notations (7.8.4) the set

$$S = V'(N) + R + V(N')$$

is a conformal set. It is immediate that each edge in G has an endpoint in S and in the preceding section we established that the sets

(7.9.2) $$T = R + V(N'),   T' = V'(N)$$

defined an M-set for every maximal matching M.

Corresponding to (7.9.2) also the sets

$$T_1 = V(N'),   T_1' = R + V'(N)$$

define a conformal set. Such sets have the following minimal property:

THEOREM 7.9.2. *Let (T, T') be a conformal set for G. Then any pair of sets*

(7.9.3) $$(T - F + F_1, T' - F' + F_1'),   F \subset T,   F' \subset T'$$

can only define a separating set when

(7.9.4) $$F_1 \supset \mu(F'),   F_1' \supset \mu(F).$$

PROOF. The edges of M connecting F and $\mu(F)$ can have no vertices in the sets (7.9.3) unless the condition (7.9.4) is satisfied.

THEOREM 7.9.3. *When G is a bipartite graph with maximal matchings M then all such matchings have the same cardinal number v(M) of edges, equal to the minimal number v (S) of vertices in a separating set.*

PROOF. According to (7.9.4) the sum

$$S = (T - F + F_1') + (T' - F' + F_1)$$

of the sets in (7.9.3) must have a cardinal number at least equal to

$$v(M) = v(T + T').$$

A special case of Theorem 7.9.3 is the theorem of König:

THEOREM 7.9.4. *In a bipartite graph G with a finite separating set there exist maximal vertex matchings M and*

$$v(M) = v(S)$$

where S is a separating set with a minimal number of vertices.

PROOF. Since $v(M_1) \leq v(S)$ for any partial matching M_1 it follows that G has maximal vertex matchings; the rest of the theorem is a consequence of Theorem 7.9.3.

In a locally finite graph one can formulate a similar result. According to Theorem 7.9.2 a conformal separating set has the property of being *finitely minimal*, that is, when two finite sets F and F' are removed from T and T' the pair of sets (7.9.3) can only be a separating set when

$$v(F_1 + F_1') \geq v(F + F').$$

In this terminology one can prove:

THEOREM 7.9.5. *A locally finite graph possesses finitely minimal separating sets S and any such set is conformal for some maximal matching.*

PROBLEMS

1. Give a proof for Theorem 7.9.5.

2.* Try to characterize all conformal separating sets: (α) when G is finite; (β) when G is a graph with a maximal matching.

7.10. **Simultaneous matchings.** As before G is a bipartite graph with the vertex sets V and V'; to simplify we assume that V is finite with $n = v(V)$. We established that a partial matching M of $n - \delta_0$ elements of V into V' exists if and only if for every subset $A \subset V$

(7.10.1)　　　　　　$\delta(A) = v(A) - v(V'(A)) \leq \delta_0.$

Higgins has considered a more general problem concerning *simultaneous matchings*. A set of m integers

(7.10.2) $d_i, \quad 0 \leq d_i \leq n,$ $i = 1, 2, \cdots, m$

is given. We ask when it is possible to determine m partial matchings M_i of V into V' such that in M_i all but d_i elements of V are matched and such that the endpoints in V' of all the matching edges in the family $\{M_i\}$ are distinct.

An equivalent formulation is the following: Given n sets

$$B_j, \quad B = \sum B_j, \qquad\qquad j = 1, 2, \cdots, n.$$

When do there exist m disjoint subsets

$$R_i, \quad v(R_i) = n_i = n - d_i, \qquad\qquad i = 1, 2, \cdots, m$$

of B such that the elements in each R_i form a partial set of representatives for the sets B_j?

If such matchings exist then under each M_i the number of vertices in V' which are matched to the vertices in a set $A \subset V$ with $k = v(A)$ elements is at least

$$k - \min(d_i, k).$$

Thus a set $V'(A)$ must contain at least

(7.10.3) $mk - \Delta(k, d), \quad \Delta(k, d) = \sum_i \min(k, d_i)$

vertices and as a consequence

(7.10.4) $\delta(A, d) = mk - v(V'(A)) - \Delta(k, d) \leq 0.$

We call the number $\delta(A, d)$ the *d-deficiency* of the set A; one may define $\delta(\emptyset, d) = 0$. We leave it to the reader to verify that the condition

(7.10.5) $\delta(A + B, d) + \delta(A \cdot B, d) \geq \delta(A, d) + \delta(B, d)$

analogous to (7.2.5) is satisfied also for this function. For $m = 1, d_1 = 0$, it reduces to the previous deficiency. When the condition (7.10.4) is fulfilled for every subset A we say that V has *no d-deficiency*.

THEOREM 7.10.1. *Let $G(V, V')$ be a bipartite graph with a finite vertex set V. When V has no d-deficiency there exists a family of m partial matching $\{M_i\}$ of V into V' with disjoint mapping sets in V' such that M_i maps all but d_i vertices of V.*

We shall prove the theorem by induction with respect to $n = v(V)$; for $n = 1$ the theorem is trivial. Suppose first there exists a proper subset A_0 of V for which

(7.10.6) $\delta(A_0, d) = 0, \quad v(A_0) = k_0.$

We shall write

(7.10.7) $d_i' = \min(k_0, d_i), \quad d_i'' = d_i - d_i'.$

Then for any set $A \subset A_0$ the condition (7.10.4) can also be written

$$\delta(A, d') \leqq 0.$$

By the induction assumption the graph

$$G_0 = G(A_0, V'(A_0))$$

has m partial matchings M_i' such that all but d_i' vertices of A_0 are matched.
Next we verify that in the graph

$$G_1 = G(V - A_0, V' - V'(A_0))$$

the set $V - A_0$ has no d''-deficiency. Let A_1 be a subset of $V - A_0$. We shall leave
it to the reader to verify the formula

$$\delta(A_0 + A_1, d) = \delta(A_0, d) + \delta(A_1, d'').$$

The conditions (7.10.4) and (7.10.6) then imply

$$\delta(A_1, d'') \leqq 0$$

as desired. As a consequence there exists in G_1 a family of matchings $\{M_i''\}$ such
that under M_i'' all but d_i'' vertices of $V - A_0$ are matched. By putting

$$M_i = M_i' + M_i''$$

one obtains a matching of the desired kind for G.

There remains the case where no proper subsets A_0 of V satisfy (7.10.6). We
notice that when $d_1 = 0$ the theorem is true because $V'(A)$ must contain at least
k vertices, hence according to Theorem 7.3.3 there exists a complete matching
M_1 of V into V'. We remove from G all endpoints of M_1 in V' and all edges
at these vertices. One sees that in the remaining graph the conditions (7.10.4)
are fulfilled for the numbers $d_2 \cdots d_m$.

For a given n we may therefore apply induction with respect to the minimal
number d_1 in (7.10.2). We replace the set (7.10.2) by

(7.10.8) $d_1 - 1, \quad d_2 + 1, \quad d_3, \cdots, d_m.$

In (7.10.4) this changes only the sum $\Delta(k, d)$ and its expression (7.10.3) shows
that it can decrease by at most one unit. In our case the inequality holds in (7.10.4)
for every proper subset A of V so that (7.10.4) is valid also for the values (7.10.8).
When $A = V$ the sum

$$\Delta(n, d_i) = d_1 + \cdots + d_m$$

is unchanged. We conclude by the induction that G has m matchings M_i' corresponding to (7.10.8). Since M_1' matches more vertices than M_2' there must be at least one vertex at which there is an edge E_1 in M_1' not in M_2'. By transferring E_1 to M_2' one obtains the desired matching

$$M_1' - E_1, \quad M_2' + E_2, \quad M_3', \cdots$$

for G.

Higgins formulated Theorem 7.10.1 in a somewhat different manner. We put

$$r_i = n - d_i$$

so that M_i matches r_i vertices of V into V'. We also write

$$(7.10.9) \hspace{4cm} N = \sum_i r_i, \hspace{3cm} i = 1, 2, \cdots, m$$

and assume that the notation is such that

$$r_1 \geqq r_2 \geqq \cdots \geqq r_m.$$

Thus the number N has the partition $\{r_i\}$. As usual such a partition can be represented by means of an $m \times n$ matrix M whose terms are zeros and ones:

$$
\begin{array}{c|ccccccc}
 & \tilde{r}_1, & \tilde{r}_2, & \cdots & & & & \\
\hline
r_1 & 1 & 1 & \cdots\cdots & 1 & 0 & \cdots & 0 \\
r_2 & 1 & 1 & \cdots\cdots & 0 & 0 & \cdots & 0 \\
\vdots & & & & & & & \\
\end{array}
$$

In the ith line the first r_i terms are 1 and the rest are 0. The column sums also form a non-increasing sequence

$$\tilde{r}_1 \geqq \tilde{r}_2 \geqq \cdots$$

which defines the *dual partition*

$$(7.10.10) \hspace{4cm} N = \sum_j \tilde{r}_j, \hspace{3cm} j = 1, 2, \cdots, n.$$

We write

$$(7.10.11) \hspace{4cm} \alpha_k = \sum_j \tilde{r}_j, \hspace{3cm} j = n - k + 1, \cdots, n$$

for the sum of all terms in the last k columns of M. The diagram shows that this sum can be written

$$\alpha_k = \sum_i (k - \min(k, d_i)) = mk - \Delta(k, d).$$

Therefore the condition (7.10.4) is equivalent to

$$(7.10.12) \hspace{4cm} v(V'(A)) \geqq \alpha_k.$$

It may be noted that for a fixed k only the left-hand side in (7.10.12) depends on A so that it is sufficient to verify that (7.10.4) or (7.10.12) hold for the sets A with the smallest value for $v(V'(A))$.

We apply the preceding result to the simple case where all vertices in V are connected to different vertices in V'. This will occur, for instance, when one shall select sets of representatives R_i for a family $\{B_j\}$ of disjoint sets. When the local degrees in V are denoted by

$$(7.10.13) \qquad \rho_1 \geq \rho_2 \geq \cdots \geq \rho_n$$

the condition (7.10.12) becomes

$$\sum_{j=n-k+1}^{n} \rho_j \geq \alpha_k.$$

From (7.10.11) we conclude:

THEOREM 7.10.2. *Let*

$$\{B_i\}, \quad v(B_i) = \rho_i, \qquad\qquad i = 1, 2, \cdots, n$$

be a family of disjoint sets where the ρ_i are arranged in the order (7.10.13). A necessary and sufficient condition that a family of m disjoint representative sets

$$\{R_j\}, \quad v(R_j) = r_j, \qquad\qquad j = 1, 2, \cdots, m$$

can be found is that

$$(7.10.14) \qquad \sum_{i=k}^{n} \rho_i \geq \sum_{i=k}^{n} \tilde{r}_i, \qquad\qquad k = 1, 2, \cdots, n$$

where the non-increasing sequence $\{\tilde{r}_i\}$ is the dual partition (7.10.10) to the partition $\{r_i\}$ in (7.10.9).

The problem may be put in a variety of popular forms, for instance: On a picnic n families of ρ_i members each shall be transported in m busses with r_j seats. When is it possible to find a seating arrangement such that no two members of the same family travel in the same bus? If the seating capacity of the busses equals the number of passengers one has in addition to the conditions (7.10.14) also

$$(7.10.15) \qquad \sum_{i=1}^{n} \rho_i = \sum_{j=1}^{m} r_j.$$

Theorem 7.10.2 is equivalent to a matrix theorem by Gale and Ryser:

THEOREM 7.10.3.   *A necessary and sufficient condition that one can construct a matrix with terms 1 and 0 such that the ith line contains $\rho(i)$ ones and the jth column $r(j)$ ones is that the conditions (7.10.14) and (7.10.15) be fulfilled where the numbers $\rho(i)$ and $r(j)$ are arranged in decreasing orders.*

The matrix constructed in this manner can be considered to be the vertex incidence matrix for a directed graph with single edges. This observation leads to:

THEOREM 7.10.4.   *A necessary and sufficient condition that there exist a directed graph with the prescribed local degrees $\rho(i)$ and $\rho^*(j) = r(j)$ is that the conditions (7.10.14) and (7.10.15) be fulfilled.*

One can extended Theorem 7.10.1 to the case where G is a locally finite graph.

CHAPTER 8

DIRECTED GRAPHS

8.1. **The inclusion relation and accessible sets.** We shall now examine some of the basic properties of *directed graphs*. Let G be such a graph with the vertex set V. When a and b are vertices such that there is a directed path of edges $P(a, b)$ from a to b we say that b is *accessible* from a and write $a > b$. As for undirected graphs one sees that a directed path $P(a, b)$ can be reduced to a directed arc $P_1(a, b)$ in which each vertex appears only once.

THEOREM 8.1.1. *When b is accessible from a and c accessible from b then c is accessible from a.*

PROOF. Let $P(a, b)$ and $Q(b, c)$ be directed arcs and d the first vertex in P which also lies on Q. Then

$$P(a, d) + Q(d, c)$$

is a directed arc from a to c.

The binary relation $a > b$ which we just defined shall be called the *inclusion relation* associated with G. Theorem 8.1.1 shows that it is transitive. Its converse we denote by $b < a$.

We write

$$D(a), \quad D^*(a)$$

for the set of all vertices accessible, resp. conversely accessible, from the vertex a. Evidently one has $a > b$ if and only if

$$D(a) \geqq D(b).$$

Two vertices a and b are *accessibly equivalent* when

(8.1.1) $$D(a) = D(b)$$

that is,

$$a > b, \quad b > a, \quad \text{for short} \quad a \sim b.$$

One sees that in order that (8.1.1) shall hold it is necessary and sufficient that a and b be *mutually connected*, that is, there exist paths $P(a, b)$ and $Q(b, a)$ in G

THEOREM 8.1.2. *Two vertices are accessibly equivalent if and only if they are mutually connected.*

145

More generally, for any set A one can define the accessible set

$$D(A) = \sum_a D(a), \qquad\qquad a \in A$$

to be the set of vertices accessible from some $a \in A$. Two sets A and B are accessibly equivalent when

$$D(A) = D(B).$$

One finds that this is the case only when each $b \in B$ is accessible from some $a \in A$ and vice versa.

A set A such that every vertex is accessible from it, that is,

(8.1.2) $D(A) = V$

may be called a *generating set*. A *minimal generating set* is a set which is minimal among the sets A with the property (8.1.2); such sets may or may not exist.

We shall examine certain questions analogous to those studied in Chapter 5 concerning leaves and lobes in undirected graphs. An edge in G is a *cyclic edge* if it belongs to some directed circuit and *acyclic* if it does not. Two vertices a_0 and b_0 are *cyclic edge connected* if there exists a sequence of directed circuits

(8.1.3) $C_1, C_2, \cdots, C_k$

such that a_0 lies on C_1 and b_0 on C_k and any pair of consecutive circuits C_i and C_{i+1} have at least one vertex in common. We shall show:

THEOREM 8.1.3. *Two vertices are cyclic edge connected if and only if they are mutually connected.*

PROOF. Suppose first that a_0 and b_0 are cyclic edge connected. When $k = 1$ in (8.1.3) there is nothing to prove. Thus we may base the proof upon induction with respect to the number k of circuits. Let c be vertex nearest to b_0 on C_k such that c lies on one of the previous circuits and there is a directed section $C_k(c, b_0)$ from c to b_0. According to the induction assumption there is a directed path from a_0 to c and this can be continued to b_0. Analogously one finds a directed path from b_0 to a_0.

Next let a_0 and b_0 be mutually connected by the directed arcs $P(a_0, b_0)$ and $Q(b_0, a_0)$. When $a_1 \neq a_0$ is the first vertex on P belonging to Q then there is a directed circuit

$$C_1 = P(a_0, a_1) + Q(a_1, a_0)$$

and the vertices a_1 and b_0 are mutually connected by the arcs

$$P(a_1, b_0), \quad Q(b_0, a_1).$$

By repeated reductions of this kind one obtains a sequence (8.1.3) of directed circuits connecting a_0 and b_0.

This discussion also shows:

THEOREM 8.1.4.   *Two vertices a_0 and b_0 in the directed graph G are mutually connected if and only if they are connected by a sequence of cyclic edges.*

A directed graph is *mutually connected* when all its vertices are mutually connected. Such a graph is also characterized by the property that each vertex is a generating set.

THEOREM 8.1.5.   *A directed graph is mutually connected if and only if it is connected and has no acyclic edges.*

PROOF.   A mutually connected graph G must evidently have a connected undirected graph G_u associated with it. No edge $E_0 = (a_0, b_0)$ in G can be acyclic since there exists a directed arc $Q(b_0, a_0)$; together with E_0 this gives a directed circuit including E_0. On the other hand if G_u is connected and all edges in G cyclic it follows from Theorem 8.1.4. that G is mutually connected.

One may ask under what conditions a given undirected graph G_0 can be considered to be the undirected graph G_u associated with a mutually connected graph G. This question has been formulated as a *traffic problem*: The graph G_0 is looked upon as being the map of a city or community; its edges are the streets or roads. When is it possible to introduce traffic directions in all streets such that any two points are connected both ways by one-way routes? This problem was solved by Robbins for finite graphs and later by Egyed for arbitrary graphs. The result is:

THEOREM 8.1.6.   *An undirected graph G_0 is the graph G_u of a mutually connected directed graph G if and only if G_0 is connected and has no separating edges.*

PROOF.   Separating edges would correspond to single bridges over a river or to dead-end streets. Suppose, therefore, that there are no separating edges in the connected graph G_0. Mutually connected directed subgraphs can be constructed by introducing suitable directions; for instance a circuit gives rise to two such graphs. These directed subgraphs form a partial order when one writes $H_1 \supset H_2$ if the edges in H_2 belong to H_1 and have the same directions. We consider an inclusion ordered family $\{H_i\}$ of mutually connected subgraphs. Their sum

$$H = \sum H_i$$

is seen to have the same property, hence by the chain sum principle there exist maximal mutually connected subgraphs H.

Next we show that such a maximal H includes all vertices of G_0. If this were not the case there would be some undirected edge $E = (b, c)$ with b in H and c not a vertex in H. In G_0 there is a circuit C including E. We denote by $C(b, c, d)$ the section of C from b through E to the next vertex d in H. Within H there exist directed paths $P(c, d)$ and $Q(d, c)$ and so by selecting any one of the two possible directions $C(b, c, d)$ one obtains a larger mutually connected graph H' contrary to the maximality of H. Finally one verifies that in a maximal H all edges in G_0 are included.

In connection with the preceding traffic problem let us mention a more difficult question: When is it possible to introduce directions in some or all streets of a city such that any two street intersections are mutually connected by directed routes having no junctions or intersections. In other words, when can one introduce directions on the edges of an undirected graph G_0 such that every pair of vertices lie on a directed circuit. Evidently this is possible when G_0 has a Hamilton circuit.

More restrictive still is the condition that any two houses in the town shall be connected by disjoint directed paths. This requires that the graph shall be so directed that any two edges shall belong to a directed circuit.

In connection with the directed paths let us mention the following result derived by Redei in connection with a study of quadratic fields:

THEOREM 8.1.7. *Let G be a finite directed graph in which each pair of vertices is connected by an edge. Then there exists a directed arc passing through all vertices.*

PROOF. The theorem is true for $n = 2$ vertices. Let G_n be a graph with n vertices for which the theorem is true and construct G_{n+1} by adding a vertex v_{n+1} from which there are directed edges to all vertices v_i in G_n. By assumption there is a directed arc

$$P_n = (v_1, v_2) \dots (v_{n-1}, v_n)$$

in G_n. If there is an edge $E = (v_n, v_{n+1})$ or (v_{n+1}, v_1) the arc can be extended through v_{n+1}. We may assume therefore that at v_{n+1} there are both incoming and outgoing edges. Suppose that all edges $E_1 \dots E_k$ are incoming while E_{k+1} is outgoing. Then

$$P_{n+1} = (v_1, v_2) \dots (v_{k-1}, v_k) (v_k, v_{n+1}) (v_{n+1}, v_{k+1}) \dots (v_{n-1}, v_n)$$

is an arc of the desired kind.

Problems

1. Apply the preceding method to assign directions in some simple road map.

2.* (Bratton's problem). For mutually connected graphs with n vertices and m edges find the minimum of lengths of directed diameters.

3.* In Redei's theorem investigate the conditions for an arc having arbitrary endpoints.

8.2. The homomorphism theorem. In a directed graph G we denote by $L(a_0)$ the set of all vertices which are mutually connected with a given vertex a_0. We shall call $L(a_0)$ the (*directed*) *leaf* to which a_0 belongs. It consists of more than one vertex when a_0 lies on a directed circuit which is not a loop. The section graph $G(L)$ we call the *leaf graph* of L. It follows from the preceding discussion that all edges in $G(L)$ are cyclic and that these leaf graphs are the maximal mutually connected subgraphs of G. The graph $G(L)$ is *circuit closed*, that is, when C is any directed circuit having a vertex in common with L then the whole circuit C lies in $G(L)$. These observations show:

THEOREM 8.2.1. *All edges touching a leaf graph $G(L)$ are acyclic.*

Next we define a directed graph to be *acyclic* if all its edges are acyclic, that is, G has no directed circuits. For directed graphs the acyclic graphs play a role similar to the trees for undirected graphs. For instance, as an analogue to Theorem 6.5.1 one finds:

THEOREM 8.2.2. *Any directed graph G has maximal acyclic subgraphs H with at least one incoming or outgoing edge at each non-isolated vertex of G. When G is connected also H is connected.*

For a directed graph G one can construct a *leaf composition graph* G' whose vertices are the leaves of G. Two leaves L_1 and L_2 are joined by a directed edge (L_1, L_2) in G' when there are directed edges from L_1 to L_2 in G. This leaf composition graph is acyclic because a directed circuit in it would produce a directed circuit in G passing through several leaves. Thus we can state a *homomorphism theorem* for directed graphs analogous to Theorem 5.3.1 for undirected graphs:

THEOREM 8.2.3. *A directed graph G has an acyclic leaf composition graph G' and G is homomorphic to G' under a correspondence τ whose inverse image sets*

$$\tau^{-1}(a_0') = L(a_0)$$

are the directed leaves of G.

In a directed graph one may also ask for the analogue to the lobes introduced for undirected graphs in Section 5.4. They were obtained by means of an equivalence relation for the edges of the graph based upon the concept of strong circuit connectedness. For a directed graph we define: Two edges E_1 and E_2 in G are *strongly cyclic edge connected* when there exists a sequence of directed circuits (8.1.3) such that E_1 lies on C_1 and E_2 on C_k while any pair of consecutive circuits C_i, C_{i+1} have at least one edge in common. Correspondingly we call a directed graph G *strongly cyclic edge connected* when all edges are strongly cyclic edge connected. Then the following analogue to Theorem 8.1.6 holds:

THEOREM 8.2.4. *An undirected graph G_0 is the graph G_u of a strongly cyclic edge connected directed graph G if and only if G_0 has no separating vertices.*

The proof is similar to that of Theorem 8.1.6 and shall be left to the reader.

Next let E_0 be an edge in a directed graph G. The subgraph consisting of all edges strongly cyclic edge connected to E_0 we call the *lobe graph* to which E_0 belongs. Its vertex set $M(E_0)$ is the lobe defined by E_0 and the lobe graph is seen to be the section graph $G(M)$. One verifies that its associated undirected graph $G_u(M)$ has no separating vertices. The lobe graph is *strongly cyclically closed*, that is, any directed circuit C which has at least two vertices in common with $M(E_0)$ lies entirely within $G(M)$.

PROBLEMS

1. Do the maximal acyclic subgraphs of a finite directed graph G all have the same number of edges?

2. Does there exist an analogue to Theorem 6.6.4 concerning the interrelations between such maximal acyclic subgraphs?

3. Prove that in an undirected graph G one can assign directions to the edges such that it becomes an acyclic graph.

8.3. **Transitive graphs and embedding in order relations.** A directed graph G is transitive when it has the property that to any two edges

$$E_0 = (a_0, a_1), \quad E_1 = (a_1, a_2)$$

there exists a resultant edge $E_2 = (a_0, a_2)$. More general, when $a > b$, there is an edge $E = (a, b)$. Every directed graph G has a transitive closure graph, that is, a least transitive graph G_t containing it. One obtains G_t from the directed paths $P(a, b)$ in G by adding an edge $E = (a, b)$ when $a > b$ and such an edge does not exist in G.

When G is a mutually connected graph one has $a > b$, $b > a$ for any pair of vertices, hence in G_t one has the edges (a, b) and (b, a). Thus when G has single edges and loops the transitive closure will be the directed complete graph $U^{(d)}$.

When G is acyclic the adjunction of the edges $E = (a, b)$, $a > b$, cannot produce any directed circuit in G_t because it would correspond to some cyclic directed sequence of edges in G. According to the definition of a partial order (Section 1.4) we see that then G_t is the graph of a partial order, provided it has no multiple edges.

From Section 8.2 the following general facts are obtained:

THEOREM 8.3.1. *Let G be a directed graph with single edges. The transitive closure G_t of G is a graph whose leaf graphs are the directed complete graphs $U^{(d)}(L)$ defined on the leaf sets L of G while the leaf composition graph G'_t of G_t is a partial order isomorphic to the transitive closure of the leaf composition graph G' of G.*

A directed graph shall be called a *quasi-order* when its transitive closure is an ordered graph. From the definition of an ordered set one sees that a quasi-order is characterized by the two properties:

1. G is acyclic: $a > b$, $b > a$ implies $a = b$.
2.   One of the relations $a > b$ or $b > a$ always holds for any pair of vertices.

A still less restrictive order concept is also of importance. A directed graph O is a *weak order* when it satisfies:

Any pair of vertices satisfy at least one of the conditions $a > b$, $b > a$. The leaf composition graph of a weakly ordered set is quasi-ordered.

We shall now deduce the result:

THEOREM 8.3.2. *Any directed graph G is a subgraph of a weak order O with the same leaf graphs as G.*

We say that two vertices in G are *comparable* when at least one of the relations $a > b$ and $b > a$ holds; when none of them is fulfilled a and b are *incomparable*. Thus a graph is a weak order if and only if all vertices are comparable.

To prove Theorem 8.3.2 we shall need the auxilliary fact:

THEOREM 8.3.3. *When a and b are incomparable vertices in G and an edge $E = (a, b)$ is adjoined to G then G and $G + E$ have the same cyclic edges.*

PROOF.   First the new edge E cannot be cyclic in $G + E$ since it would imply the existence of a path $P(b, a)$ in G. Secondly, when $F = (c, d)$ is an acyclic edge in G it cannot become cyclic in $G + E$ because a path

$$Q(d, a) + E + Q_1(b, c)$$

would produce a path

$$Q_1(b, c) + F + Q(d, a)$$

connecting b with a.

To obtain Theorem 8.3.2 we consider the family of all graphs $H > G$ which have the same cyclic edges as G. Let $\{H_i\}$ be an inclusion ordered family of such graphs and

$$H_0 = \sum H_i$$

its sum graph. Then H_0 is a graph of the same kind: if H_0 should contain a directed cyclic path C not in G the edges in C would have to belong to one of the graphs H_i. We conclude from the maximal principle that there must exist maximal graphs $H_0 \supset G$ with the same cyclic edges. Theorem 8.3.3 shows that in H_0 all vertices must be comparable, hence H_0 is a weak order.

Instead of adjoining the edge $E = (a, b)$ to G in Theorem 8.3.3 one could have used the reverse edge $E' = (b, a)$. We conclude that for any edge E between incomparable vertices a and b there exists a weakly ordered graph $O \supset G$ satisfying the conditions of Theorem 8.3.3 and not including E. This observation gives the following representation for directed graphs:

THEOREM 8.3.4.   *Any directed graph G can be represented as the intersction*

$$G = \bigwedge O_i$$

of weak orders $O_i \supset G$ having the same cyclic edges as G.

In the case of acyclic graphs this result becomes:

THEOREM 8.3.5.   *Every acyclic graph is the intersection of the quasi-orders in which it is contained.*

8.4.   **Basis graphs.**   We shall study the accessibility of vertices under directed paths. We may assume that all edges are single and there are no loops. In Section 8.3 we constructed the transitive closure of a directed graph G by adding an edge $E = (a_0, a_n)$ whenever there existed a directed path $P(a_0, a_n)$. We shall now consider the opposite operation consisting in the removal of *superfluous edges* $E = (a_0, a_n)$, that is, edges for which a directed path $P(a_0, a_n)$ not including E exists. Such a reduction cannot change the accessible set for any vertex.

A subgraph H of G is called a *generating subgraph* when the accessible sets for all vertices are the same for H and G

(8.4.1) $$D_G(a) = D_H(a), \qquad\qquad a \in V.$$

In order that H have this property it is necessary and sufficient that for every edge $E = (a, b)$ in G there exists a directed path $P_H(a, b)$ in H. The condition (8.4.1) shows:

THEOREM 8.4.1.   *Any generating subgraph H of G has the same leaf sets as G and the leaf composition graph H' of H is a generating subgraph of G'.*

A minimal generating graph for G shall be called a *basis graph*. Thus a generating graph H is a basis graph if and only if the removal of any edge changes the accessibility in H, that is, when $E = (a, b)$ is an arbitrary edge in H it cannot be superfluous in the sense that there exists some path $P_H(a, b)$ in H not including E.

When G is finite there exist basis graphs and these can be obtained by successive removal of edges as indicated. In case G has a directed Hamilton circuit this may be taken as a basis graph. When a basis graph exists it need not be unique. In Figure 8.4.1 any radial edge and the directed polygonal circuit defines a basis graph.

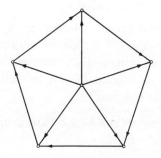

Figure 8.4.1.

In Figure 8.4.2 the five edges $(1,0)(3,0)(5,0)(0,2)(0,4)$ constitute a unique basis graph. We notice that the subgraph obtained by omitting the edges $(0,2)$ and $(0,4)$ has a unique basis consisting of seven edges.

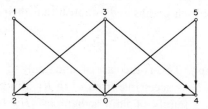

Figure 8.4.2.

As a further example one may take the directed complete graph $U_0^{(d)}$ defined on a vertex set with n elements. The directed Hamilton paths form one type of basis graphs; each has n edges. Another basis type are the star graphs $S(a_0)$ consisting of all outgoing and incoming edges at a vertex a_0; these graphs have $2(n-1)$ edges.

This latter construction is a special case of the following result:

THEOREM 8.4.2. *Let G_d be a directed graph obtained by duplication of a connected undirected graph G. Then one obtains a basis graph for G_d by duplication of any maximal tree in G.*

The proof is left to the reader.

In a finite ordered set

$$a_0 < a_1 < \cdots < a_n$$

the basis graph is unique and consists of all edges $E_i = (a_i, a_{i+1})$. If an infinite ordered set shall have a basis graph B then one sees that in any edge $E = (a, b)$ in B the vertices a and b must be immediate successors in the order. Furthermore, no two vertices can have an infinite number of vertices lying between them. From these observations one concludes:

THEOREM 8.4.3. *An ordered set can have a basis graph only when it is isomorphic to the order of a set of integers.*

We shall formulate certain general conditions under which basis graphs exist. A directed graph G shall be said to have *compact edge separation* when it has the property: For any edge $E = (a_0, b_0)$ let H be a subgraph (including E) such that after the removal of the edges in H the vertex b_0 is no longer accessible fro m a_0 Then there shall exist a finite subgraph H_0 of H with the same property.

THEOREM 8.4.4. *A directed graph with compact edge separation has a basis graph.*

PROOF. To show that there exists minimal generating graphs we consider an ordered family $\{K^{(i)}\}$ of such graphs and establish that their intersection

$$(8.4.2) \qquad\qquad\qquad K_0 = \bigwedge_i K^{(i)}$$

is also a generating graph. This is the case if and only if for every edge $E = (a_0, b_0)$ in G the vertex b_0 is accessible from a_0 in K_0. Since G has compact edge separation there exists a family of finite subgraphs $\{H_0^{(j)}(E)\}$ for each E such that b_0 is accessible from a_0 in a subgraph K only when the complement $\bar{K}$ does not contain any of these graphs $H_0^{(j)}$. If K_0 should exclude all edges of some $H_0^{(j)}$ there would be a graph $K^{(i)}$ in (8.4.2) with the same property contrary to the assumption that all $K^{(i)}$ are generating graphs.

A special case of Theorem 8.4.4 is:

THEOREM 8.4.5. *If in G any two endpoints a_0 and b_0 of an edge are connected by a finite number of directed paths then G has a basis graph.*

These conditions are fulfilled when G is locally finite and the paths from a_0 to b_0 have bounded lengths.

Another result is:

THEOREM 8.4.6. *A directed graph G has a basis graph if and only if each of its leaf graphs G(L) and its leaf composition graph G' has a basis graph.*

PROOF. Suppose first that G has a basis graph B. For any vertex a_0 in a leaf L every other vertex $b_0 \in L$ is accessible from a_0 only in paths lying entirely in $G(L)$. Consequently, in B the vertex b_0 is accessible from a_0 in the section graph $B(L)$. No edge in $B(L)$ can be superfluous since it would lead to a reduction of B. Within B there is only a single edge connecting a pair of leaves L_1 and L_2 in G (and B) because if one such edge is included in B the others are seen to be superfluous. The edges in B' form a generating subgraph for G' and no edges in B' can be superfluous since it would again lead to a reduction of B.

Conversely, assume that there exists a basis graph $B(L)$ for each leaf L in G and also a basis graph for the leaf composition graph G'. Each edge in G' is the image of all edges in G connecting a pair of leaves. To each edge in G' we assign a single such edge in G. Then one verifies that these edges corresponding to edges in B' together with all edges in the basis graphs $B(L)$ form a generating graph for G and it actually is a basis graph.

Theorem 8.4.6 reduces the problem of the existence of a basis graph to the case of acyclic graphs and mutually connected graphs.

To conclude let us make a few observations on the question when the basis graph is unique. An edge E of G is *essential* if it belongs to every generating graph of G. This as one sees is equivalent to E not being superfluous in G. Thus the essential edges belong to every basis graph which exists. We shall show:

THEOREM 8.4.7. *Let G be a graph with the property that every generating graph contains a basis graph for G. A necessary and sufficient condition that G has a unique basis graph is that for every edge $E = (a, b)$ there exists a path $P(a, b)$ consisting of essential edges.*

PROOF. According to the preceding there is a unique basis graph if and only if the essential edges form a basis graph and this is the case only if the condition of the theorem are fulfilled. Theorem 8.4.6 applies in particular to finite graphs.

PROBLEMS

1.* When is it possible to assign directions to the edges of an undirected graph G such that it becomes the basis graph of a directed graph?

2.*   Determine the largest number of edges in a basis graph defined on a vertex set with n vertices.

8.5. **Alternating paths.** A path

(8.5.1) $$P = (a_0, a_1)(a_1, a_2) \cdots (a_{n-1}, a_n)$$

in a directed graph G shall be called *alternating* when the edges $E_i = (a_i, a_{i+1})$ alternately belong to G and its converse G^*. Such paths may be classified according to the character of the initial edge E_0: It is an α-*path* when E_0 is an α-*edge*, i.e., belongs to G and an α^*-*path* when E_0 is an α^*-*edge*, i.e., belongs to G^*. Often one may wish to take into account also the character $\beta = \alpha$ or $\beta = \alpha^*$ of the last edge E_{n-1}. For instance, P is an (α, α^*)-*path* when E_0 is in G and E_{n-1} in G^*. This yields four types of paths characterized by the symbols

$$(\beta, \gamma) = (\alpha, \alpha^*);\ (\alpha^*, \alpha)\ ;\ (\alpha, \alpha);\ (\alpha^*, \alpha^*).$$

The two first types of paths have even lengths while the others have odd lengths. An alternating path is cyclic when $a_0 = a_n$. We also extend the concept of alternating paths to one or two-way infinite paths. When P in (8.5.1) is a (β, γ)-path we say that a_n is (β, γ)-*accessible* from a_0.

THEOREM 8.5.1.   *When the vertex b is (β, γ)-accessible from the vertex a and c a vertex which is (γ^*, δ)-accessible from b then c is (β, δ)-accessible from a.*

PROOF.   If the two connecting paths $P(a, b)$ and $Q(b, c)$ have no edges in common they can be combined into a single (β, δ)-path

$$P(a, b) + Q(b, c).$$

When they have common edges let $E = (e, f)$ be the first such edge in P. One of the paths

$$P(a, e, f) + Q(f, c);\ P(a, e) + Q(e, c)$$

is then a (β, δ)-path depending on whether E appears in the same or opposite directions in P and Q.

The set of all (β, γ)-accessible vertices from a vertex a we denote by

(8.5.2) $$V(a, \beta, \gamma).$$

We include a in this set when $\beta = \gamma$; in the *singular case* where $\rho(a) = 0$ one has

$$V(a, \alpha, \alpha^*) = a.$$

This definition of accessible sets can be extended to arbitrary sets A by putting

(8.5.3) $$V(A, \beta, \gamma) = \sum_a V(a, \beta, \gamma), \qquad\qquad a \in A.$$

Denote as before (Section 1.2) by $G[A]$ the set of endpoints of those edges which have their initial vertex in A. We can state:

THEOREM 8.5.2.   *A set A is an (α, α^*)-accessible set if and only if all incoming edges to $G[A]$ have their initial vertex in A, that is,*

(8.5.4) $$G^*[G[A]] \subseteq A.$$

PROOF.   It is evident that this property insures

(8.5.5) $$A = V(A, \alpha, \alpha^*).$$

On the other hand if there should be some edge

$$F = (c, b), \qquad\qquad b \in G[A], \quad c \notin A$$

one could construct an (α, α^*)-path $E + F^*$ from A to c, hence (8.5.5) is not satisfied.

From Theorem 8.5.2 follows as a special case:

THEOREM 8.5.3.   *A finite set A with finite local degrees $\rho(a)$ is an (α, α^*)-accessible set if and only if*

$$\rho(A) = \rho^*(G[A]).$$

Next we mention:

THEOREM 8.5.4.   *The accessible sets (8.5.5) form two complete fields of sets.*

PROOF.   The definition (8.5.3) shows that any sum of sets $V(A)$ is of the same kind When

$$d \in D = \bigwedge V_i$$

is a vertex belonging to an intersection of accessible sets then also $V(d)$ must belong to D. Finally it must be shown that a difference set

$$V_1 = V(A) - V(B), \quad V(A) \supset V(B)$$

is an accessible set. For any edge

$$E = (a, a'), \qquad\qquad a \in V_1$$

one must have

$$a' \in G[V(A)]$$

and so for any other edge $F = (a'', a')$ to a' also $a'' \in V(A)$. But $a'' \in V(B)$ is not possible since the path $F + E$ would lead from a'' to the vertex a not in $V(B)$.

Two vertices a and b are α-*accessibly equivalent* when any vertex v which is (α, β)-accessible from a $(\beta = \alpha$ or $\beta = \alpha^*)$ is also (α, β)-accessible from b and vice versa. We consider a to be α-accessibly equivalent to itself. We shall show:

THEOREM 8.5.5. *The accessible set $V(a)$ consists of all vertices α-accessibly equivalent to a.*

PROOF. First we observe that when $b \in V(a)$ there exists an (α, α^*)-path $P(a, b)$ with a reverse (α, α^*)-path $P(b, a)$, hence a and b must be α-accessibly equivalent according to Theorem 8.5.1. Secondly, suppose that a and b are α-accessibly equivalent. Since a must be α-accessible from b there is an α-path $P(b, a)$. When P is an (α, α^*)-path there is nothing to prove. Suppose, therefore, that P is an (α, α)-path. Let c be the last vertex in $P(b, a)$ before a such that c is (α, α^*)-accessible from b; possibly $c = b$. Then c must be (α, α^*)-accessible from a in a path $Q(a, c)$ and

$$Q(a, c) + P(c, b)$$

is an (α, α^*)-sequence from a to b which may be reduced to an (α, α^*)-path between the two vertices; hence $b \in V(a)$.

Similarly one finds that the set $V^*(a)$ consists of all vertices which are α^*-accessibly equivalent to a. One can also say that a vertex b is (α, α^*)-accessibly equivalent to a when any vertex accessible from a in an (α, β)-path is accessible from b in an (α^*, β)-path and conversely. One verifies that the set of all such vertices form the set

$$V(G[a]; \alpha^*, \alpha) = G[V(a)].$$

In connection with the alternating paths we introduce the *alternating composition graph* $G(\alpha, \alpha^*)$ which is of importance for various applications. It is defined as the graph product

$$G(\alpha, \alpha^*) = G \cdot G^*$$

of G and its converse G^*. This means that $G(\alpha, \alpha^*)$ and G have the same vertex set V and two vertices a and c are connected by an edge $E_\alpha = (a, c)$ in $G(\alpha, \alpha^*)$ if and only if a and c are connected by an alternating (α, α^*)-path of length 2 in G, that is, there exist edges

$$E_1 = (a, b), \quad E_2 = (b, c)$$

in G and G^* respectively. The graph $G(\alpha, \alpha^*)$ can be considered to be undirected. Its connected components are the accessible sets $V(a)$ defined above.

8.6. **Subgraphs of first degree.** Any directed graph has an equivalent representation as a bipartite graph: To the vertex set V of the given graph G one constructs a replica V' which is in a one-to-one correspondence $a \rightleftarrows a'$ with V. To G we associate the bipartite graph $G(V, V')$ constructed in the manner that $G(V, V')$ has an edge (a, b') if and only if there exists an edge (a, b) in G. Conversely, it is evident that when in a bipartite graph $G(V, V')$ there is a one-to-one correspondence between the vertex sets it can be represented as a directed graph in V.

This correspondence between bipartite graphs and directed graphs makes it possible to translate the previous results on bipartite graphs into directed graphs. When a bipartite graph $G(V, V')$ has a complete matching M there exists a unique sequence of edges

$$\cdots (a_0, a_1') (a_1, a_2') \cdots$$

in M beginning at any vertex a_0 in V. In the associated directed graph this sequence corresponds to a directed path

$$\cdots (a_0, a_1) (a_1, a_2) \cdots.$$

Through each vertex of G there passes exactly one path so that the matching in $G(V, V')$ corresponds to a subgraph of first degree in G, or (Section 2.3) a permutation graph for the vertex set V.

The matching theorems for locally finite graphs depended, as we saw in the preceding chapter, upon the concept of the deficiency of a set and this is readily transferred to the directed graphs. The *deficiency* of a finite set A is the quantity

(8.6.1) $$\delta(A) = v(A) - v(G[A])$$

where as before $G[A]$ denotes the set of all endpoints of edges having their initial vertex in A. Similarly there exists a *converse deficiency*

(8.6.2) $$\delta^*(A) = v(A) - v(G^*[A])$$

where $G^*[A]$ is the set of all initial vertices of edges having their endpoint in A. One finds that these deficiencies have the same properties as those derived in Section 7.2 for bipartite graphs.

As before we denote the maximal deficiencies by

(8.6.3) $$\delta_0 \geqq 0, \quad \delta_0^* \geqq 0$$

and as an analogue to Theorem 7.4.3 one obtains:

THEOREM 8.6.1. *In a locally finite directed graph a necessary and suf-*
ficient condition that it have a subgraph of first degree is that its maximal
deficiencies are

(8.6.4) $$\delta_0 = \delta_0^* = 0.$$

As in Theorem 7.5.1. one sees that a regular directed graph has no deficiency,
consequently it has a subgraph of first degree. When this subgraph is removed
from G the remaining graph is also regular. This leads to an analogue of Theorem
7.5.2:

THEOREM 8.6.2. *A regular directed graph with the vertex set V and local*
degrees

$$\rho(v) = \rho^*(v) = m, \qquad\qquad v \in V$$

is the edge direct sum of m permutation graphs

$$G = \sum P_i$$

on V.

One concludes as in Theorem 7.5.8 that this theorem is valid also when G has
a countable vertex set and each vertex is connected to a countable number of
different vertices by incoming and outgoing edges.

The other matching theorems of Chapter 7 all have their counterparts for
directed graphs but we shall leave many of the reformulations to the reader.
A vertex matching for the bipartite graph will correspond to a subgraph H of
the directed graph G such that H has at most one outgoing and one incoming
edge at each vertex in V. We shall call H a subgraph of *at most first degree*.
The vertices at which H does not have both an incoming and outgoing edge
are the *deficient vertices*. When the sets of deficient vertices are minimal then
H is a *maximal subgraph of at most first degree*. This subgraph consists of disjoint arcs covering the vertices of G. The arcs may be one or two way infinite
or they may be nite; in the latter case they can be cyclic or non-cyclic including
those of length zero.

The maximal subgraphs of at most first degree correspond to the maximal
matchings in the associated bipartite graph. When they exist one sees that there
will be subsets N and N' such that the vertices in N are deficient for outgoing
edges and those in N' deficient for incoming edges in some maximal H. The
disjoint decompositions

$$V = N + G^*[N'] + R = N' + G[N] + R'$$

follow as in Section 7.8. Here the sets

$$G[N] + R + G^*[N'], \; G[N] + R' + G^*[N']$$

are separating sets for G, that is, every edge has a vertex in one of them; these particular separating sets have strong minimal properties corresponding to those described in Theorem 7.9.2.

There will exist maximal subgraphs of at most first degree in the particular case where G has a finite separating set (Theorem 7.9.4). The same is true when G is locally finite (Theorem 7.8.6). In the latter case when G has finite maximal deficiencies (8.6.3) the number of vertices at which there is no outgoing edge in H is δ_0 and the number of vertices at which there is no incoming edge is δ_0^*. Since these deficient vertices are the initial and terminal vertices respectively of the arcs of H we conclude that for finite G

$$\delta_0 = \delta_0^*$$

a relation which also follows from Theorem 7.6.3.

CHAPTER 9

ACYCLIC GRAPHS

9.1. **Basis graphs.** We assume that G is an acyclic graph with single edges. Then $a > b$, $b > a$ implies $a = b$ and the inclusion relation $a > b$ associated with G is a partial order whose graph G_t is the transitive closure of G. When $a > c > b$ we say that c *lies between* a and b or c is an *intermediate vertex* for a and b.

Let $E = (a, b)$ be some edge. When there are intermediate vertices between a and b the edge E is superfluous in the sense of Section 8.4; when there are no vertices between a and b the edge E is essential. In this case b is an *immediate successor* to a and a an *immediate predecessor* to b. A directed path $P(a, b)$ in G is *maximal* when all its edges are essential, that is, any vertex in P is an immediate successor to the preceding.

The paths between a and b are said to be finite when there exists no infinite descending sequence of vertices

$$a > a_1 > a_2 > \cdots > b$$

nor any infinite ascending sequence

$$a > \cdots > b_2 > b_1 > b.$$

In this case the paths between any pair of vertices $a' > b'$ are also finite when

$$a \geqq a' > b' \geqq b.$$

When the paths between a and b are finite let $P(a, b)$ be any path from a to b and $E_i = (a_i, a_{i+1})$ a non-essential edge in P. One can then refine P by replacing E_i by some longer path $P_1(a_i, a_{i+1})$. One verifies that by repeating this process a finite number of times in any way one must finally reach a maximal path $Q(a, b)$. Conversely, it is easy to see that when the paths between a and b have this refinement property all paths between them are finite.

THEOREM 9.1.1. *An acyclic graph G has at most one basis graph B and when B exists it consists of the essential edges.*

PROOF. The essential edges must belong to every generating graph. On the other hand let $E_0 = (a_0, a_1)$ be an edge in a basis graph B. If E_0 should be superfluous in G there would exist some vertex c between a_0 and a_1. Since B is a basis there are paths $P(a_0, c)$ and $P(c, a_1)$ in B. But E_0 cannot be superfluous in B so the combined path

$$P(a_0, c) + P(c, a_1)$$

162

must include E_0. But this leads to a directed circuit passing through a_0 or a_1 contrary to the fact that G is acyclic.

THEOREM 9.1.2. *A necessary and sufficient condition that an acyclic graph have a basis is that the endpoints of any edge $E_0 = (a_0, a_1)$ be connected by a maximal path.*

PROOF. When a basis graph exists the condition is fulfilled. On the other hand when it holds all essential edges define a basis. An immediate consequence is:

THEOREM 9.1.3. *An acyclic graph has a basis when for each edge $E_0 = (a_0, a_1)$ the paths connecting a_0 and a_1 are finite.*

One can propose the following problem: Let G be an undirected graph. When is it possible to assign directions to its edges in such a manner that it becomes the basis graph of a partial order? One finds readily that for a triangle, that is, a circuit consisting of three edges, such a construction is not possible. Thus an immediate condition on the graph G is that its circuits have lengths $l \geq 4$. This condition is, however, not sufficient. The general problem is unsolved.

PROBLEMS

1. In an acyclic graph with a basis does every subgraph have a basis?
2. Construct a graph without triangles which cannot be directed into the basis graph of a partial order.
3.* Determine the graphs with the smallest number of edges with this property.
4.* Determine the largest number of edges in an acyclic basis graph defined on a vertex set with n elements.

9.2. **Deformations of paths.** We shall derive certain results for acyclic graphs which include as special cases the well-known Jordan-Hölder type theorems for groups and other algebraic systems.

Suppose that in the acyclic graph G the two vertices a and b are connected by directed maximal paths

$$(9.2.1) \quad \begin{aligned} A(a, b) &= (a_0, a_1) \cdots (a_{k-1}, a_k), \quad a_0 = a, a_k = b, \\ B(a, b) &= (b_0, b_1) \cdots (b_{l-1}, b_l), \quad b_0 = a, b_l = b. \end{aligned}$$

We define: The two paths A and B in (9.2.1) are *simply related* when they have only the endpoints a and b in common and there exists no vertex c with maximal paths

$$(9.2.2) \quad P(a, c) + Q(c, a_i), \quad P(a, c) + R(c, b_j)$$

or

$$(9.2.3) \quad Q_1(a_i, c) + P_1(c, b), \quad R_1(b_j, c) + P_1(c, b)$$

for any pair of intermediate vertices a_i and b_j (see Figure 9.2.1).

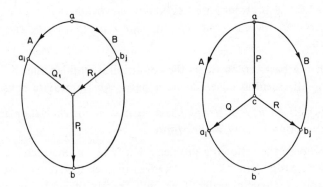

Figure 9.2.1.

When a_r and a_s are two vertices in the maximal path $A(a, b)$ in (9.2.1) they will be connected by the section $A(a_r, a_s)$. If there exists another maximal path $B_1(a_r, a_s)$ also

$$A_1(a, b) = A(a, a_r) + B_1(a_r, a_s) + A(a_s, b)$$

is a maximal path from a to b. We say that A_1 has been obtained from A by *deformation*. We call the deformation *simple* when

$$A(a_r, a_s), \quad B_1(a_r, a_s)$$

are simply related. A pair of paths (9.2.1) is *deformation equivalent* when one is obtainable from the other by a finite number of simple deformations.

THEOREM 9.2.1. *In an acyclic graph G let the paths between the vertices $a > b$ be finite. Then any pair of maximal paths (9.2.1) connecting them are deformation equivalent.*

PROOF. Suppose that $A(a, b)$ and $B(a, b)$ were not deformation equivalent. Then if they have common vertices aside from a and b there will be a decomposition of each into sections A_i and B_i such that $A_i = B_i$ or they have only the endpoints in common. If all A_i and B_i are simply related the paths A and B will be deformation equivalent. Thus we may suppose that A and B have only the endpoints a and b in common and are not deformation equivalent. Then they are not simply related and there exists some vertex c with paths (9.2.2) or (9.2.3). In the first case also the maximal paths

$$P(a, c) + Q(c, a_i) + A(a_i, b),$$
$$P(a, c) + R(c, b_j) + B(b_j, b)$$

join a and b. Since A and B are not deformation equivalent at least one of the three pairs of paths

$$A(a, a_i); \quad P(a, c) + Q(c, a_i),$$

$$Q(c, a_i) + A(a_i, b); \quad R(c, b_j) + B(b_j, b),$$

$$P(a, c) + R(c, b_j); \quad B(a, b_j)$$

cannot be deformation equivalent. An analogous result is obtained when there exist paths (9.2.3). These observations may be summarized as follows: When $A(a, b)$ and $B(a, b)$ are not deformation equivalent then there exist vertices a' and b' with

$$a \geqq a' > b' \geqq b$$

where not both equalities hold, such that a' and b' are also connected by a pair of non-equivalent paths. This argument can be repeated and so one is led to sequences

$$a \geqq a' \geqq a'' \geqq \cdots \geqq b'' \geqq b' \geqq b$$

of pairs of vertices with the same property. Since at least one of these sequences is infinite we have arrived at a contradiction. (See Ore and MacLane.)

From Theorem 9.2.1 follows as an immediate consequence:

THEOREM 9.2.2. *Let G be an acyclic graph with finite paths between any vertices $a > b$. A necessary and sufficient condition that maximal paths $A(a, b)$ and $B(a, b)$ always have the same length is that any pair of simply related paths have this property.*

The algebraic applications of this theorem to the Jordan-Hölder theorems depend on the fact that in the systems considered the following special condition is satisfied:

Quadrilateral condition. When

$$a > a_1 > b, \quad a > b_1 > b$$

where $a_1 \neq b_1$ are immediate successors to a then there exists a vertex c between a and b which is an immediate successor to both a_1 and b_1 (Figure 9.2.2).

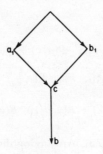

Figure 9.2.2.

When the quadrilateral condition holds, simply related paths have the form

$$(a, a_1) + (a_1, c); \quad (a, b_1) + (b_1, c)$$

consequently both have the length 2.

To obtain the ordinary Jordan-Hölder theorem for *principal series* in groups one need only consider the partial order consisting of all normal subgroups of the given group G_0. If in this system a subgroup A contains the two maximal normal subgroups A_1 and B_1 then the intersection $C = A_1 \cap B_1$ is also normal in G_0 and maximal in A_1 and B_1 according to the law of isomorphism. Thus the quadrilateral condition holds.

To deduce the Jordan-Hölder theorem for *composition series*, that is, series of subgroups in which every term is normal in the preceding, one applies the same considerations to the partial order of all composition subgroups, that is, the subgroups appearing in some composition series.

Problems

1. Carry through a complete proof of the Jordan-Hölder theorem for composition series based on the preceding graph results.

2. Can Theorem 9.2.1 be so formulated that it holds for an arbitrary directed graph?

9.3. **Reproduction graphs.** We turn next to an application of graph theory arising from the field of biology. Let V be a population of some sort consisting of individual organisms capable of sexual reproduction. The interrelations of the members in V in regard to descendence from each other may then be described by a binary *progeny relation* π such that

$$a \pi b, \qquad\qquad a, b \in V$$

whenever b is a progeny (child, off-spring) of the individual a. To π corresponds a directed graph $G = G(\pi)$, the *reproduction graph* for V. It has single edges and no loops; there is an edge (a, b) in G if and only if b is a progeny of a. When there exists a directed path $P(c, d)$ between two vertices we write $c > d$ as before and call d a *descendent* of c and c a *predecessor* of d. The corresponding *descendence graph* G is the transitive closure of G.

According to our assumptions the vertex set V must fall into two disjoint sexual groups, males m and females f such that

$$(9.3.1) \qquad\qquad V = M + F, \qquad\qquad m \in M, \quad f \in F.$$

By the mating of two individuals of opposite sex one or more off-spring will result. Two properties are immediate in this reproduction process:
1. Each individual has two parents.
2. No individual descends from itself.
In graph terminology this means:
1. The number of incoming edges at each vertex $a \in V$ is

$$(9.3.2) \qquad\qquad \rho^*(a) = 2.$$

2. The graph is acyclic.

We shall here examine the graph implications of these properties and pose the following question: Suppose that in a graph the two preceding conditions are satisfied. When is it possible to assign a *sex* to the vertices of G, that is, when does there exist a disjoint decomposition (9.3.1) of the vertex set such that at each vertex there is one edge coming from each set?

We shall prefer to consider the problem first in a somewhat more general form by dropping the condition that G shall be acyclic. Furthermore, we shall assume instead of (9.3.2) that only the condition

$$(9.3.3) \qquad\qquad \rho^*(a) \leqq 2$$

holds. In this connection it is convenient to use the terminology for an arbitrary directed graph G that a is a *parent* of b when there exists an edge (a,b) from a to b. We shall also say that G has a *sex dichotomy* when there exists a disjoint decomposition (9.3.1) such that each individual with at least two parents has exactly two of them, one from each set M and F.

Suppose now that G satisfies (9.3.3). We assign the sexual character m to some arbitrary vertex a_0. If a_0 has a progeny a_1 then a_1 may also be the progeny of some other parent a_2. In this case a_2 must be assigned the character f. From a_2 one proceeds in the same manner: When a_2 has some progeny a_3 and a_3 some other parent a_4 then a_4 must have the character m. By continuing this process a character is assigned to all vertices a_{2n} accessible from a_0 in (α,α^*)-paths, that is, using the terminology of Section 8.5, to the vertices in the set

$$(9.3.4) \qquad\qquad V(a_0; \alpha, \alpha^*).$$

However, in order that the characters m and f thus obtained be unique all paths to a_{2n} must assign the same character. One sees readily that for this to be the case it is necessary and sufficient that the length of all cyclic (α,α^*)-paths be divisible by 4. When this condition is satisfied characters with the desired pro- perties can be assigned in each set (9.3.4). This yields the result:

THEOREM 9.3.1. *A necessary and sufficient condition that a directed graph satisfying (9.3.3) have a sex dichotomy is that the lengths of all cyclic alternating (α, α^*)-paths be divisible by 4.*

The condition (9.3.3) can be omitted from the theorem by a suitable refor- mulation. Let us say that an alternating (α, α^*)-sequence is *proper* when no edge $A = (a,b)$ is followed immediately by the reverse edge A^*. Then we have:

THEOREM 9.3.2. *A necessary and sufficient condition that a directed graph have a sex dichotomy is that the lengths of all cyclic alternating proper (α, α^*)- sequences be divisible by 4.*

PROOF. The condition is evidently necessary. On the other hand it implies (9.3.3). If at some vertex there should be 3 or more incoming edges (Figure 9.3.1) then one sees that there is a cyclic proper (α, α^*)-sequence of length 6.

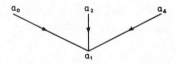

Figure 9.3.1.

Theorem 9.3.1 can be reformulated in terms of the alternating composition graph introduced in Section 8.5. An (α, α^*)-sequence in G corresponds to a unique edge sequence in $G.G^*$. The loops in $G.G^*$ are defined by the 2-sequences consisting of an edge and its reverse. These are excluded when we restrict ourselves to proper (α, α^*)-sequences. When the cyclic proper (α, α^*)-sequences in G have lengths which are divisible by 4 the cyclic paths in $G.G^*$ have even lengths, hence $G.G^*$ is a bipartite graph when the loops are disregarded, and vice versa. Furthermore, the sets (9.3.4) are the connected components of $G.G^*$. In each of them one can assign a character m or f to a given vertex a_0 and the characters of the remaining vertices are uniquely determined. Thus Theorem 9.3.2 can be stated:

THEOREM 9.3.3.   *A necessary and sufficient condition that a directed graph G have a sex dichotomy is that the alternating composition graph G.G* without loops be bipartite. The number of ways in which the characters can be assigned is 2^k where k is the number of connected components of G.G*.*

Let us return to the reproduction graphs. One can construct such a graph successively by letting pairs of vertices a and b give rise to a new vertex c connected to them by edges (a, c) and (b, c). If in such an acyclic graph every individual has two parents the graph must be infinite. In genetic experiments or descriptions of them one usually starts from some given limited population or generating set B from which the subsequent generations are produced. The predecessors of these individuals are unknown and one puts $\rho^*(b) = 0$ in B. One might also begin with some generating set in which the family relations are but incompletely known. Thus one is led to consider the condition (9.3.3) as being characteristic for the general reproduction graphs. By this definition one concludes from Theorem 9.3.2:

THEOREM 9.3.4.   *A directed graph G is a reproduction graph if and only if it is acyclic and its alternating composition graph G.G* is bipartite.*

In a reproduction graph one can introduce the usual concepts of family relationships: Father, mother, brother, sister, half-brother, half-sister, uncle, aunt, cousins, nieces and nephews, in-laws, etc. Most of the common taboos of human society can be represented as simple restrictions on the reproduction graph. For instance, mating with a descendent is not permitted. In graph terms this means that when there exists a directed path $P(a_0, a_n)$ there can exist no edge (a_0, a_n), in other words, the reproduction graph must be a basis graph in the sense of Section 8.4. The reader may verify the graph form of other taboos.

PROBLEMS

1. Characterize the theoretical reproduction graphs for a society with an absolute monogamy for both sexes, that is, no individual can have more than one mate. The same problem when the monogamy is restricted to one sex.

2. Give the graph formulation for the restriction that intermarriages between siblings or half-siblings are not permitted. The same question for a taboo against marriage between uncle and niece or aunt and nephew.

3.* Suppose that in a graph one has

$$\rho^*(a) \leqq n$$

for every vertex a. When can the vertex set be decomposed into n disjoint sets such that the incoming edges to each vertex come from different sets?

CHAPTER 10

PARTIAL ORDER

10.1. **Graphs of partial order.** In Section 1.4 we introduced the concept of partial order: A *partial order relation* $a \geqq b$ has the three properties:

1. $a \geqq b$ and $b \geqq a$ implies $a = b$.
2. Reflexivity: $a \geqq a$.
3. Transitivity.

The converse $a \leqq b$ of a partial order is a partial order. With each partial order $a \geqq b$ is associated a *strict partial order* $a > b$ which is the intersection of the two relations

$$a \geqq b, \quad a \neq b.$$

The graph G of a strict partial order is characterized by the properties:

1. G is directed with single edges.
2. Acyclic.
3. Transitive.

The graph of the corresponding partial order is obtained by adding loops at each vertex.

As previously for acyclic graphs we say that a vertex b is an immediate successor to a vertex a when $a > b$ and there is no vertex c such that

$$a > c > b;$$

in other words, the edge (a, b) is essential. A directed path $P(a, b)$ is maximal when all its edges are essential. For such maximal paths one has the Jordan-Hölder properties expressed in Theorems 9.2.1 and 9.2.2.

A partial order is the transitive closure of any of its generating graphs. As in Theorem 9.1.1 one finds that a partial order has at most one basis graph B and when B exists it consists of the essential edges. It should be noted that when a partial order is represented graphically one usually does not draw the graph of the partial order itself, but rather its basis graph B. A basis graph exists according to Theorem 9.1.2 if and only if for any edge (a, b) the vertices (a, b) are connected by a maximal path $P(a, b)$. This is the case in particular when the paths between a and b are finite.

10.2. **Representations as sums of ordered sets.** Next we turn to the subgraphs of at most first degree and show that the special properties of the partial orders

170

makes it possible to derive more specific results than those obtained in Section 8.6 for directed graphs. As in this section we represent the directed graph G as a bipartite graph $G(V, V')$ where V' is a replica of V with a one-to-one correspondence $a \leftrightharpoons a'$ between the vertices of these sets. Each edge (a, b) in G corresponds to a unique edge (a, b') in $G(V, V')$ and vice versa. Any matching M of $G(V, V')$ corresponds to a subgraph H of G of at most first degree. The components C_i of H are directed circuits and directed arcs. Let V_i be the vertex set of C_i. Then the V_i are disjoint and one has the decompositions

$$(10.2.1) \qquad\qquad H = \sum C_i, \quad V = \sum V_i.$$

Some of the V_i may possibly consist of a single vertex.

Suppose now that G is an acyclic graph. Then the components C_i of H in (10.2.1) are finite or infinite directed arcs, hence the section graphs $G(V_i)$ represent quasi-orders. Thus any matching M in $G(V, V')$ corresponds to a decomposition (10.2.1) of V in which each $G(V_i)$ is a quasi-order with a countable number of vertices. When G is a partial order the sets V_i become ordered sets.

The deficient vertices of H are those at which there is no outgoing edge so these vertices are the endpoints of arcs C_i. The conversely deficient vertices are those at which there is no incoming H-edge, hence they are initial vertices of arcs C_i. When all arcs C_i are finite there is both an initial and a terminal vertex, hence a one-to-one correspondence between the deficient and conversely deficient vertices. When G is finite the minimal number of deficient vertices equals the maximal deficiency of G

$$(10.2.2) \qquad\qquad \delta_0 = \delta_0{}^*$$

as we observed in Section 8.6. This shows:

THEOREM 10.2.1.   *In a finite acyclic graph G with the vertex set V let*

$$(10.2.3) \qquad\qquad V = \sum V_i$$

be a disjoint decomposition of V such that for each block V_i the section graph $G(V_i)$ is a quasi-ordered set. Then the smallest number of components V_i in any such decomposition is equal to the maximal deficiency (10.2.2) of G.

We notice that when $v_e(H)$ is the number of edges in a subgraph H of at most first degree including a maximal number of edges then

$$(10.2.4) \qquad\qquad v_e(H) = v(V) - \delta_0.$$

This shows that the graphs H with a minimal number of quasi-ordered components are also those with a maximal number of edges.

We shall examine the case of a strict partial order G in some further detail. A subset S of V shall be called a *lower section* when $x < s$ for some $s \in S$ implies $x \in S$. An *upper section* is defined analogously. Each set B generates a lower section $S(B)$ consisting of all $x \leqq b$ for some $b \in B$; thus B is a generating set for $S(B)$ in the sense of Section 8.1. A *minimal generating set* B_0 is such that no subset of B_0 generates $S(B_0)$. A set B_0 is a minimal generating set if and only if it is an *independent set*, that is, no relation $b_1 > b_2$ can hold for any pair b_1 and b_2 of its elements.

Suppose now first that G is a finite partial order. When A is a subset of the vertex set V its deficiency is given by the formula

$$\delta(A) = v(A) - v(G[A])$$

where $G[A]$ is the set of vertices v with $v < a$ for some $a \in A$, that is,

$$S(A) = A + G[A].$$

Suppose that for some such v one has $v \notin A$. Since G is transitive

$$G[v] \subseteq G[A];$$

consequently

$$\delta(A + v) = \delta(A) + 1.$$

This shows any set of maximal deficiency must be a lower section. For such a section A let B_0 be the minimal generating set. From

$$B_0 = A - G[A]$$

one concludes that

$$\delta(A) = v(B_0),$$

that is, the deficiency of a section set is equal to the number of vertices in its minimal generating set B_0. As a consequence we have:

THEOREM 10.2.2. *In a finite partial order the maximal deficiency is*

$$\delta_0 = v(B_0)$$

where B_0 is an independent set with a maximal number of elements.

The critical sets, i.e., the sets with maximal deficiency, are the section sets for which B_0 is a greatest independent set with $v(B_0) = \delta_0$. From Theorem 7.2.2 it follows that the critical sets form a ring of sets; in particular, there is a smallest such set $N_0 = S(B_0)$ contained in all others and a largest set $M_0 = S(B_0')$ containing all others. Correspondingly, among the greatest independent sets there is a unique lowest one B_0 and a unique highest one B_0' such that all elements of any other greatest independent set are contained between B_0 and B_0'.

By combining the results of Theorems 10.2.1 and 10.2.2 one concludes for finite partial orders:

THEOREM 10.2.3.   *Let G be a partial order in which the greatest independent sets have δ elements. Then the vertex set V has a disjoint decomposition* (10.2.3) *into δ components V_i such that each $G(V_i)$ is an order graph.*

Theorem 10.2.3 is due to Dilworth who also extended it to infinite partial orders. The proof is based upon the finite case and uses induction with respect to the maximal number δ of independent vertices. It is clear that for a given δ there can be no disjoint order decomposition with less than δ terms since that would preclude the existence of δ independent elements. For $\delta = 1$ the theorem is trivial.

In the general case each finite subset F of V has a disjoint order decomposition with δ terms

(10.2.5) $$F = \sum F_i$$

where some F_i may be void. We shall call a set C *strongly dependent* when it has the property that for any finite set F there exists some order decomposition (10.2.5) such that

$$C \cdot F \subseteq F_1$$

for a suitable component F_1. A single vertex is strongly dependent. When the condition is applied to two elements it follows that C must be ordered. The sum

$$C_0 = \sum C_i$$

of any inclusion ordered family $\{C_i\}$ of strongly dependent sets is also strongly dependent since one must have

$$C_0 \cdot F = C_k \cdot F$$

for some suitable set C_k. From the maximal principle one concludes that there exists maximal strongly dependent sets.

To complete the induction we prove that when C is a maximal strongly dependent set the remaining set

$$V_1 = V - C$$

contains a maximal number $\delta_1 = \delta - 1$ of independent vertices. One cannot have $\delta_1 < \delta - 1$ because it would lead to an order decomposition of V with less than δ terms. Suppose therefore that $\delta_1 = \delta$ so that V_1 contains δ independent elements

(10.2.6) $$a_1, a_2, \cdots, a_\delta.$$

Since the sets $C + a_i$ cannot be strongly dependent there exists for each a_i some finite set S_i for which there is no order decomposition where $(C + a_i) \cdot S_i$ belongs to the same component. One sees that $a_i \in S_i$ and so the finite set

$$S = S_1 + S_2 + \cdots + S_\delta$$

includes all vertices (10.2.6). Let

$$S = T_1 + T_2 + \cdots + T_\delta$$

be some direct order decomposition of S such that

$$C \cdot S \subseteq T_1.$$

Since S contains the independent vertices (10.2.6) there is some $a_i \in T_1$. But then

$$S_i = S_i \cdot T_1 + \cdots + S_i \cdot T_\delta$$

is a direct order decomposition of S_i with

$$(C + a_i) \cdot S_i \cdot T_1 \subseteq S_i \cdot T_1$$

contrary to the definition of S_i.

Dilworth's theorem concerns partially ordered sets for which the largest independent sets have a bounded number of elements. Under certain conditions the theorem can be extended to partial orders with infinite independent sets.

We shall say that a decomposition (10.2.3) of a partial order into disjoint ordered sets is an *independent order decomposition* when there exists an independent set

$$B_0 = \{b_i\}, \qquad\qquad\qquad b_i \in V_i.$$

When an independent decomposition exists any other independent set can have at most one vertex in each V_i. We observe that Theorem 10.2.3 is equivalent to:

THEOREM 10.2.4. *A partial order in which the greatest independent sets have δ elements has an independent order decomposition.*

PROOF. Under the given condition an independent decomposition contains at least δ orders and it can have no more. On the other hand, when Theorem 10.2.3 holds there must be one of the δ vertices in each V_i.

A partial order G is locally finite when for a given v there exists only a finite number of vertices x satisfying either of the conditions $v > x$ or $v < x$. This implies that all arcs in G are finite. Since the bipartite graph $G(V, V')$ corresponding to G is then also locally finite, it follows from Theorem 7.8.6 that it has a maximal matching M. From this property one can deduce

THEOREM 10.2.5 *Any locally finite partial order has an independent order decomposition.*

PROBLEMS

1.* Give a proof for Theorem 10.2.5.

2.* Prove the same result under the two slightly weaker conditions: $(\alpha)G(V, V')$ has a maximal matching. (β) All directed paths in G are finite.

10.3. Lattices and lattice operations. Closure relations. We shall suppose that the partial order P has the property: To every pair of elements a and b there exists a unique element

$$m = a \cup b$$

the *union* of a and b such that

$$x \geqq a, \; x \geqq b$$

if and only if $x \geqq m$.

From this definition one readily obtains the rules

$$1. \quad \text{Idempotency:} \quad a \cup a = a,$$

(10.3.1) $$2. \quad \text{Commutativity:} \quad a \cup b = b \cup a,$$

$$3. \quad \text{Transitivity:} \quad (a \cup b) \cup c = a \cup (b \cup c).$$

When a union exists in P it may be considered to be an algebraic operation which from any two elements a and b produces a unique third $a \cup b$. Furthermore one has $a \geqq b$ in P if and only if

(10.3.2) $$a \cup b = a.$$

An operation satisfying the conditions (10.3.1) we shall call a *lattice operation*. For these one can prove also the converse result:

THEOREM 10.3.1. *A lattice operation defines a partial order with the union $a \cup b$ when one puts $a \geqq b$ whenever the relation (10.3.2) holds.*

The proof is simple and may be left as an exercise to the reader.

Instead of a union one may suppose that the partial order has a unique element $a \cap b$, the *cross-cut*, such that

$$y \leqq a, \; y \leqq b$$

if and only if

$$y \leqq a \cap b.$$

The cross-cut satisfies the same rules (10.3.1) as the union. The analogue of Theorem 10.3.1 also holds when one defines $a \geqq b$ whenever

$$(10.3.3) \qquad\qquad a \cap b = b.$$

A partial order is a *lattice* when any pair of elements a and b has both a union $a \cup b$ and a cross-cut $a \cap b$. Instead of introducing a lattice by means of an original partial order one can also consider a lattice to be an algebraic system with a union operation $a \cup b$ and a cross-cut operation $a \cap b$. These operations satisfy the dual set of axioms:

$$
\begin{aligned}
a \cup a &= a, & a \cap a &= a, \\
a \cup b &= b \cup a, & a \cap b &= b \cap a, \\
a \cup (b \cup c) &= (a \cup b) \cup c, & a \cap (b \cap c) &= (a \cap b) \cap c, \\
a \cup (a \cap b) &= a, & a \cap (a \cup b) &= a.
\end{aligned}
$$

(10.3.4)

The first three axioms in each set in (10.3.4) define a partial order as we have seen. The last two conditions are the *absorption laws*. They insure that the two partial orders $a \geqq b$ defined respectively by (10.3.2) and (10.3.3) are the same. For instance, from (10.3.2) it follows that

$$a \cap b = (a \cup b) \cap b = b.$$

Conversely (10.3.2) follows from (10.3.3).

The theory of lattices permeates large parts of mathematics, but it is beyond the scope of this exposition to discuss these applications in any detail and the reader is referred to the special works on this topic. Let us add only a few observations.

A lattice we defined as a partial order in which any two elements a and b have a least upper bound $a \cup b$ and a greatest lower bound $a \cap b$. Thus these concepts are defined for the combination of any finite set of elements. A lattice is called *complete* when an arbitrary set

$$A = \{a_i\}, \qquad\qquad i \in I,$$

has a union or least upper bound and also a cross-cut or greatest lower bound

$$V = \bigvee_i a_i, \quad \Lambda = \bigwedge_i a_i, \qquad\qquad i \in I.$$

Then one of the set of conditions

$$x \geqq a_i; \quad y \leqq a_i; \qquad\qquad i \in I$$

will be fulfilled if and only if correspondingly

$$x \geqq V, \quad y \leqq \Lambda.$$

A complete lattice L possesses a unique maximal element m_1 which is the union of all elements in L and a unique minimal element m_0 which is the cross-cut of the elements.

For complete lattices the axiom system can be reduced. It suffices to assume:
1. Every set has a cross-cut.
2. There exists a unique maximal element m_1 containing all others.
The union of a set A may then be defined as the cross-cut

$$\bigvee a_i = \bigwedge u, \qquad\qquad u \in U, \quad a_i \in A$$

where U is the non-void set of all elements u which contain all $a_i \in A$.

The complete lattices are connected with the *closure relations* in sets. Let S be some basic set. A closure relation in S is a correspondence

$$A \to \Gamma(A)$$

which associates with each subset A of S a set $\Gamma(A)$ with the following properties:

1. $\Gamma(A) \geq A$,

2. $\Gamma(\Gamma(A)) = \Gamma(A)$,

3. $A \geq B$ implies $\Gamma(A) \geq \Gamma(B)$.

The image sets $\Gamma(A)$ are the *closed sets* of the relation. Condition 1 shows that $S = \Gamma(S)$ is a closed set.

THEOREM 10.3.2. *The closed sets in a closure relation Γ form a complete intersection ring R of sets including S and the closure $\Gamma(A)$ of a set A is the least set in R containing it. Conversely any complete intersection ring R including S defines a closure relation in this manner.*

PROOF. A *complete intersection ring R* of sets is a family of sets such that the intersection of any subfamily is again contained in R. Suppose that

$$\{D_i\}, \quad \Gamma(D_i) = D_i$$

is a family of closed sets under the closure relation Γ. To show that their intersection

$$D = \prod D_i$$

is closed we observe that from

$$D \subseteq D_i, \quad \Gamma(D) \subseteq \Gamma(D_i) = D_i$$

follows that

$$\Gamma(D) = \prod D_i = D.$$

Conversely let R be a complete intersection ring of sets sets including S. One may define

$$\Gamma(A) = \prod C_i$$

where C_i runs through all sets in R containing A; one sees readily that $\Gamma(A)$ satisfies the three conditions for a closure relation.

The theory of complete lattices and the theory of closure relations are equivalent in the following sense: The closed sets in a closure relation form a complete lattice. The cross-cut of a family of closed sets $\{\Gamma(A_i)\}$ is their intersection while the union is the closure of their sum

(10.3.5) $$\bigvee_i \Gamma(A_i) = \Gamma(\sum_i \Gamma(A_i)).$$

Conversely, in a complete lattice the sets $\Gamma(a)$ of all $x \leq a$ form an intersection ring of sets, hence define a closure relation in the vertex set V.

PROBLEMS

1. Show that in (10.3.5) one can put

$$\bigvee_i \Gamma(A_i) = \Gamma(\sum_i A_i).$$

2. Prove that the operation of forming transitive closures of a graph is a closure operation.

3. Prove that the transitive graphs on a set form a complete lattice under graph inclusion.

4.* A partial order is a lattice when there is a unique minimal element $a \cup b$ containing a and b and a maximal element $a \cap b$ contained in a and b. In a more general case there may be a minimal set of elements $\{c_i\}$ such that $x \geq a$, $x \geq b$ if and only if $x \geq c_i$ for some i and similarly for $x \leq a$, $y \leq b$. This suggests the definition of the partial order P as a multilattice in which there are defined many-valued operations

$$a \cup b = \{c_i\}, \quad a \cap b = \{d_i\}.$$

Try to formulate suitable axioms for this purpose.

10.4. **Dimension in partial order.** In Section 8.3 we established that every acyclic graph G is contained in a quasi-order O on the same vertex set. When G is transitive, hence a partial order, it will be contained in the transitive closure of O so that we have the result first proved by Szpilrajn: A partial order is contained in an order. In this case the same reasoning which led to Theorems 8.3.4 and 8.3.5 yields a theorem due to Dushnik and Miller:

THEOREM 10.4.1. *Any intersection of orders on a set V is a partial order and any partial order is the intersection of the orders containing it.*

On the basis of this theorem one can define: The *order dimension* $d_0(G)$ of a partial order G is the smallest cardinal number of orders O_i on V such that

$$(10.4.1) \qquad\qquad\qquad G = \bigwedge_i O_i.$$

It is possible to introduce the dimension concept in a partial order also in another manner which shows greater analogy to the ordinary Cartesian dimension for product spaces. Suppose that $\{Q_i\}$ is a family of orders, each defined on a set V_i; the index i may run through an arbitrary index set I. To the set V_i we introduce the product set

$$(10.4.2) \qquad\qquad V = V_1 \times V_2 \times \cdots \times V_k = \underset{i}{\times}\, V_i, \qquad\qquad i \in I$$

consisting of all k-tuples

$$v = (v_1, v_2, \cdots, v_k), \qquad\qquad v_i \in V_i.$$

The orders $\{Q_i\}$ define a partial order Q, the *order product*

$$(10.4.3) \qquad\qquad\qquad Q = \underset{i}{\times}\, Q_i, \qquad\qquad i \in I$$

in the product set (10.4.2) in the sense of Section 2.6: When

$$w = (w_1, w_2, \cdots, w_k)$$

then $v > w$ in Q if and only if for each i

$$v_i \geqq w_i$$

where the equality does not hold for all indices. The partial order Q is in fact a lattice with the operations

$$v \cup w = (\max\ (v_i, w_i)), \quad v \cap w = (\min\ (v_i, w_i)).$$

Furthermore, this lattice is *distributive*, that is, the lattice operations satisfy the dual *distributive laws*

$$u \cap (v \cup w) = (u \cap v) \cup (u \cap w),$$

$$u \cup (v \cap w) = (u \cup v) \cap (u \cup w)$$

as the reader may verify.

We now define: A partial order G has the *product dimension* $d_p(G)$ when this is the smallest cardinal number of orders Q_i such that G is isomorphic to a section subgraph of their order product Q. We shall prove:

THEOREM 10.4.2. *The order dimension and the product dimension of a partial order G are the same:*

(10.4.4) $$d_0(G) = d_p(G).$$

PROOF. Assume first that G has a representation (10.4.1) as the intersection of $k = d_0(G)$ orders of its vertex set V. We introduce k replicas V_i' of V and for each an order O_i' isomorphic to O_i. To every $a \in V$ there will corespond a unique element a'

(10.4.5) $$a \rightleftarrows a' = (a_i')$$

in the product space

(10.4.6) $$V' = \underset{i}{\times} V_i'.$$

According to the representation (10.4.1) one has $a > b$ in G if and only if $a > b$ for each O_i in V, hence $a_i' > b_i'$ for each O_i' in V_i'. This means that the one-to-one correspondence (10.4.5) is such that $a > b$ in G if and only if $a' > b'$ in the order product

(10.4.7) $$O' = \underset{i}{\times} O_i'.$$

This expresses that G is isomorphic to a section subgraph of the order product O' with k factors. We conclude

$$d_0(G) \geq d_p(G).$$

Secondly, let Q be an order product (10.4.3) of $l = d_p(G)$ orders $\{Q_i\}$ defined on sets V_i with the product set (10.4.2). We construct a family of orders $\{O_i\}$ of V such that Q has a representation (10.4.1). For this purpose we well-order the index set I of the orders Q_i and define each order O_i of V as follows: One has $v > w$ for two elements v and w in V when either $v_i > w_i$ or in case $v_i = w_i$, then $v_j > w_j$ where j is the first index in I for which one has $v_j \neq w_j$. The reader may verify that O_i actually is an order of V. To show

(10.4.8) $$Q = \underset{i}{\wedge} O_i;$$

we observe that one can only have $v > w$ in Q when this inclusion holds for each order O_i and conversely.

Suppose now that G is a section subgraph of Q. Then (10 4.8) gives

$$G = \underset{i}{\wedge} (G \cap O_i);$$

hence G is the intersection of l orders. We conclude that

$$d_0(G) \leq d_p(G)$$

and (10.4.4) follows.

As a consequence of Theorem 10.4.2 we may denote the dimension of a partial order G simply by $d(G)$. We shall derive a few other properties of this dimension function.

THEOREM 10.4.3.   *The dimension of order product* (10.4.3) *with k factors is $d(Q) = k$.*

PROOF.   We have just seen that Q can be represented as an intersection (10.4.8) of k orders so that $d(Q) \leq k$. To prove $d(Q) = k$ it suffices to establish that Q cannot be the intersection of fewer than k orders of V. To verify this we select two vertices $a_i > b_i$ in the set V_i of each order Q_i and construct the vertices in V

$$\alpha^{(i)} = (\cdots b_x \cdots a_i \cdots b_y \cdots),$$

$$\beta^{(i)} = (\cdots a_x \cdots b_i \cdots a_y \cdots)$$

where all components in $\alpha^{(i)}$ except a_i are equal to b_x while in $\beta^{(i)}$ all components except b_i equal a_x. In Q

$$\beta^{(j)} > \alpha^{(i)}, \qquad\qquad\qquad i \neq j$$

while $\alpha^{(i)}$ and $\beta^{(i)}$ are incomparable.

Since Q is the intersection of orders there exists some order O_i of V with

$$\alpha^{(i)} > \beta^{(i)}$$

and also some O_i^* with the reverse relation. But in no O_i can one have

$$\alpha^{(j)} > \beta^{(j)}, \qquad\qquad\qquad j \neq i$$

because it would lead to the directed cycle

$$\alpha^{(i)} > \beta^{(i)} > \alpha^{(j)} > \beta^{(j)} > \alpha^{(i)}.$$

Thus for each i there must exist at least one O_i in the intersection representation (10.4.8) for Q. This completes the proof of Theorem 10.4.3. A special case is a theorem due to Komm:

THEOREM 10.4.4.   *The dimension of the lattice L of all subsets of a set S is equal to the cardinal number of S.*

PROOF.   The family of subsets of S is isomorphic to a product set (10.4.2) in which the components are $v_i = 0$ or $v_i = 1$.

PROBLEMS

1. Let L be an order product with two factors

$$L = O_1 \times O_2$$

of lengths respectively α_1 and α_2. Determine the maximal number of independent elements in L and also an explicit Dilworth decomposition of L as the sum of ordered sets.

2.* The same problem for an arbitrary order product.

CHAPTER 11

BINARY RELATIONS AND GALOIS CORRESPONDENCES

11.1. Galois correspondences. We shall denote by P and Q two partial orders defined in the vertex sets V_P and V_Q respectively. We assume that there exists a correspondence ρ of P into Q

$$(11.1.1) \qquad\qquad p \to \rho(p) \in Q$$

and a correspondence π of Q into P

$$(11.1.2) \qquad\qquad q \to \pi(q) \in P.$$

These correspondences shall be called a pair of *Galois correspondences* between P and Q when the following two conditions are fulfilled:

1. When $p_1 \geq p_2$ are two elements in P and $q_1 \geq q_2$ elements in Q then

$$(11.1.3) \qquad\qquad \rho(p_1) \leq \rho(p_2), \quad \pi(q_1) \leq \pi(q_2).$$

2. For any elements $p \in P$ and $q \in Q$

$$(11.1.4) \qquad\qquad \pi\rho(p) \geq p, \quad \rho\pi(q) \geq q .$$

When a pair of Galois correspondences are defined we say there exists a *Galois connection* between P and Q. This terminology is inspired by the Galois theory of equations. Here one examines the correspondence between the subfields of a given field F and the subgroups of the group of automorphisms A of F. To each set of elements $X \subseteq F$ there exists a subgroup $A(X)$ consisting of those automorphisms which leave each element in X invariant. Conversely, to each subset $Y \subset A$ there exists a field $F(Y)$ consisting of those elements in F which are invariant by the automorphisms in Y. One verifies that the conditions

$$A(X) \subseteq A(X_1) \qquad\qquad \text{when } X \supset X_1,$$
$$F(Y) \subseteq F(Y_1) \qquad\qquad \text{when } Y \supset Y_1$$

are fulfilled; furthermore

$$F(A(X)) \supseteq X, \quad A(F(Y)) \supseteq Y$$

so that a Galois correspondence is defined between the subsets of F and A.

Among the numerous examples of Galois correspondences let us mention the following:

1.   In a vector space V there corresponds to each subset A of V a set $O(A)$ consisting of all vectors orthogonal to the vectors in A. One verifies that

$$O(A) \subseteq O(B), \qquad\qquad \text{when } A \supset B,$$

$$O(O(A)) \supseteq A$$

so that a Galois connection is defined for the subsets of V.

2.   In a group G there corresponds a centralizer $C(A)$ to each subset A of G. Here $C(A)$ consists of all elements c commuting with each element a of A:

$$a \cdot c = c \cdot a.$$

3.   In a ring there corresponds an annihilator $N(A)$ to each subset A. It consists of the elements n for which $n \cdot a = 0$ for each $a \in A$.

We shall examine the properties of the Galois correspondences. The conditions (11.1.3) state that the Galois correspondences are inclusion inverting. Through a combination of the properties (11.1.3) and (11.1.4) one sees that for any $p \in P$ one must have simultaneously

$$\rho\pi\rho(p) \geq \rho(p), \quad \rho\pi\rho(p) \leq \rho(p)$$

and so we conclude:

THEOREM 11.1.1.   *Under Galois correspondences ρ and π one has*

(11.1.5) $\rho\overline{\pi\rho}(p) = \rho(p), \quad \pi\overline{\rho\pi}(q) = \pi(q).$

The combined correspondences $\pi\rho$ and $\rho\pi$ map P and Q into themselves. They may be called the *Galois closure operations* while the images

(11.1.6) $\Gamma_P(p) = \pi\rho(p), \quad \Gamma_Q(q) = \rho\pi(q)$

are the *Galois closures* of p and q respectively. The reader may verify that they possess the following properties:

THEOREM 11.1.2.   *The Galois closures* (11.1.6) *have the three closure properties in P:*

1.   *When $p_1 \geq p_2$ then $\Gamma_P(p_1) \geq \Gamma_P(p_2)$,*

2. $\Gamma_P(p) \geq p,$

3. $\Gamma_P\Gamma_P(p) = \Gamma_P(p)$

and analogously in Q.

It may be noted that the elements

$$\bar{p} = \Gamma_P(p), \quad \bar{q} = \Gamma_Q(q)$$

are the *closed elements* in P and Q:

THEOREM 11.1.3. *The closed elements $\bar{p}$ and $\bar{q}$ in P and Q are those which are images of elements in the other set*

(11.1.7) $$\bar{p} = \pi(q), \quad \bar{q} = \rho(p)$$

and the Galois connection defines one-to-one correspondences for the closed sets.

PROOF. The elements $\bar{p}$ of the form (11.1.7) are closed according to (11.1.5). On the other hand when $\bar{p}$ is a closed element it is an image under π

$$\bar{p} = \pi(\rho(p)).$$

Finally when

$$\bar{p} = p, \quad \bar{q} = q$$

in (11.1.7) one of the relations

$$\bar{p} = \pi(\bar{q}), \quad \bar{q} = \rho(\bar{p})$$

implies the other.

Let P_1 and Q_1 be the sets of closed elements in P and Q respectively. The Galois connection is called *perfect in P* when $P = P_1$, that is, every $p \in P$ is closed

$$\pi\rho(p) = p.$$

The connection is *perfect* when it is perfect both in P and Q. For several questions, for instance, for the Galois theory of equations, it is of importance to decide when this is the case. The following criterion is useful:

THEOREM 11.1.4. *A Galois connection between P and Q is perfect in P if and only if any two distinct elements $p_1 > p_2$ have distinct images*

$$\rho(p_1) < \rho(p_2).$$

The proof is left to the reader.

Let us consider the general construction of Galois connections. The set P_1 of closed elements is a partially ordered subset of P such that to each $p \in P$ there exists a unique minimal element $\bar{p} \in P_1$ with $\bar{p} \geq p$. Analogously, the closed elements $\bar{q}$ form a subset Q_1 of Q such that for any $q \in Q$ there is a minimal element $\bar{q} \in Q_1$ with $\bar{q} \geq q$. Between P_1 and Q_1 there exists a converse isomorphism, that is, a one-to-one correspondence π

$$P_1 = \pi(Q_1), \quad Q_1 \pi^{-1}(P_1)$$

for which $q_1 > q_2$ in Q_1 implies

$$\pi(q_1) < \pi(q_2)$$

in P_1 and vice versa. Conversely, when such subsets P_1 and Q_1 of P and Q exist a Galois correspondence can be defined.

In most applications the sets P and Q are complete lattices. We shall verify that then the sets P_1 and Q_1 are also complete lattices. For this purpose let $\{\bar{p}_i\}$ be a set of closed elements. The largest element in P contained in all $\bar{p}_i$ is the cross-cut

$$d = \wedge \bar{p}_i.$$

But from

$$d \leqq \bar{p}_i, \; \bar{d} \leqq \bar{p}_i$$

one concludes that

$$\bar{d} \leqq \wedge \bar{p}_i = d, \qquad\qquad\qquad \bar{d} = d.$$

Since d is closed the cross-cuts in P and P_1 are the same. The smallest element in P containing all $\bar{p}_i$ is the union

$$u = \vee \bar{p}_i.$$

Thus the smallest closed element containing all $\bar{p}_i$ is the closure

$$\bar{u} = \overline{\vee \bar{p}_i} = \overline{\vee \bar{p}_i}.$$

One sees that unions in P and P_1 will in general not coincide. We call P_1 a *complete sublattice of P with respect to cross-cut* and similarly for Q_1 in Q.

The complete lattices P and Q will have maximal and minimal elements

$$\overset{(P)}{m}, \; \overset{(Q)}{m}, \; \overset{(P)}{n}, \; \overset{(Q)}{n}$$

respectively. Similarly P_1 and Q_1 have the maximal and minimal elements

$$\overset{(P_1)}{m}, \; \overset{(Q_1)}{m}, \; \overset{(P_1)}{n}, \; \overset{(Q_1)}{n}.$$

It is clear that

(11.1.8) $$\overset{(P)}{m} \overset{(P)}{\bar{m}} = \overset{(P_1)}{m}, \; \overset{(Q)}{m} \overset{(Q)}{\bar{m}} = \overset{(Q_1)}{m}$$

and that

$$\overset{(P)}{m} \to \overset{(Q_1)}{n}, \; \overset{(Q)}{m} \to \overset{(P_1)}{n}$$

under the Galois connection.

Conversely, let P and Q have complete sublattices P_1 and Q_1 with respect to cross-cut such that (11.1.8) holds. When P_1 and Q_1 are conversely isomorphic a Galois connection is defined between P and Q by associating with each $p \in P$ as its closure $\bar{p}$ the smallest element in P_1 containing p and analogously for Q. The Galois correspondences are defined by

$$\rho(\bar{p}_1 \cap \bar{p}_2) = \overline{\bar{q}_1 \cup \bar{q}_2},$$

$$\rho(\overline{\bar{p}_1 \cup \bar{p}_2}) = \bar{q}_1 \cap \bar{q}_2$$

and analogously for π.

The preceding observations apply in particular when $P = Q$, that is, for Galois connections within the complete lattice P. Various special cases may occur. One may have $P_1 = Q_1$ and the Galois correspondence is self-dual; this requires that P_1 has a converse or dual automorphism, a one-to-one correspondence taking unions into cross-cuts and vice versa. Such a Galois connection is involutory when the dual automorphism π is an involution or correspondence of order 2 so that

$$\bar{p} \to \bar{q} = \pi(\bar{p}), \quad \bar{q} \to \pi(\bar{q}) = \bar{p}.$$

Finally, assume that P_1 is a complemented lattice so that each $p_1 \in P_1$ has at least one complement p_1' defined by

$$p_1 \cup p_1' = m_1, \quad p_1 \cap p_1' = n_1.$$

A polarity or orthogonality is an involutory Galois connection which takes every $p_1 \in P_1$ into its special polar or orthogonal complement p_1^* which has the properties

$$p_1 \to p_1^* = \pi(p_1), \quad p_1^{**} = p_1,$$

$$p_1 \cup p_1^* = m_1, \quad p_1 \cap p_1^* = n_1.$$

11.2. **Galois connections for binary relations.** We shall illustrate the theory of Galois connections through an application to binary relations. Let V and V' denote two sets which may coincide. As we have already stated, a binary relation R is an association

(11.2.1) $a \, R \, a'$

which holds for certain pairs of elements (a, a') in the product space $V \times V'$. We denote by $R(a)$ the subset of V' consisting of all vertices a' for which the relation (11.2.1) holds. A converse relation R^* is defined as before by putting

$$a' \, R^* \, a$$

whenever (11.2.1) is fulfilled. The set $R^*(a')$ consists of all $a \in V$ satisfying (11.2.1).

The relation R associates with each set A in V two derived sets

(11.2.2) $\hat{R}(A) = \prod_a R(a), \quad \check{R}(A) = \sum_a R(a),$ $a \in A$

lying in V'. The set $\hat{R}(A)$ consists of all $a' \in V'$ such that (11.2.1) holds for every $a \in A$ while $\check{R}(A)$ consists of all a' for which (11.2.1) holds for some $a \in A$. To begin with we shall only examine the sets $\hat{R}(A)$. The definition (11.2.2) shows that they form a complete intersection ring of sets. The minimal set of this ring is $\hat{R}(V)$ consisting of all a' such that (11.2.1) holds for every a. The maximal set is

$$\hat{R}(\emptyset) = V'.$$

For the converse relation the same situation obtains. To each subset A' of V' there exists a set $\hat{R}*(A')$ consisting of all $a \in V$ for which (11.2.1) holds for every $a' \in A'$. As in (11.2.2) one has

$$(11.2.3) \qquad\qquad \hat{R}*(A) = \prod_{a'} R*(a'), \qquad\qquad a' \in A'.$$

These sets form a complete intersection ring with $\hat{R}*(V')$ as the minimal element. From (11.2.2) and (11.2.3) follows

$$\hat{R}(A_1) \subseteq \hat{R}(A_2), \qquad\qquad A_1 \supseteq A_2$$

and similarly for $\hat{R}*$; furthermore

$$\hat{R}*\hat{R}(A) \supseteq A, \quad \hat{R}\hat{R}*(A') \supseteq A'$$

so that we can state:

THEOREM 11.2.1. *Every binary relation R and its converse $R*$ define Galois correspondences*

$$(11.2.4) \qquad\qquad A \to \hat{R}(A), \; A' \to \hat{R}*(A')$$

for the subsets of the sets V and V'.

The consequences of the theory of Galois connections follow, in particular:

THEOREM 11.2.2. *For a binary relation R and its converse $R*$ one has*

$$(11.2.5) \qquad \hat{R}\,\hat{R}*\,\hat{R}(A) = \hat{R}(A), \; \hat{R}*\hat{R}\,\hat{R}*(A') = \hat{R}*(A').$$

The closures (11.1.6) of sets A and A' become in this case

$$\Gamma(A) = \hat{R}*\hat{R}(A), \; \Gamma*(A') = \hat{R}\,\hat{R}*(A').$$

It is of importance to note that to Theorem 11.2.1 one has the converse:

THEOREM 11.2.3. *Any Galois connection Γ between the lattices P and Q of all subsets of sets V and V' is obtainable from correspondences (11.2.4) for a suitable relation R.*

PROOF. In Γ let P_1 and Q_1 be the sublattices of closed sets with the dual isomorphism α connecting them

$$\bar{A} \to \alpha(\bar{A}), \quad \bar{A}' \to \alpha^{-1}(\bar{A}').$$

Between V and V' we introduce the relations

(11.2.6) $a \, R \, a', \; a' \, R^* \, a$

defined to hold respectively when

(11.2.7) $a' \in \alpha(\bar{a}), \; a \in \alpha^{-1}(\bar{a}').$

The first of these conditions implies

$$\bar{a}' \subset \alpha(\bar{a})$$

and by applying α^{-1}

$$\alpha^{-1}(\bar{a}') \supset \bar{a} \supset a$$

so that R^* is the converse of R. Furthermore

$$\hat{R}(A) = \prod_a \hat{R}(\bar{a}) = \prod_a \alpha(\bar{a}), \qquad\qquad a \in A$$

and so by the converse isomorphism

$$\hat{R}(A) = \alpha(\overline{\bigvee \bar{a}}) = \alpha(\bar{A}).$$

This shows that the closed sets under Γ are the same as those for R and R^*.

We assume in the following that R is a binary relation within a set V. In order that R be self-dual, that is, the lattices of closed sets be the same it is necessary and sufficient that for each a

$$R(a) = \prod_b R^*(b), \qquad\qquad b \in B_a^*,$$

$$R^*(a) = \prod_b R(b), \qquad\qquad b \in B_a$$

for suitable sets B_a and B_a^*. This property can be expressed in the form:

THEOREM 11.2.4. *A necessary and sufficient condition for a relation R to define a self-dual Galois connection is that for each $a \in V$ there exist sets B_a and B_a^* such that the relations*

$$a \, R \, x, \; a \, R^* y$$

hold respectively if and only if

$$B_a^* \, R^* \, x, \; B_a \, R \, y.$$

Such relations can therefore also be termed *weakly symmetric*.

Next let $R = R^*$ be a symmetric relation. In this case (11.2.5) reduces to

$$\hat{R}\,\hat{R}\,\hat{R}(A) = \hat{R}(A).$$

This can be expressed that the correspondence between the closed sets is of order 2, hence an involution. Conversely, every involutory Galois correspondence between the subsets of V can be defined by a symmetric relation, because then the conditions (11.2.7) reduce to a single one and the relations (11.2.6) are the same.

THEOREM 11.2.5.   *A symmetric relation defines an involutory Galois connection in the family of all subsets of the basic set V; conversely every Galois connection of this kind is obtainable in this way from a symmetric relation.*

A relation R is reflexive when $a\,R\,a$ for every a and antireflexive when this holds for no a. The converse relation R^* is reflexive or antireflexive at the same time as R. When R is antireflexive $R(a)$ does not contain a, hence

$$A \cdot \hat{R}(A) = \emptyset$$

for any set A, hence in particular

$$\hat{R}(A) \cdot \hat{R}\,\hat{R}(A) = \emptyset.$$

In the Galois correspondence defined by R this last property of the closed sets implies that for the images under the dual isomorphisms one has

$$\hat{R}^*\,\hat{R}(A) \cup \hat{R}^*\hat{R}\,\hat{R}(A) = V$$

in Q_1. In P_1 one finds analogously

$$\hat{R}\,\hat{R}^*(A) \cup \hat{R}\,\hat{R}^*\,\hat{R}^*(A) = V.$$

Assume now that R is symmetric, hence $P_1 = Q_1$ for the closed sets. The results just stated reduce to

$$\hat{R}(A) \cdot \hat{R}\,\hat{R}(A) = \emptyset, \quad \hat{R}(A) \cup \hat{R}\,\hat{R}(A) = V.$$

Thus the lattice of closed sets is complemented and R defines a polarity in it. The converse is readily established from (11.2.6) and (11.2.7) as before, so that we state:

THEOREM 11.2.6.   *A symetric antireflexive relation defines a Galois connection with a polarity for the family of all subsets of V; conversely any such polarity is obtainable from a suitable symmetric antireflexive relation in V.*

Among the several relations which may be derived by means of Galois connections let us mention the *closed relations* in which

(11.2.8) $$\hat{R}^*(\hat{R}(A)) = A.$$

The associated sets $\check{R}(A)$ defined in (11.2.2) for a relation R have properties analogous to those derived for the $\hat{R}(A)$. Denote for the moment by $S = \tilde{R}$ the complementary relation to R, that is,

$$a \,\tilde{R}\, a'$$

only when (11.2.1) does not hold. One verifies then that for R the associated sets are

$$\hat{S}(A) = C'(\check{R}(A)), \ \check{S}(A) = C'(\hat{R}(A))$$

where C' indicates the set complement in V'. For the converse of R one has the analogous formulas.

PROBLEM

1. Examine the properties of the closed relations defined in (11.2.8), in particular for finite sets.

11.3. **Alternating product relations.** *The product of two relations R and S* is defined in the same way as the graph product: The relation

$$a \, R \, S \, a''$$

holds if and only if there is a vertex $a' \in V'$ such that

$$a R a', \ a' S a'' \ ;$$

in other words, there exists an edge sequence (a, a'), (a', a'') of length 2 from a to a''. The product of several relations is defined analogously so that

$$R_1 R_2 \cdots R_k [A] = \check{R}_k \cdots \check{R}_1(A)$$

is the set of vertices which can be reached from vertices in A by sequences of k edges lying successively in $R_1, \cdots, R_k$. When all R_i are equal $R_i = R$ one obtains the sets $R^n[A]$ defined by the *power relation* R^n.

We shall consider various relations characterized by product properties. The simplest case is a *transitive relation* in a set V defined by

(11.3.1) $R^2 \subseteq R.$

We denote by E the *identity relation* $a = b$ in V. Then the *reflexive relations* are defined by

(11.3.2) $R \cup E = R$

while the *antireflexive relations* have

$$R \cap E = 0$$

where 0 is the *null-relation* holding for no pair of vertices. A relation is *acyclic* when

(11.3.3) $$R^n \cap E = 0, \qquad n = 1, 2, \cdots.$$

Thus a *strict partial order* is defined by (11.3.1) and (11.3.3) while an *equivalence relation* is characterized by $R = R^*$ in addition to (11.3.1) and (11.3.2). The *transitive closure* of R is the union

(11.3.4) $$\Gamma(R) = E \cup R \cup R^2 \cup \cdots$$

which holds

$$a\Gamma(R)b$$

if and only if there is a directed path of R-edges from a to b.

Let R be a relation from V to V' and S a relation from V' to V. The products

(11.3.5) $$RS, \; SR$$

are relations in V and V' respectively. Their transitive closures

$$\Gamma(RS), \; \Gamma(SR)$$

will hold

$$a\Gamma(RS)b, \; a'\Gamma(SR)b'$$

when there is an even path from a to b consisting alternatingly of edges in R and S, respectively, an even path from a' to b' in S and R-edges.

Two relations R and S shall be called *mutually transitive* when

(11.3.6) $$RSR \subseteq R, \; SRS \subseteq S.$$

These represent quadrilateral conditions upon the edges in R and S (Figure 11.3.1). When there exists edges

$$E_1 = (a, a') < R, \; E_3 = (b, b') < R, \; E_2 = (a', b) < S$$

then there shall exist an edge $E_4 = (a, b')$ in R, and analogously for S.

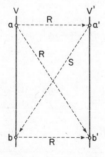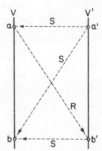

Figure 11.3.1.

When R and S are mutually transitive also R^* and S^* are mutually transitive. Each of the conditions (11.3.6) insures that both product relations (11.3.5) are transitive. When $V = V'$ and $R = S$ the conditions (11.3.6) become

$$R^3 \subseteq R.$$

This condition of *weak transitivity* seems to be a natural substitute for transitivity in bipartite graphs. Such relations have been studied by Rainich.

Let us call a relation *self-transitive* when R and R^* are mutually transitive. Also in this case the conditions (11.3.6) reduce to a single one

(11.3 7) $$R R^* R \supseteq R.$$

Such self-transitive relations have been studied in particular by Jacotin-Dubreil and Riguet; the latter used the term *difunctional relations*. When (11.3.7) holds the relations $R^*.R$ and $R. R^*$ are both transitive and symmetric and one has

$$a R R^* a$$

assuming there is an R-edge from each a and to each a'. This leads to the principal result for self-transitive relations (compare Section 8.5):

THEOREM 11.3.1. *All self-transitive relations are obtainable by the following construction: The basis sets V and V' are partitioned*

$$V = \sum B_i, \quad V' = \sum B_i'$$

such that the cardinal number of blocks B_i and B_i' is the same and in each pair of corresponding blocks B_i and B_i' every vertex $b_i \in B_i$ is connected by an R-edge to each $b_i' \in B_i'$ and conversely.

Thus these relations may be considered as a correspondence between two. equivalence relations.

11.4.   **Ferrers relations.**   We assume that R and S are relations from V to V' and construct the *alternating products*

$$\Delta(R,S) = (R \cap \tilde{S}) \cdot (S^* \cap \tilde{R}^*),$$

(11.4.1)

$$\Delta(S^*, R^*) = (S^* \cap \tilde{R}^*) \cdot (R \cap \tilde{S})$$

where as before $\tilde{R}$ is the complementary relation to R. One sees that $\Delta(R, S)$ is a relation in V and $\Delta(S^*, R^*)$ a relation in V'. Furthermore

$$a \, \Delta(R, S) \, b$$

holds if and only if there exists some $a' \in V'$ such that

$$a(R \cap \tilde{S})a', \quad a'(S^* \cap \tilde{R}^*)b,$$

that is, there exists an edge (a, a') in R but not in S and an edge (a', b) in S^* but not in R^*.

The transitive closure $\Gamma(\Delta(R, S))$ consists of the vertices in V which can be reached from a vertex a by even alternating paths whose edges belong to the two relations

$$(11.4.2) \qquad R \cap \tilde{S}, \quad S^* \cap \tilde{R}^* = (S \cap \tilde{R})^*.$$

The vertices $a' \in V'$ which can be reached from a by odd alternating paths of the same kind are those which satisfy

$$a\Gamma(R, S) \cdot R \cap \tilde{S} a'.$$

When the relations (11.4.2) are mutually transitive they fulfill the conditions

$$(R \cap \tilde{S}) \cdot (S \cap \tilde{R})^* \cdot (R \cap \tilde{S}) \subset R \cap \tilde{S},$$

$$(11.4.3)$$

$$(S \cap \tilde{R})^* \cdot (R \cap \tilde{S}) \cdot (S \cap \tilde{R})^* \subset (S \cap R)^*.$$

The special case $S = \tilde{R}$ is of some interest. The conditions (11.4.3) reduce to

$$(11.4.4) \qquad R \tilde{R}^* R \subset R, \quad \tilde{R}^* R \tilde{R}^* \subset \tilde{R}^*,$$

i.e., the relations R and $\tilde{R}^*$ are mutually transitive. Relations with this particular property are known as *Ferrers relations*; they have been examined by Wiener and Riguet. The reader may verify that when one of the relations

$$R, \tilde{R}, R^*, \tilde{R}^*$$

is a Ferrers relation so are the three others and the conditions (11.4.4) reduce to a single one provided R and R^* are defined over the whole sets V and V'. These relations can be characterized in another manner:

THEOREM 11.4.1. *A relation R is a Ferrers relation if and only if the associated sets $R(a)$ form an inclusion ordered family.*

PROOF. When R is a Ferrers relation for which

$$a R a', \quad b \tilde{R} a'$$

then

$$(11.4.5) \qquad a' \in R(a), \quad a' \notin R(b)$$

and the condition (11.4.4) shows that

$$(11.4.6) \qquad R(a) \supset R(b).$$

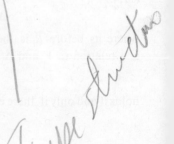

Conversely when the sets $R(a)$ form an inclusion ordered family and (11.4.5) holds, then (11.4.6) and (11.4.4) follow.

The Ferrers relations first made their appearance in connection with the additive partitions of integers. Suppose that for some integer N one has

$$N = \sum r_i, \qquad\qquad r_1 \geq r_2 \geq \cdots \geq r_m.$$

This partition can be represented by means of an incidence matrix or *Ferrers diagram*

	r_1^*,	r_2^*, $\cdots$			
r_1	1	1	1	0 $\cdots$	0
r_2	1	1	0	0 $\cdots$	0
$\vdots$	.	.	.	. $\cdots$	0

where in the ith line the first r_i terms are 1 and the remaining 0. Then the column sums also form a non-increasing sequence

$$r_1^* \geq r_2^* \geq \cdots$$

defining the dual or converse partition

$$N = \sum r_i^*.$$

Various other formal conditions, in addition to those we have already mentioned, have been investigated. Two relations *commute* when

$$R \cdot S = S \cdot R.$$

This means that when

$$a\,R\,b, \quad b\,S\,c$$

then there shall exist some b' with

$$a\,S\,b', \quad b'\,R\,c$$

and conversely. A *weak commutativity* is introduced in the *hexagonal condition* of Dubreil

$$R\,S\,R = S\,R\,S.$$

Of a more topological character is the T_0-condition that $R(a) = R(b)$ shall imply $a = b$. We shall not go into further details.

PROBLEMS

1. Prove that when R is a Ferrers relation then

$$R \, \tilde{R}^* R$$

has the same property.

2. If R and S are equivalence relations, when is $R \cdot S$ an equivalence?

3. Let G be a group with subgroups A and B. The coset expansions

$$G = \sum g A = \sum g' B$$

define equivalence relations in G. Show that these commute if and only if A and B are commuting subgroups: $AB = BA$.

4. Show that the equivalence relations defined by a left and a right coset expansion

$$G = \sum g A = \sum B g_1$$

always commute.

CHAPTER 12

CONNECTING PATHS

12.1. **The cross-path theorem.** Several of the preceding results were based upon the matching theorems established in Chapter 7. They were concerned with the existence of families of disjoint edges connecting the two vertex sets in a bipartite graph. We shall extend these results by replacing the edges by paths connecting two disjoint vertex sets in a graph. To obtain a unified method for the proof of two different theorems we shall first deduce an auxilliary *cross-path theorem*

We assume that t disjoint directed graph arcs

(12.1.1) $$A_i = E_{i1}, E_{i2}, \cdots, E_{in_i} \qquad\qquad i = 1, 2, \cdots, t$$

are given; here the edges are

(12.1.2) $$E_{i,j} = (a_{i, j-1}, a_{ij}), \qquad\qquad j = 1, 2, \cdots, n_i$$

and

(12.1.3) $$a_{i0}, a_{i1}, \cdots, a_{i,n_i}$$

the vertices lying on A_i. To these arcs (12.1.1) we adjoin a family of directed *cross-edges*

(12.1.4) $$C_l = (c_l, c_{l+1}), \qquad\qquad t = 0, 1, \cdots, m$$

such that for each cross-edge the endpoints c_l and c_{l+1} coincide with vertices (12.1.3) with the exception of c_0 and c_m which do not lie on any arc A_i. The ends of C_l may possibly lie on the same A_i.

The family of cross-edges (12.1.4) shall be called *alternating* when it possesses the following characteristics: At a vertex a_{ij} there shall be at most one outgoing and one incoming cross-edge. Furthermore, on any given arc A_i these cross-edges shall form an ordered sequence of alternately outgoing and incoming edges. In case there are both types of edges at some vertex the incoming edge shall be considered to precede the outgoing. The first cross-edge, if it exists, shall be outgoing, hence it is single. We observe also that by joining certain sections of an arc A_i into single edges E_{ij} one can suppose that there is at least one cross-edge at each intermediate vertex a_{ij} (see Figure 12.1.1).

197

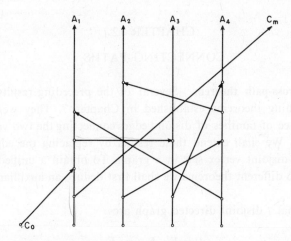

Figure 12.1.1

The cross-path theorem states:

THEOREM 12.1.1. *A family $\{A_i\}$ of t disjoint arcs (12.1.1) shall be given together with an alternating family (12.1.4) of cross-edges $\{C_l\}$. From the edges in $\{A_i\}$ and $\{C_l\}$ one can construct $t+1$ disjoint arcs $\{A_i'\}$ connecting the set of initial vertices*

(12.1.5) $c_0, \quad a_{i0},$ $i = 1, 2, \cdots, t$

with the set of terminal vertices

(12.1.6) $c_m, \quad a_{in_i},$ $i = 1, 2, \cdots, t.$

PROOF. Each $\{A_i\}$ gives rise to a new arc A_i' by the following construction. One puts $A_i' = A_i$ when there are no cross-edges on A_i. Otherwise, one proceeds from a_{i0} on A_i to its first cross-edge C. By assumption C is outgoing; we continue A_i' along C to some vertex a_{kl} on an arc A_k. One then proceeds on A_k to the next cross-edge C' which must also be outgoing and so on. To these t paths A_i' we can add another A_0' of the same kind by starting the construction from b_0 along the cross-edge C_0. The family of these $t+1$ paths $\{A_i'\}$ may be called the *cross-paths* defined by $\{A_i\}$ and $\{C_j\}$.

It remains to show that the cross-paths have the properties indicated in the theorem. At each vertex a_{ij} including the vertices (12.1.6) there is only one edge through which a cross-path can enter. This is clear for the vertices at which there is no entering cross-edge. A vertex a_{ij} with an incoming cross-edge cannot be entered through the edge E_{ij} in A_i of which it is the endpoint because the preceding cross-edge at $a_{i,j-1}$ is outgoing by assumption. From this observation follows first that the A_i' can have no cyclic sections, hence they are arcs; secondly, the construction can only come to a halt when it reaches one of the vertices (12.1.6); thirdly, at no vertex a_{ij} can there be more than one cross-path A_i', hence they are all disjoint.

By proceeding from a vertex a_{ij} in reverse direction on the single possible entering edge for an arc A_i' one must eventually reach one of the vertices (12.1.5). We conclude that for any a_{ij} there is a single cross-path passing through it. It may be noted also that the only edge in the families $\{A_i\}$ and $\{C_l\}$ which do not occur in the cross-paths are the sections E_{ij} in (12.1.2) connecting a vertex $a_{i,j-1}$ with an outgoing cross-edge with the next vertex a_{ij} with an incoming cross-edge.

The cross-path theorem is evidently valid also when some of the vertices in (12.1.5) coincide and similarly for the vertices (12.1.6), with the only change in the formulation that the arcs $\{A_i\}$ and also $\{A_i'\}$ may have endpoints in common. For instance, the sets (12.1.5) and (12.1.6) can consist of single vertices.

The cross-path theorem holds in a slightly modified form also for a family of arcs $\{A_i\}$ about which one supposes only that they are edge disjoint. In this case a cross-edge C_l in (12.1.4) will join a pair of vertices lying on arcs A_i and A_j but these are not uniquely determined by the endpoints of C_l as above since several A_i may pass through the same vertex. We suppose, therefore, that the cross-edges are *arc designated*, that is, we shall write

$$(12.1.7) \qquad\qquad C_l = (c_l, c_{l+1}; A_i, A_j)$$

so that not only are the endpoints and the direction of C_l given as in (12.1.4) but we also specify which arcs A_i and A_j it shall be considered to connect. Such a cross-edge may possibly be a loop with $c_l = c_{l+1}$ but then we suppose $A_i \neq A_j$ in (12.1.7). As before the vertices c_l and c_{l+1} in (12.1.7) are on A_i and A_j respectively, except that c_0 may not be on any A_i or if it does, coincides with a_{i0}; similarly c_m is either on no arc A_i or it coincides with a vertex a_{in_i}.

The cross-edge family (12.1.7) is *alternating* when at each vertex a_{ij} on an arc A_i there is at most one incoming and one outgoing cross-edge and these shall alternate on A_i, the first edge being outgoing. The preceding method may now be used to construct a family of $t + 1$ edge disjoint *cross-paths* $\{A_i'\}$ connecting the initial vertices (12.1.5) with the terminal vertices (12.1.6). When in the construction one follows a cross-edge C_l in (12.1.7) the designated arcs A_i and A_j indicate on which arc one shall proceed in the next step. As before, at any a_{ij} considered as a vertex on A_i there is only one possible incoming edge. We observe that in this case a path A_i' may pass through the same vertex a_{ij} several times, but each time the vertex is considered to belong to a different arc A_i. The family $\{A_i'\}$ may be reduced to $t+1$ edge disjoint arcs by omitting cyclic sections.

12.2. **Vertex separation.** In an undirected graph G let A and B be two disjoint subsets of the vertex set V. An arc (path)

$$(12.2.1) \qquad\qquad P(a, b), \qquad\qquad a \in A, \; b \in B$$

shall be called a *connecting arc* (path) for A and B. A set of vertices

$$(12.2.2) \qquad\qquad S = \{s_i\}$$

is a *separating set* for A and B when every connecting arc must pass through at least one vertex in S. One verifies that every separating set contains a minimal separating set. The sets A and B are $\sigma-vertex$ *separated* when there exists a finite separating set (12.2.2) with a minimal number σ of vertices. We shall prove the following *vertex separation theorem* due to Menger:

THEOREM 12.2.1. *For two σ-vertex separated sets A and B in an undirected graph G there exists a family $\{A_i\}$ of σ disjoint connecting arcs.*

PROOF. Evidently σ is the maximal number of arcs in such a family $\{A_i\}$. We may suppose $\sigma \geq 1$ so that there exists at least one connecting arc (12.2.1). To prove the theorem it is sufficient to show that when $\{A_i\}$ is a family of $t < \sigma$ disjoint connecting arcs then one can construct another such family $\{A_i'\}$ with $t+1$ members.

For the given family $\{A_i\}$ we adopt the notations of Section 12.1. Each A_i is considered directed from A to B. We may suppose

$$a_{i0} \in A, \; a_{in_i} \in B$$

while none of the intermediate vertices belong to either one of these sets. A *reverse cross-sequence* for the arcs $\{A_i\}$ shall be defined as follows. One begins the sequence in some edge

$$C_0 = (c_0, c_1), \qquad\qquad c_0 \in A, c_1 \notin A$$

which does not belong to any arc A_i. Such an edge exists since the t vertices a_{i0} cannot form a separating set. From c_1 one continues the sequence till one reaches a vertex a_{ij} on some A_i. From a_{ij} one proceeds in reverse direction (toward A) on A_i to some vertex a_{ik}, $k < j$. Next follows a section from a_{ik} of edges not in $\{A_i\}$ to some other a_{rs} on A_r and so on.

A vertex shall be called *accessible* from A when it lies on some such reverse cross-sequence. The first step in the proof of Theorem 12.2.1 is the

LEMMA. *There are accessible vertices in B.*

PROOF.   If this were not true there would be a vertex $a_i \neq a_{i,n_i}$ on each A_i such that a_i but no vertex beyond a_i is accessible. Again the t vertices $\{a_i\}$ cannot form a separating set and there exists a connecting arc P not passing through any of them. If P should not include any vertices of the arcs $\{A_i\}$ it is the desired further connecting arc. Assume next that p is the first vertex on P lying in B or beyond a_i on some A_i. We denote by p' the vertex preceding p on P lying in A or some arc A_j with p' not beyond a_j. Since a_j is accessible so is p'. By continuing in $P(p', p)$ also p becomes accessible contrary to its definition.

Denote by Q some reverse cross-sequence connecting A and B. If any edges should appear more than once the corresponding cyclic sections of Q may be eliminated; hence Q may be supposed to be a path. It consists alternately of sections C_k of edges not in arcs A_i connecting two vertices of such arcs and of reverse sections of arcs A_i. We direct the *cross-paths* C_k in the direction of Q from A to B.

A number of other reductions of Q may be made, all shortening its length. When $g_0 \in A$ and $g_m \in B$ are its end vertices we may suppose that none of its intermediate vertices belong to these sets. One can also assume that two cross-paths C_k and C_l have no vertices in common outside the arcs A_i because then a cyclic section of Q could be deleted.

Suppose next that on the same arc A_i there are two different sections

(12.2.3) $$A_i(g_k, g_{k+1}), \quad A_i(g_l, g_{l+1})$$

belonging to Q in this order. If g_{l+1} should be nearer to A than g_k one can shorten Q by replacing the section from g_k to g_{l+1} by $A_i(g_k, g_{l+1})$. Thus on each A_i one can assume that the common sections (12.2.3) with Q appear in increasing order and any two consecutive ones have at most one vertex in common. This implies that on each A_i any vertex can have at most one incoming and one outgoing cross-path. There can be paths of both kinds only at the common endpoints of two consecutive sections (12.2.3). The construction of Q shows that any incoming cross-path to A_i must be preceded by an outgoing one. Thus the cross-paths C_k satisfy the conditions for an alternating family of cross-edges to the arcs A_i. We conclude from the cross-path theorem that there exist $t + 1$ disjoint connecting paths $\{A_i'\}$ between A and B. This completes the proof for Menger's theorem.

The theorem may be modified in various ways. One may suppose that

$$A = a, \quad B = b$$

are single elements not joined by any edge and σ the smallest number of separating vertices, different from a and b. Then there exist σ paths $\{A_i\}$ having only the vertices a and b in common. The theorem applies also to direct graphs.

When σ is the minimal number of separating vertices for directed paths from A to B there exist σ disjoint directed paths between these sets.

12.3. Edge separation. To the vertex separation theorem which we just derived there exists an analogous *edge separation theorem*. As before let A and B be two disjoint vertex sets for an undirected graph G. We say that a family of edges

$$(12.3.1) \qquad\qquad\qquad T = \{E_i\}$$

form a *separating edge set* for A and B when every connecting path between these sets must pass through at least one edge in T. Clearly one can suppose that no E_i lies within A or B. Every separating edge set contains a minimal such set. Any set S containing one endpoint of each edge in an edge separating family is a vertex separation set; any family of edges containing all edges from the vertices in a vertex separation set is edge separating.

A and B are *τ-edge separated* when there exists a finite separating family of edges (12.3.1) with a minimal number τ of edges. If A and B are σ-vertex separated then according to a preceding remark one has $\tau \geq \sigma$. The edge separation theorem states:

THEOREM 12.3.1. *When A and B are two τ-edge separated sets in an undirected graph G then there exists a family of τ edge disjoint arcs $\{A_i\}$ connecting A and B.*

PROOF. We proceed along the same lines as in the proof of Theorem 12.2.1. One may suppose $\tau \geq 1$. It is sufficient to show that when $\{A_i\}$ is a family of $t < \tau$ edge disjoint connecting arcs then one can construct another such family $\{A_i'\}$ with $t + 1$ arcs.

We use the notations of Section 12.1. Each A_i is considered directed from A to B and only the end vertices belong to these sets. The definition of *reverse cross-sequences* requires a refinement from the previous concepts. Since the t initial edges in the arcs $\{A_i\}$ cannot form a separating edge family, there is a connecting path with an initial edge different from them. Beginning in such an edge we construct a sequence C_0 containing no edges in any A_i until one reaches a vertex a_{ij}. In this case it need not necessarily be the first such vertex. At a_{ij} there may be several arcs A_k but we select a particular one A_i and assign this character to the sequence C_0. In the next step one proceeds on the arc A_i in reverse direction to a vertex a_{ik}, $k < j$. From a_{ik} one constructs another sequence

$$(12.3.2) \qquad\qquad\qquad C_1(a_{ik}, a_{lm}; A_i, A_l)$$

having no edges from any arc, but we specify the arcs A_i and A_l it connects. A sequence obtained by continued construction of this kind is a *reverse cross-sequence*. Any vertex in such a sequence is *accessible* from A and any edge in it is *cursal*. As before we show:

LEMMA.   *B contains accessible vertices.*

PROOF.   If this were not the case case there would be some cursal edge

$$E^{(i)} = (a_i, b_i), \qquad\qquad a_i > b_i$$

on each arc A_i such that $E^{(i)}$ is cursal from a_i to b_i while no edge beyond $E^{(i)}$ on A_i is cursal. The t edges $E^{(i)}$ cannot form a separating family so there exists a connecting path P not containing any $E^{(i)}$. There will be a first vertex p on P lying in B or on some A_i beyond a_i and a vertex p' preceding p lying in A or on some arc A_j not beyond its a_j. Since p' is accessible also p must have this property and so an edge in A_i beyond $E^{(i)}$ is cursal.

The remaining part is analogous to the proof of Theorem 12.2.1. There exists a reverse cross-sequence Q from A to B. Reductions of Q may be performed as before, only it is necessary to take their arc designations into account. One obtains an alternating family of designated cross-arcs (12.3.2) as in Section 12.1, hence $t + 1$ edge disjoint connecting paths $\{A_i'\}$ can be constructed.

12.4. **Deficiency.**   The vertex separation theorem of Menger is an extension of the matching theorem of König (Theorem 7.9.4) for bipartite graphs. In analyzing the matching theorems we made use of the concept of deficiency for a bipartite graph. This, as we shall show, may be generalized to connecting arcs in an arbitrary directed or undirected graph G. When G is directed we consider only directed paths.

As before let A and B be disjoint sets. When A is finite the expression

$$(12.4.1) \qquad\qquad \delta(A) = \delta(A, B) = v(A) - \sigma(A)$$

shall be called the *deficiency* of A with respect to B; here $v(A)$ is the number of vertices in A and

$$\sigma(A) = \sigma(A, B)$$

is the minimal number of vertices in a separation set for connecting paths between A and B. We put

$$(12.4.2) \qquad\qquad \delta(\emptyset) = 0.$$

For a general set A the *maximal deficiency* with respect to B is defined as

$$(12.4.3) \qquad\qquad \delta_0(A) = \max \delta(D), \qquad\qquad D \subset A$$

where D runs through all finite subsets of A. In evaluating $\delta_0(A)$ in (12.4.3) one need only consider those finite subsets D which have a minimal separation set $S(D)$ disjoint from D. If namely

$$D_1 = D \cdot S(D) \neq \emptyset$$

then one sees that

$$\delta(D) = \delta(D - D_1).$$

According to (12.4.2) one has $\delta_0 \geqq 0$. When

(12.4.4) $\delta_0(A) = 0$

we say that A is *without deficiency*.

Let D_1 and D_2 be finite sets disjoint from B and $S(D_1)$ and $S(D_2)$ vertex separation sets with the minimal number $\sigma(D_1)$ and $\sigma(D_2)$ of vertices. Then

$$S(D_1) + S(D_2)$$

is a vertex separation set for $D_1 + D_2$ and we conclude that

$$\sigma(D_1 + D_2) \leqq \sigma(D_1) + \sigma(D_2) - \sigma(D_1 \cdot D_2).$$

As in Theorem 7.2.1 one finds that the deficiency function satisfies the inequality

(12.4.5) $\delta(D_1 + D_2) + \delta(D_1 \cdot D_2) \geqq \delta(D_1) + \delta(D_2).$

Next let A be some set disjoint from B having a maximal deficiency δ_0. Subsets D of A with

$$\delta(D) = \delta_0$$

are called *critical sets*. It follows as in Theorem 7.2.2 that the sum and intersection of critical sets are critical. This shows as in Theorem 7.2.3 that there exists a unique minimal critical set N contained in all others; when A is finite there is a unique maximal critical set M containing all others.

We say that the set A is *matched* into B when there exists a family of disjoint arcs $\{A_i\}$, one from each vertex $a_i \in A$ having its other endpoint in B.

THEOREM 12.4.1. *A necessary and sufficient condition that a finite set A can be matched into the set B disjoint from A is that A have no deficiency with respect to B.*

PROOF. The condition is evidently necessary. To show the sufficiency assume that (12.4.4) holds. Then A itself has a minimal separating set with at least $v(A)$ vertices, hence according to Theorem 12.2.1, there are $v(A)$ disjoint arcs from A to B.

The reformulation Theorem 12.4.1 of Menger's theorem has the advantage that it can be extended to infinite sets to give results which are analogous to those of Section 7.8 for bipartite graphs. Here instead of local finiteness we require *path finiteness*: From each $a \in A$ it shall be possible to reach only a finite number of vertices by paths whose intermediate vertices belong neither to A nor B. One can then show:

THEOREM 12.4.2. *Let A and B be two disjoint sets satisfying the path finiteness condition for vertices in A. Then A can be matched into B by disjoint arcs if and only if*

$$\delta_0(A, B) = 0.$$

When also B satisfies the path finiteness condition for reverse paths the two sets can be mutually matched upon each other by disjoint paths if and only if

$$\delta_0(A, B) = \delta_0^*(B, A) = 0.$$

This result corresponds to Theorems 7.3.3 and 7.4.3 for bipartite graphs. The proofs shall be left to the reader. Also the results in Sections 7.8 and 7.9 have analogues for connecting disjoint arcs.

Similar theorems hold for edge disjoint arcs from A to B when one uses a deficiency function defined with respect to separating edges. Instead of the vertex deficiency (12.4.1) we now introduce the *edge deficiency*

$$\delta^{(e)}(A) = \rho(A) - \tau(A)$$

where $\rho(A)$ is the number of edges from A to outside vertices and $\tau(A)$ the minimal number of edges in an edge separation family. When one considers matchings of A upon B by means of edge disjoint arcs the analogues of Theorems 12.4.1 and 12.4.2 follow immediately.

PROBLEM

1.* Derive theorems for edge disjoint and vertex disjoint arc matchings analogous to Theorems 7.8.6 and 7.9.1.

CHAPTER 13

DOMINATING SETS, COVERING SETS AND INDEPENDENT SETS

13.1. **Dominating sets.** Let G be a directed or undirected graph with the vertex set V. A subset D of V is a *dominating set* for G when every vertex not in D is the endpoint of some edge from a vertex in D. Clearly, V itself is a dominating set. To illustrate, if one considers G to represent a game with the vertices corresponding to positions and the edges to moves then a dominating set D represents a set of positions such that all other positions can be reached from D in a single move. A *minimal dominating set* is a dominating set such that no subset has this property.

THEOREM 13.1.1. *When G is locally finite any dominating set contains a minimal one.*

PROOF. We apply the minimal principle. Let $\{D_i\}$ be a family of inclusion ordered dominating sets with the intersection D_0. Suppose that for some $a_0 \notin D_0$ there are no edges from D_0. Then there would be some set D_i such that there are no edges from D_i to $a_0 \notin D_i$, contrary to the definition of this set.

THEOREM 13.1.2. *A dominating set D_0 is a minimal dominating set if and only if for each $d_0 \in D_0$ one of the two following conditions hold:*
1. *At d_0 there are no entering edges $E_0 = (d_1, d_0)$ within D_0.*
2. *There exists an edge $E = (d_0, d)$ touching D_0 such that E is the only edge from D_0 to v.*

PROOF. In order that $D_0 - d_0$ not be a dominating set it is necessary and sufficient that at least one of these conditions be fulfilled. For finite graphs Theorem 13.1.2 may be used for the reduction of a dominating set to a minimal one. We note that any vertex v at which there are no entering edges must belong to every dominating set.

By considering the converse graph G^* one can define the *converse dominating sets*.

We turn to the case where G is undirected and show first:

THEOREM 13.1.3. *Any undirected graph without isolated vertices has a dominating set D such that its complement $\bar{D}$ is also a dominating set.*

PROOF. We may suppose that G is connected. Let T be a maximal tree in which some root a_0 is selected. Then the vertices in T and G fall into two disjoint

206

sets D and $\bar{D}$ consisting respectively of the vertices with an even and odd distance from a_0 in T. Evidently D and $\bar{D}$ are dominating sets for G.

We observe next:

THEOREM 13.1.4. *Let G be undirected without isolated vertices. Then the complement $\bar{D}$ of a minimal dominating set D is a dominating set.*

PROOF. If at some $d \in D$ there were no edges to $\bar{D}$ the set $D-d$ would be a dominating set.

By combining Theorems 13.1.1 and 13.1.4 one concludes:

THEOREM 13.1.5. *Let G be undirected, locally finite and without isolated vertices. Then to any minimal dominating set there exists another disjoint from it.*

The *domination number* $\delta(G)$ of a graph G is the smallest number of vertices in any minimal domination set. It appears in various puzzle questions. One instance is the so-called *Five Queens Problem* on the chessboard: It is required to place five queens on the board in such positions that they dominate each square. A solution is indicated in Figure 13.1.1; no smaller number of queens will suffice so that $\delta(G) = 5$. Analogous problems may be formulated for the other pieces or combinations of pieces; and similarly for other board games. (See for instance Rouse-Ball, Bibl. Chapter 1.)

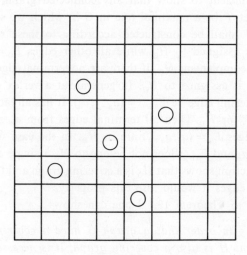

Figure 13.1.1.

PROBLEMS

1. Determine minimal domination sets and the domination number for the Platonic graphs.

2.* Try to extend some of the preceding results to directed graphs.

13.2. **Covering sets and covering graphs.** We suppose that G has no isolated vertices. A set of vertices K shall be called a *covering set* when each edge has at least one endpoint in K. The minimal principle shows readily that each covering set contains a minimal one.

Dually we call a family of edges $D(E_i)$ a *covering edge family* when it has at least one edge E_i at each vertex. In our previous terminology this means that

$$H = \sum E_i$$

is a *covering subgraph* for the vertices of G. We recall the definition of a *star graph* (Section 1.3); it consists of edges issuing from a vertex, loops possibly included.

THEOREM 13.2.1. *A covering subgraph H is minimal if and only if its connected components are single loops or star graphs without loops.*

The proof is a consequence of the fact that if for an edge $E = (a, b)$ in H there are other edges of H both at a and b then $H - E$ is still a covering graph.

THEOREM 13.2.2. *Any covering graph contains a minimal covering graph.*

PROOF. It is sufficient to show that any connected graph G has a minimal covering graph. Let T be a maximal tree in G in which we select a root a_0. A subgraph H_0 of T shall be constructed according to these rules: All terminal edges from a_0 are assigned to H_0 while all other edges $E_0 = (a_0, a_1)$ from a_0 shall belong to the complement $\bar{H}_0$. If there are no terminal edges from a_0 a single non-terminal edge is assigned to H_0. In general, at a vertex a_n at a distance n from a_0 let the entering edge be $E_{n-1} = (a_{n-1}, a_n)$. It has already been designated as belonging to H_0 or $\bar{H}_0$. Then all terminal edges from a_n shall belong to H_0 while the other edges $E_n = (a_n, a_{n+1})$ are in $\bar{H}_0$. In the case where there are no terminal edges at a_n and E_{n-1} does not belong to H_0 a single edge E_n is assigned to H_0. The construction shows that H_0 is a covering graph and that by the removal of any one of its edges it would lose this property.

As an analogue to Theorem 13.1.3 one can show:

THEOREM 13.2.3. *In order that a graph G have a covering graph H such that its complement $\bar{H}$ is also a covering graph, it is necessary and sufficient that G have no terminal edges and none of its connected components consist of a single odd length circuit.*

PROOF. The conditions are evidently necessary. We suppose they are satisfied and that G is connected. The first step in the proof consists in showing that there exists a pair of non-trivial edge disjoint subgraphs H and H' such that if H has an edge at a vertex a_0 of G then also H' has such an edge and vice versa. If there exists some two-way infinite path P one can construct H and H' by assigning the edges in P alternately to each subgraph. If G has no two-way infinite paths it must contain circuits since there are no terminal edges. If there is a cyclic path of even length the preceding construction applies. If all circuits are odd let C be one of them. According to assumption there is an edge $E = (a_0, b)$ not in C at a vertex a_0 on C. Beginning in E we construct an arc P disjoint from C and continue it as far as possible. It may return to C or be infinite or end in some circuit C_1 disjoint from C. In either case one verifies that a pair of graphs H and H' is obtained as follows. The edges of C belong alternately to H and H' with two H-edges at a_0. The edge E belongs to H' and the successive edges in P alternately to H and H'.

To complete the proof we consider all pairs of graphs (H, H') with the covering properties just indicated. They form a partial order when the inclusion

$$(H_1, H_1') \geqq (H_2, H_2')$$

is defined to hold when both conditions

$$H_1 \geqq H_2, \quad H_1' \geqq H_2'$$

are fulfilled. When

$$\{(H_i, H_i')\}$$

is an inclusion order family of pairs then one sees that the sum pair

$$(H_0, H_0') = (\textstyle\sum H_i, \ \sum H_i')$$

also belongs to the partial order.

We conclude that there exist maximal pairs (H_0, H_0') and shall show finally that

(13.2.1) $$G = H_0 + H_0'.$$

In any case

$$G(A) = H_0 + H_0'$$

is a section graph since any edge connecting two vertices of H_0 could be assigned arbitrarily to H_0 and H_0' if it did not already belong to these graphs. Consider now the complementary graph $\overline{G(A)}$ and any path P in it from a vertex $a_0 \in A$. Such a path cannot return to $G(A)$ because one could enlarge H_0 and H_0' by assigning the edges in P alternately to these graphs. For the same reason P cannot be infinite nor lead to any circuit disjoint from $G(A)$. This would make

$\overline{G(A)}$ circuit free, contradicting the fact that G has no terminal edges. We conclude that (13.2.1) holds, completing the proof.

Our result may also be expressed that the edges in a graph can be divided into two disjoint classes, each represented at every vertex, only when the conditions of Theorem 13.2.3 are fulfilled. Another formulation is the following: We say that H is a *proper subgraph* when it covers G, but does not include all edges at any vertex. Then G has a proper subgraph only under the restrictions of Theorem 13.2.3. Theorem 13.2.2 shows that in this case G has two edge disjoint minimal covering graphs.

The *edge covering number* $\alpha_e(G)$ is the smallest number of edges in any covering graph H for G; the *vertex covering number* $\alpha_v(G)$ is the smallest number of vertices in a covering set.

THEOREM 13.2.4.   *The edge covering number has the bounds*

(13.2.2) $$v(V) - 1 \geqq \alpha_e(G) \geqq \tfrac{1}{2} v(V)$$

where $v(V)$ is the number of vertices in G.

PROOF.   For the number of edges and vertices in a star graph one has

$$v_e = v_v - 1$$

and by summation the first inequality (13.2.2) follows. The second is a consequence of the fact that a covering graph has at least one edge at each vertex. It is assumed that G is not a sum of single loops.

PROBLEMS

1. Determine the edge covering numbers for the Platonic graphs.

2. Show that the inequality (13.2.2) can be improved to

$$\alpha_e(G) \leqq v(V) - \tfrac{1}{2}(d(G) + 1)$$

where $d(G)$ is the diameter of G.

3. Examine the bounds (13.2.2) when the conditions of Theorem 13.2.3 are satisfied.

4.* A covering graph H for a directed graph G may be defined as having at least one incoming and one outgoing edge at each vertex of G. Try to extend the previous results to such covering subgraphs, in particular, establish an analogue to Theorem 13.2.3.

13.3. **Independent sets.** We assume G undirected and without loops. A set I of vertices is called *independent*, sometimes *unrelated*, when there are no connecting edges between any of its vertices. In a *dependent set* (*related set*) at least two vertices are connected by an edge. A counterpart of the independent sets are the *completely dependent sets* in which each pair of vertices is edge connected. If one assumes that G defines a binary relation R, that is, all edges are single, then the completely dependent sets under R are the independent sets under the complementary relation $\bar{R}$.

A *maximal independent* set I_0 is an independent set which becomes dependent by the adjunction of any vertex. One verifies that every independent set is contained in a maximal one.

THEOREM 13.3.1. *An independent set is maximal if and only if it is a dominating set.*

PROOF. If I is maximal independent there cannot be any vertex $j\varepsilon\bar{I}$ not connected to I by an edge because the set $j+I$ would also be independent. On the other hand let I be an independent dominating set. Then no j can be transferred from $\bar{I}$ to I without making $I+j$ dependent.

The maximal number $\beta_v(G)$ of vertices in any independent set we call the (*vertex*) *independence number*. Theorem 13.3.1 shows that it cannot be less than the domination number, hence

(13.3.1) $$\beta_v(G) \geqq \delta(G).$$

In graph representations of games an independent set of vertices is a set of positions such that none of them can be reached in a move from another. An example is the problem of placing a maximal number of queens on the chessboard such that none of them can take another. The maximal number is $\beta_v(G) = 8$ while we saw in Section 13.1 that $\delta(G) = 5$ for the corresponding domination problem. One solution of the problem is given in Figure 13.3.1.

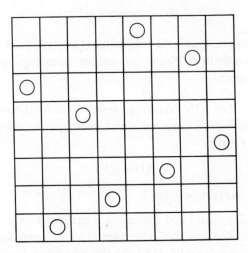

Figure 13.3.1.

Another illustration may be taken from combinatory analysis. Among N objects one can select $\binom{N}{n}$ combinations of n elements. Two such combinations may be called *k-related* when they have at least k elements in common. This relation can be represented by a graph

$$G_k = G(k; N, n).$$

Its independence number $\beta_v(G_k)$ gives the maximal number of combinations which are not k-related. Several puzzle problems concering the selections of groups or committees depend on the determination of maximal k-unrelated sets, for instance the *Kirkman school girl problem*; related to this are questions concerning the so-called *Steiner triples* in geometry and other problems in combinatory analysis. (See for instance Netto.)

According to Theorem 13.3.1 there is, when I is a maximal independent set, at least one edge from I to each vertex in the complement $\check{I}$. Thus the number of edges from I is at least as great as the number of vertices in $\check{I}$

$$\rho(I) \geqq v(\check{I}).$$

By adding the vertices in I to both sides one obtains

(13.3.2) $$\rho(I) + v(I) = (\rho + 1)\ (I) \geqq v(V).$$

Among the consequences of this inequality we mention first:

THEOREM 13.3.2.   *When ρ_1 is an upper bound for the local degrees of G then*

$$\beta_v(G) \geqq \frac{1}{\rho_1 + 1} \cdot v(V).$$

When G is an infinite graph the inequality (13.3.2) applies also to the corresponding cardinal numbers. From well-known properties of infinite cardinals one readily concludes:

THEOREM 13.3.3.   *Let $v(V)$ denote the infinite cardinal number of the vertex set V of G. If there exists a cardinal upper bound ρ_1 for the local degrees of G such that $\rho_1 < v(V)$ then*

(13.3.3) $$v(I) = v(V)$$

for any maximal independent set I.

A result due to Sierpinski and Piccard is a particular case: When G is locally finite and V infinite and not countable then (13.3.3) holds for any maximal independent set. The same equality (13.3.3) holds also when V is countable provided the local degrees have a finite bound.

There exists a considerable number of studies on the special case where V is the set of real numbers and R a relation defined on V. It has been proved by Fodor that (13.3.3) holds when no vertex v is a limit point of its associated set $R(v)$; one can even show that I can be taken to have a positive outer measure. Stronger results can be obtained when one makes certain assumptions on the distance $d(v)$ between v and $R(v)$. Other related papers have been published by Erdös and Bagemihl; for a more complete bibliography we shall refer to a recent article by Marcus.

An analogue to the independent vertex sets are the *independent edge families* consisting of edges having no vertices in common. Each independent family of edges is contained in a maximal one. The maximal number of edges in such a family is the *edge independence number* $\beta_e(G)$ of G. Gallai has pointed out an interesting reciprocity between maximal independence numbers and minimal covering numbers:

THEOREM 13.3.4.   *In a graph with n vertices*

(13.3.4) $$\alpha_v + \beta_v = \alpha_e + \beta_e = n.$$

PROOF.   (1a) A set I is an independent set if and only if its complement $\bar{I}$ is a covering set. Thus when I is a minimal independent set with β_v elements one must have

$$\alpha_v + \beta_v \leq n.$$

(1b) A set K is a covering set if and only if $\bar{K}$ is independent so that when K is a minimal covering set with α_v elements

$$\alpha_v + \beta_v \geq n.$$

(2a) Let F be a maximal family of $v_e(F)$ independent edges; the vertex set K defined by the edges in F has $2 \cdot v_e(F)$ vertices. The complementary set $\bar{K}$ must be independent; we select an edge E_k at each vertex $k \in \bar{K}$. The other end of E_k must lie in K. The graph

$$H = F + \sum E_k$$

covers G and

$$v_e(H) = v_e(F) + v_v(\bar{K}).$$

On the other hand

$$v_v(K) + v_v(\bar{K}) = n$$

and by addition one obtains

$$v_e(H) + v_e(F) = n.$$

This implies

$$\alpha_e + \beta_e \leq n.$$

(2b) Let H be a minimal covering graph for G; according to Theorem 13.2.1 H is a sum of star graphs. We select a subgraph H' of H consisting of a single edge E_a from each center a of the stars in H. Then there is a one-to-one correspondence between the edges in $H + H'$. counting those in H' double, and the vertices in G so that

$$v(H) + v(H') = n.$$

Since the edges in H' are independent this gives

$$\alpha_e + \beta_e \geqq n.$$

13.4. The theorem of Turan. When a finite graph with n vertices has few edges one may expect its independence number to be relatively large. For fixed n and k there must exist graphs $G_0(n, k)$ with a minimal number $N_0(n, k)$ of edges such that

$$(13.4.1) \qquad\qquad\qquad \beta(G_0) < k, \qquad\qquad\qquad 3 \leqq k \leqq n.$$

These graphs as we shall show have a very simple form and are essentially unique:

THEOREM 13.4.1. *The graphs $G_0(n, k)$ satisfying (13.4.1) and having a minimal number of edges are the disjoint sum of $k - 1$ complete graphs*

$$(13.4.2) \qquad\qquad\qquad G = C_1 + \cdots + C_{k-1}.$$

When one writes

$$(13.4.3) \qquad\qquad\qquad n = t \cdot (k - 1) + r, \qquad\qquad\qquad 0 \leqq r \leqq k - 2$$

then r of the complete components C in (13.4.2) are defined on $t + 1$ vertices and the remaining ones on t vertices.

The number of edges in the graph G in (13.4.2) is

$$N = \tfrac{1}{2}t(t + 1) \cdot r + \tfrac{1}{2}t(t - 1) \, (k - 1 - r)$$

and by means of (13.4.3) this reduces to

$$(13.4.4) \qquad\qquad\qquad N = \tfrac{1}{2}t(n - k + 1 + r).$$

The proof of Theorem 13.4.1 proceeds by induction with respect to n. For the lowest values $n = 1, 2, 3, 4$ it is readily verified. By the removal of an edge from a graph the independence number can at most increase by one unit. Therefore a graph $G_0(n, k)$ must possess some maximal independent set I with

$$v(I) = \beta(G_0) = k - 1$$

vertices. Theorem 13.3.1 shows that each vertex in the complement $\bar{I}$ has at least one edge connecting it with a vertex in I. Since the section graph $G_0(\bar{I})$ can have no independent set with more than $k - 1$ vertices the number of its edges is at least

$$N_0(n - k + 1, k);$$

consequently

(13.4.5) $N_0(n, k) \geq n - k + 1 + N_0(n - k + 1, k).$

Since

(13.4.6) $n - k + 1 = (t - 1)\ (k - 1) + r$

it follows by the induction assumption from (13.4.4) that

$$N_0(n - k + 1, k) = \tfrac{1}{2}(t - 1) \cdot (n - 2k + 2 + r).$$

When this is substituted in (13.4.5) the inequality reduces to

(13.4.7) $N_0(n, k) \geq \tfrac{1}{2}t(n - k + 1 + r).$

The equality sign can hold in (13.4.5) and (13.4.7) only under the conditions
1. There is a single edge from each vertex in $\bar{I}$ to I.
2. $G_0(\bar{I})$ is a minimal graph of type (13.4.2) where according to (13.4.6) r graphs C are defined on t vertices and the remaining ones on $t - 1$ vertices.
  We write $I = (v_1, v_2, \cdots, v_{k-1})$.
  Let

$$\bar{v}_1 \in C_1, \quad \bar{v}_2 \in C_2$$

be vertices in two different components in $\bar{I}$. These cannot be edge connected to the same vertex $v_1 \in I$ since the k vertices

$$\bar{v}_1, \bar{v}_2, v_{k-1}, \cdots, \ v_{k-1}$$

would be independent. We conclude that each $v_i \in I$ can only receive edges from a single component C_i in $\bar{I}$. But then the resulting graph is also of the type (13.4.2). This completes the proof.
  A consequence of Theorem 13.4.1 is:

THEOREM 13.4.2. *Let ρ_1 be the maximal local degree in a graph. For a given ρ_1 there exists graph G satisfying (13.4.1) if and only if*

(13.4.8) $\rho_1 \geq t - 1.$

PROOF. For a graph of the type (13.4.2) one has $\rho_1 = t - 1$ and (13.4.1) is fulfilled. When $\rho_1 \leq t - 2$ the maximal number of edges in the graph is

$$\tfrac{1}{2}(t - 2)n$$

and one verifies readily that this number is smaller than (13.4.4).

When Theorem 13.4.1 is applied to the complementary graph on n vertices it becomes a theorem of Turan: The maximal number of edges in a graph without complete subgraphs on k vertices is

$$M(n, k) = \tfrac{1}{2} \cdot \frac{k-2}{k-1} \cdot (n^2 - r^2) + \tfrac{1}{2} r(r - 1).$$

The graphs of this kind with the maximal number of edges $M(n, k)$ are the complements of the graphs G in (13.4.2) within the complete graph on n vertices. When Theorem 13.4.2 is applied to the complementary problem it gives a result by Zarankiewicz.

PROBLEMS

1.* Determine the connected graphs satisfying (13.4.1) and having a minimal number of edges.

2.* For a given number of edges in a graph with n vertices determine bounds for the number of independent sets.

3.* Determine the graphs with the minimal property that the removal of any edge increases the independence number.

13.5.   **The theorem of Ramsey.**   There exists a combinatorial theorem due to Ramsey which has applications to a wide variety of mathematical problems:

Let S_n denote a set with n elements and m some integer. For any r one forms all $\binom{n}{r}$ combinations of r elements in S_n. These combinations are divided arbitrarily into μ disjoint classes. Then there exists a number $n_0 = n_0(m, r, \mu)$ such that when $n \geq n_0$ there will be a subset S_m of S_n for which all $\binom{m}{r}$ combinations belong to the same class.

We shall show that the theorem of Ramsey is a consequence of certain general graph results. Let G be a graph, directed or undirected, with the vertex set V. Suppose that there exists a decomposition of G into μ edge disjoint subgraphs

$$(13.5.1) \qquad G = H_1 + H_2 + \cdots + H_\mu.$$

We construct a family of edges in G in the following manner. Take an arbitrary vertex $a_0 \in V_0 = V$. From a_0 a family F_1 of edges is selected, all belonging to the same graph H_1' in (13.5.1). The set of endpoints of these edges is denoted by V_1. We take $a_1 \in V_1$ and construct a family of edges F_2 from a_1 to $V_2 \subset V_1$ such that all edges in F_2 belong to the same graph H_2' in (13.5.1). Next take $a_2 \in V_2$ and continue the process. A family of edges

$$(13.5.2) \qquad F_1, F_2, \cdots, F_s \neq \emptyset$$

obtained in this way shall be called an *interlocking chain*. In (13.5.2) each F_i consists of edges in the same component graph H_i' in (13.5.1). One has

(13.5.3) $$V \supset V_1 \supset V_2 \supset \cdots \supset V_s \neq \emptyset$$

and the edges in F_i connect the vertex $a_{i-1} \in V_{i-1}$ with the set $V_i \subset V_{i-1}$. We call a_{i-1} a *center* belonging to the graph H_i' in the interlocking chain (13.5.2).

THEOREM 13.5.1. *Let*

(13.5.4) $$c_1, c_2, \cdots, c_k$$

be a family of centers in the interlocking chain (13.5.2) *all belonging to the same component graph H in* (13.5.1). *Then the section graph*

(13.5.5) $$G(c_1, c_2, \cdots, c_k)$$

is a subgraph of H.

PROOF. Let c_1 and c_2 be two centers in (13.5.4) and $E = (c_1, c_2)$ an edge in G, hence in (13.5.5) connecting them. Then according to (13.5.3) E is an edge from c_1 to V_{c_1+1} so that E is in H.

We assume next that G is finite and denote the number of vertices in V_i by v_i so that

(13.5.6) $$n = v_0 \supset v_1 \supset \cdots \supset v_s.$$

If n is large and the v_i do not decrease too fast the interlocking chain can be relatively long. Since there is only a fixed number μ of graphs in (13.5.1) there must be many centers belonging to the same H, hence a large section graph (13.5.5) is a subgraph of H.

One can construct an interlocking chain (13.5.2) by the process of selecting at each center all edges in that graph H having the largest number of edges. Denote the local degrees of G with $\rho(v) \geq 2$ and put

$$\rho_0 = \min \rho(v), \qquad\qquad v \in V.$$

Then at each vertex there will be at least

$$v = \frac{1}{\mu}(\rho(v) - 1) \geq \frac{1}{2\mu} \cdot \rho(v) \geq \frac{1}{2\mu} \cdot \rho_0$$

edges in some H and in the same manner one obtains in (13.5.6)

$$v_i > \frac{1}{2\mu} \cdot v_{i-1}, \quad v_i > \left(\frac{1}{2\mu}\right)^i \cdot \rho_0.$$

As a consequence

$$v_i \geqq 1, \quad \text{when} \quad i = \frac{\log \rho_0}{\log 2\mu}.$$

From this we conclude:

THEOREM 13.5.2.   *Let* G *be a finite graph with an edge disjoint decomposition* (13.5.1). *The minimal local degree in* G *shall be* $\rho_0 \geqq 2$. *Then one of the components* H *in* (13.5.1) *must include a section graph of* G *with at least*

$$m = \frac{1}{\mu \log 2\mu} \cdot \log \rho_0 - 1$$

vertices.

Better estimates could have been made. When G_n is a complete graph without loops on n vertices one has $\rho_0 = n - 1$. Theorem 13.5.2 then yields the following result which is the theorem of Ramsey in the case $r = 2$.

THEOREM 13.5.3.   *Let the complete graph* G_n *on* n *vertices have an edge disjoint decomposition* (13.5.1). *Then there exists a number* n_0 *such that when*

$$n \geqq n_0(\mu, m)$$

then at least one of the components H *contains a complete subgraph* G_m.

The special case $\mu = 2$ yields:

THEOREM 13.5.4.   *For a given* m *there exists a number* n_0 *such that when* $n \geqq n_0$ *any graph with* n *vertices includes either an independent set with* m *vertices or a complete subgraph on* m *vertices.*

In a more popular version this becomes: In any sufficiently large party there exists either m individuals all strangers to each other or a clique of m friends all knowing each other.

The exact lower bounds for n in Theorems 13.5.3 and 13.5.4 are not known except for a few special cases. For $m = 3$ it suffices to take $n_0 = 6$ in the last party problem. A few other exact bounds have been determined by Goodman and by Gleason and Greenwood. In these papers as well as a paper by Erdös one finds improved estimates for n_0 much better than those obtained by the preceding method of proof.

The general Ramsey theorem may be obtained by induction with respect to r; we shall sketch a proof. Consider the set C consisting of all combinations of r elements taken from the set V and assume that C is decomposed

(13.5.7) $C = C_1 + \cdots + C_\mu$

into μ disjoint sets. Select some vertex $a_0 \in V = V_0$. The set C' of all combinations P' of $r - 1$ elements from $V_0 - a_0$ will also decompose into μ classes

$$(13.5.8) \qquad\qquad C' = C_1' + \cdots + C_\mu'$$

depending on the set C_i in (13.5.7) to which the r-combination $a_0 + P'$ belongs. We begin the construction of an interlocking chain in the complete graph G on V by selecting the edges from the center a_0 to a set V_1 with the property that all $(r - 1)$-combinations of elements in V_1 belong to the same class C_1'' in (13.5.8). According to the induction assumption such sets V_1 exist and can be made arbitrarily large by taking the number n of elements in V sufficiently large. Next select a vertex $a_1 \in V_1$ and repeat the construction with respect to the set V_1. It is clear that in this manner for large n one can obtain an interlocking chain of such length that it includes m centers

$$c_1, c_2, \cdots, c_m$$

whose associated edges in the chain connect them to sets

$$V_{c_1} > V_{c_2} > \cdots > V_{c_m}$$

whose $(r - 1)$-combinations belong to the same class C_i'' in (13.5.8). Then all r-combinations of these m centers belong to the same class in (13.4.7) since in any

$$(c_{i_1}, c_{i_2}, \cdots, c_{i_r}), \qquad\qquad i_1 < i_2 < \ldots < i_r$$

all centers except c_1 belong to V_{i_1+1}, hence when combined with c_i, they give an r-combination in C_t.

Ramsey introduced his theorem to examine the possibility of satisfying certain types of logical expressions. A curious application is due to Erdös and Szekeres in connection with the solution of a problem proposed by Esther Klein: Let n points be given in the plane. Show that there exists a number $n_0(m)$ such that when $n \geq n_0(m)$ there must be some m among the points which form a convex polygon. To prove this result one observes that a polygon is convex if and only if any four of its vertices define a convex quadrangle. The 4-combinations of the n points can be divided into two classes consisting respectively of convex and concave quadrangles. Among 5 points it is always possible to select 4 points determining a convex quadrilateral. Then the assumption that there should be no convex polygons with $m \geq 5$ vertices leads to a contradiction, for according to Ramsey's theorem when $n \geq n_0(m)$ there would have to exist m points whose 4-combinations are all concave, contrary to the preceding observation for 5 points.

Another consequence of Ramsey's theorem is a result due to Schur: When the numbers $1, 2, \cdots, n$ are distributed into μ classes, then for $n \geq n_0(\mu)$ one of the classes contains three numbers: $x, y, x - y$. This may be used to derive a theorem of Dickson that for any sufficiently large prime q the congruence

$$x^n + y^n \equiv z^n \pmod{q}$$

is always solvable.

We mention finally that Erdös and Radó have investigated Ramsey's theorem for infinite sets and arbitrary cardinal numbers.

PROBLEMS

1. (Bostwick, C.W.) Prove that at any gathering of six people some three of them are either mutually acquainted or complete strangers.

2. Prove Schur's theorem.

3. (Makai, E.) Show that when $n \geq 9$ there is always a convex pentagon included among n points in the plane.

4.* Extend the problem of E. Klein to space or to an arbitrary number of dimensions.

13.6. **A problem in information theory.** As pointed out by Shannon the theory of independent sets in a graph is of importance for fundamental problems in information theory. Suppose that some transmission code for information is given. Its basic signals may be denoted by the symbols

(13.6.1) $$S = (s_1, s_2, \cdots, s_n).$$

As an illustration one may think of the signals as being letters of the alphabet and the transmission process as ordinary spelling over the telephone. By experience one may know that some signals can be mistaken for others, while some signals cannot be confounded. We note that in many applications such mistakes will occur with only a certain probability; however, here we shall consider only the definite case where two signals can be confounded or not.

The signals received we denote by

(13.6.2) $$S^* = (s_1^*, s_2^*, \cdots, s_m^*).$$

For each $s_i \in S$ there will be a certain subset $S^*(s_i)$ of S^* consisting of the received symbols which can be construed as having s_i as a possible origin. In the same way there is a subset $S(s_j^*)$ of S consisting of all signals in (13.6.1) which can possibly give rise to s_j^*. Thus the transmission process can be represented by means of a *transmission graph* $T(S, S^*)$ such that there is an edge (s_i, s_j^*) in T if and only if s_j^* can have originated from s_i.

Two signals s_i and s_k in (13.6.1) are called *related* when there are two edges

(13.6.3) $$(s_i, s_j^*), \quad (s_k, s_j^*)$$

in T with a common endpoint s_j^*; if not s_i and s_k are *unrelated*. Thus one can also describe the possibilities for confounded signals by a *signal (relation) graph*

$C(S)$. It has the vertex set S and two vertices in C are connected by an edge (s_i, s_k) only when there exist neighboring edges (13.6.3) in T. Analogously there is a signal relation graph $C(S^*)$ in (13.6.2) in which two vertices s_j^* and s_l^* are connected by an edge only when these two signals may have originated from the same s_i.

The signal graph $C(S)$ is evidently determined by the transmission graph but the converse is not generally true (see Figure 13.6.1).

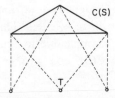
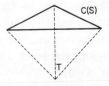

Figure 13.6.1.

One can show, however, that every graph $C(S)$ in S can be considered to be the signal graph of some transmission graph T and usually in many ways. Suppose that in a given $T(S, S^*)$ the vertex $s^* \in S^*$ is the endpoint of k edges

$$(s_1, s^*), \cdots, (s_k, s^*).$$

Then the corresponding vertices s_i in $C(S)$ will all be related among each other, that is, they define a complete subgraph U_k on k vertices. Conversely, any edge E in a graph $C(S)$ will be contained in a maximal complete subgraph U of S, usually in several. We associate a vertex $s^*(U)$ with each U and connect all vertices in each U in C with s^*. The graph $T(S, S^*)$ thus obtained is seen to have C for its signal graph. One can also make the construction in the manner that with each edge $E = (s_1, s_2)$ in C there is associated a vertex $s^*(E)$ and the edges (s_1, s^*) and (s_2, s^*) in T. In this case the graph $C^*(S^*)$ becomes the interchange graph for $C(S)$ (see Figure 13.6.2).

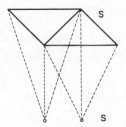
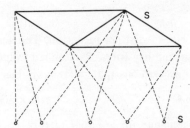

Figure 13.6.2.

Let us turn now to the actual transmission process. To obtain an errorless code in which no confusion can occur one must restrict the signals to an independent subset I of S. The maximal number of signals in such an errorless group is therefore the independence number $\beta(C)$ of $C(S)$.

In practice messages are not restricted to a single signal; rather they are sent out as words or combinations of signals. In the simplest case where the words are restricted to two letters one obtains β^2 unmistakable messages by using the signals in a maximal independent set in C. In general, by words of n letters one obtains β^n distinct ones in the same manner. One might believe that in general this would be the maximal number of errorless words of n letters. This, however, is not the case as one may see from the following example due to Shannon. Take the transmission graph in Figure 13.6.3 where $C(S)$ and $C(S^*)$ are circuits consisting of 5 edges.

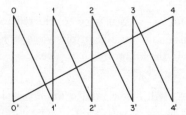 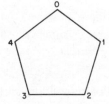

Figure 13.6.3.

Evidently $\beta = 2$ and for instance, an independent set in C is $(0, 2)$ producing the 4 errorless words

$$0\,0, \quad 0\,2, \quad 2\,0, \quad 2\,2$$

of length 2. But one verifies readily that also the five words

$$0\,0, \quad 1\,2, \quad 2\,4, \quad 3\,1, \quad 4\,3$$

give rise to distinct reception. The general problem is to determine the independence number for a Cartesian product of graphs (Section 2.6). One sees from our observations that one always has

(13.6.4) $\beta(G \times H) \geqq \beta(G) \times \beta(H)$

in particular for n equal factors

(13.6.5) $\beta(G \times \cdots \times G) \geqq \beta(G)^n.$

It seems to be very difficult to establish the exact value in (13.6.4) and (13.6.5) or the necessary and sufficient conditions for the equality sign to hold. Shannon examined these problems for all graphs of orders up to 7 and found by a special reduction procedure that with the exception of circuits with 5 or 7 edges the equality sign holds in (13.6.5) for all of them. However, for higher order graphs this seems to be the exceptional case.

PROBLEMS

1.   Prove that the equality sign holds in (13.6.5) when no signal can be confounded with more than one other.

2.* Examine the value of $\beta(C^n)$ when C is a circuit.

CHAPTER 14

CHROMATIC GRAPHS

14.1. The chromatic number. We assume that G is an undirected graph with single edges and no loops. G is *k-colorable* when there exists a decomposition of its vertices into k disjoint classes

$$(14.1.1) \qquad C_1, C_2, \cdots, C_k, \quad V = \sum_i C_i, \quad C_i \cdot C_j = \emptyset$$

such that the vertices in each class are independent. This means that the edges in G connect only vertices belonging to different classes. The representation (14.1.1) is a *k-coloration* of G. This terminology is suggested by considering each class to represent a color. Then each vertex is colored in such a manner that the endpoints of an edge always have different colors. One can also represent the colors of the blocks C_i in (11.4.1) by the integers $1, 2, \cdots, k$ and introduce a *color function* f such that

$$f(v_i) = i, \qquad\qquad v_i \in C_i.$$

The smallest number $k = \kappa(G)$ of classes in any coloration (14.1.1) is the *chromatic number* of G. Then G is *k-chromatic* and (14.1.1) is a *chromatic decomposition* of V. A graph is 2-chromatic only when it is bipartite. Thus a graph which is more than 2-chromatic must contain an odd circuit. A complete graph on n vertices has the chromatic number n.

There exists a particular type of color function, sometimes called a *Grundy function*, characterized by the following property: For each v let

$$\{v_i'\}, \qquad\qquad i = 1, 2, \cdots, \rho(v)$$

be the set of neighboring vertices. Then $f(v)$ shall be the smallest number $1, 2, \cdots$ such that for all i

$$f(v) \neq f(v_i').$$

One sees that

$$f(v) \leq \rho(v) + 1.$$

Furthermore, for any $f(v)$ the values

$$1, 2, \cdots, f(v) - 1$$

must be assumed at neighboring vertices.

A Grundy function can be constructed in the following manner. A maximal independent set S_1 in V is selected and one puts

$$f(s_1) = 1, \qquad\qquad\qquad s_1 \in S_1.$$

We saw that all vertices in G are connected by an edge to S_1 so that one must have $f(v) \geq 2$ when $v \notin S_1$. Next we select a maximal independent set S_2 in $G(V - S_1)$ and define

$$f(s_2) = 2, \qquad\qquad\qquad s_2 \in S_2.$$

When this process is continued a Grundy function must result.

When a Grundy function satisfies

(14.1.2) $$\max f(v) = k, \qquad\qquad\qquad v \in V$$

it defines a coloration in k colors. When G is k-chromatic with a decomposition (14.1.1) one can construct a Grundy function fulfilling (14.1.2) as follows. Define the maximal independent set S_1 as a sum

$$S_1 = C_1 + C_2' + C_3' + \cdots + C_k'$$

where C_2' consists of the vertices in C_2 not connected to C_1 while C_3' in the set of vertices in C_3 not connected to $C_1 + C_2'$ and so on. The set S_2 is formed from the sets

$$C_2 - S_1, \quad C_3 - S_1, \quad \cdots$$

in the same manner; since G is k-chromatic the process stops in k steps.

We point out a few simple properties of the chromatic number:

THEOREM 14.1.1. *For the independence number $\beta(G)$ and the chromatic number $\kappa(G)$ of a graph G of order n one has*

(14.1.3) $$\beta(G) \cdot \kappa(G) \geq n.$$

PROOF. Since all C_i in (14.1.1) are independent sets one has

$$v(C_i) \leq \beta(G)$$

and consequently

$$n = \sum v(C_i) \leq k \cdot \beta(G) = \kappa(G) \cdot \beta(G).$$

Another immediate observation is:

THEOREM 14.1.2. *When G contains a complete subgraph U_m on m vertices then*

$$\kappa(G) \geq m.$$

Next let us consider the connection between the colorations of a graph G and those of its finite subgraphs. We select a finite vertex set F such that no intersections $F \cdot C_1$ in (14.1.1) are void. It is clear that the section graph $G(F)$ is $\kappa(G)$-colorable. If one should have

$$k_1 = \kappa(G(F)) < \kappa(G)$$

there would be k_1-chromatic decompositions of F in $G(F)$. Since the vertices in these blocks do not remain independent in G one can raise the chromatic number for $G(F)$ by adding a finite number of edges from G. We conclude that G contains finite section graphs $G(F)$ with the same chromatic number as G.

In the reverse direction one has the result due to de Bruijn and Erdös:

THEOREM 14.1.3. *When all finite subgraphs of G are k-colorable then G is k-colorable.*

The proof is a consequence of Radó's theorem (Theorem 7.1.4). We construct a bipartite graph $G(V, V')$ where V is the vertex set for G and V' the set of k colors. For any finite set $F \subset V$ a choice function is defined by means of the vertex coloration in the graph $G(F)$ such that vertices connected by an edge have different colors. We conclude that there exists a choice function with the same property for the whole set V.

The following theorem gives an upper bound for the chromatic number:

THEOREM 14.1.4. *When ρ_1 is the least upper bound for the local degrees then*

(14.1.4) $$\kappa(G) \leq \rho_1 + 1.$$

PROOF. According to the preceding theorem it suffices to consider G finite. The theorem is evident when $n = 1$ and $n = 2$ so that it may be derived in general by induction with respect to n. Suppose that a graph G_{n-1} is k-colorable with $k = \rho_1 + 1$. The addition of a vertex v_n with $\rho(v_n) \leq \rho_1$ to G_{n-1} gives a new graph G_n in which v_n is not connected to all k blocks C_i in a k-coloration (14.1.1) for G_{n-1}. Thus v_n can be added to one of these blocks without raising k.

The bound (14.1.4) has been improved by Brooks who showed that

$$\kappa(G) \leq \rho_1.$$

PROBLEMS

1. Determine the chromatic number and a Grundy function for each of the Platonic graphs.

2. (Mycielski, J.) Prove that for each k there are k-chromatic graphs without triangles.

3.* Find a lower bound for the order of such graphs.

4. (Tutte, W. T., also Kelly, J. B. and Kelly, L. M.) Give examples of k-chromatic graphs without circuits of length ≤ 5.

14.2. Sums of chromatic graphs. We observe first :

THEOREM 14.2.1. *For graphs G and G' on the same vertex set one has*

(14.2.1) $$\kappa(G + G') \leq \kappa(G) \cdot \kappa(G').$$

PROOF. Let $V = \sum_j C'_j, j = 1, 2, \cdots, k'$ be a k'-coloration of G'. From (14.1.1) one obtains the $k \cdot k'$ coloration of $G + G'$

$$V = \sum C_i \cdot C'_j.$$

The following result is due to Gaddum and Nordhaus:

THEOREM 14.2.2. *For the chromatic numbers of a graph and its complement $\bar{G}$ one has the inequalities*

(14.2.2) $$2n^{1/2} \leq \kappa(G) + \kappa(\bar{G}) \leq n + 1,$$

(14.2.3) $$n \leq \kappa(G) \cdot \kappa(\bar{G}) \leq (\tfrac{1}{2}(n + 1))^2.$$

PROOF. The lower bound in (14.2.3) is a consequence of Theorem 14.2.1 for $G' = \bar{G}$. From it follows the lower bound in (14.2.2) by means of the general inequality

$$(a + b)^2 \geq 4ab.$$

The same inequality yields the upper bound in (14.2.3) from the upper bound in (14.2.2). Thus it remains only to prove that

$$\kappa(G) + \kappa(\bar{G}) \leq n + 1.$$

This is true for $n = 1$ and $n = 2$ and may be derived in general by induction with respect to n. For a graph G_n with n vertices

$$G_n + \bar{G}_n = U_n.$$

From this complete graph U_n we construct U_{n+1} by adding a vertex v_{n+1}. We adjoin q of the n edges from v_{n+1} to V_n to the graph G_n and the remaining $n - q$ edges to $\bar{G}_n$ to obtain the general complementary graphs G_{n+1} and $\bar{G}_{n+1}$ in U_{n+1}. Since the addition of a vertex with its edges to a graph can at most increase the chromatic number by one it follows that

(14.2.4) $$\kappa(G_{n+1}) \leq \kappa(G_n) + 1, \quad \kappa(\bar{G}_{n+1}) \leq \kappa(\bar{G}_n) + 1.$$

By adding these two inequalities the desired result is obtained except when both chromatic numbers are increased. Let us consider this case. Since the chromatic number of G_n is increased by the adjunction of v_{n+1} one must have $q \geq \kappa(G_n)$ for otherwise v_{n+1} could be added to one of the classes C_i in (14.1.1) such that it remained independent. Similarly

$$n - q \geq \kappa(\bar{G}_n)$$

so that in this case

$$\kappa(G_n) + \kappa(\bar{G}_n) \leq n$$

and the desired inequality follows from the induction assumption by adding (14.2.4).

As an example let G be bipartite. Then

$$\tfrac{1}{2}n \leq \kappa(\bar{G}) \leq n - 1.$$

One can construct special examples to show that the bounds given in Theorem 14.2.2 cannot be improved.

When a coloration (14.1.1) is given a homomorphic image graph G/C is defined in which the inverse image sets are the independent blocks C_i (Section 5.3). In G/C a pair of vertices (C_i, C_j) are joined by an edge if and only if there exists an edge in G

$$(c_i, c_j), \qquad\qquad\qquad c_i \in C_i, c_j \in C_j.$$

But if $k = \kappa(G)$ such an edge must always exist because otherwise $C_i + C_j$ could be joined into a single block. This shows:

THEOREM 14.2.3. *Let G have a k-chromatic decomposition (14.1.1). Then G has an independent homomorphism such that the image graph G/C is a complete graph on k vertices.*

We shall make use of this representation to derive certain additive decompositions of a k-chromatic graph. Suppose that $a < k$ is some integer and divide k by a

(14.2.5) $$k = a \cdot b + r, \qquad\qquad 0 \leq r \leq a - 1.$$

We decompose the k blocks C_i in (14.1.1) into classes correspondingly

(14.2.6)
$$
\begin{array}{cccc}
C_{11} & C_{12} & \cdots & C_{1a}, \\
C_{21} & C_{22} & \cdots & C_{2a}, \\
\multicolumn{4}{c}{\dotfill} \\
C_{b1} & C_{b2} & \cdots & C_{ba}, \\
C_{b+1,1} & C_{b+1,2} & \cdots & C_{b+1,r}.
\end{array}
$$

Two subgraphs A and B shall be constructed as follows: The graph A consists of all edges in G connecting any two blocks in different lines in (14.2.6) while

B includes all edges connecting blocks in two different columns. This definition shows that

(14.2.7) $G = A + B$

and also that A is $(b + 1)$-colorable and B is a-colorable when $r \neq 0$. For $r = 0$ we obtain a theorem by Zykov:

THEOREM 14.2.4. *When the chromatic number of a graph G is a product $k = a \cdot b$ then G is the sum of two graphs (14.2.7) such that A is b-chromatic and B is a-chromatic.*

PROOF. The inequality (14.2.1) shows that the chromatic numbers cannot be less than a and b.

The same argument applies in certain cases where $r \neq 0$ in (14.2.5). One must always have $\kappa(A) = b + 1$ for $\kappa(A) \leq b$ leads to a contradiction as one sees from (14.2.1). But one may possibly have $\kappa(B) \leq a - 1$; this leads to the condition

$$a \geq r + b + 1 \geq 3$$

which cannot be satisfied for $a = 2$. We conclude that G can always be written as a sum (14.2.7) where

$$\kappa(A) = b + 1, \quad \kappa(B) = 2,$$

that is, B is bipartite and one can take A such that

$$\kappa(A) = \tfrac{1}{2}k, \quad \kappa(A) = \tfrac{1}{2}(k + 1)$$

depending on the parity of k. By repeated applications follows:

THEOREM 14.2.5. *A k-chromatic graph can be written as the sum of t bipartite graphs where t is the smallest exponent such that $k \leq 2^t$.*

PROBLEMS

1.* Try to obtain inequalities for the chromatic numbers of an arbitrary pair of graphs G and G_1 generalizing the inequalities (14.2.2) and (14.2.3).

2.* Determine other kinds of sum representations for chromatic graphs.

14.3.   **Critical graphs.** A number of interesting properties of chromatic graphs have been obtained by Dirac through the introduction of the concept of *critical graphs*. A graph K shall be called *(vertex) critical* when the removal of any vertex and the edges from it reduces the chromatic number $k = \kappa(K)$. A critical 1-chromatic graph is a single vertex; a critical 2-chromatic graph is a single edge. A critical 3-chromatic graph becomes a bipartite graph by the removal of a single vertex, hence it is a circuit of odd length.

THEOREM 14.3.1. *A critical graph K has the properties*:

1. K *is finite and connected.*

(14.3.1)   2. *For every vertex $\rho(v) \geqq k-1$.*

3. K *has no separating vertices.*

PROOF. 1. We saw that a k-chromatic graph contains a finite section graph with the same chromatic number. As a consequence every k-chromatic graph contains a finite critical subgraph with the same chromatic number. If K should not be connected a component could be removed without changing k.

2. The removal of a vertex and its edges can at most reduce the chromatic number by one unit. When v is removed from K the reduced graph has the chromatic number $k-1$. If $\rho(v) < k-1$ the vertex could be restored without increasing the chromatic number.

3. Suppose that K has a separating vertex s. Then K consists of two section graphs $K(A)$ and $K(B)$ having only the vertex s in common. The chromatic numbers for $K(A)$ and $K(B)$ are at most $k-1$ and by using the same color for s in both graphs K would also be colorable in $k-1$ colors.

The result in (3) in Theorem 14.3.1 can be extended. Let A be a subset of the vertex set V of the critical graph K. When A and all edges to its vertices are removed from K there remains the graph $K(V-A)$ which in general decomposes into a number of connected components

$$(14.3.2) \qquad K(V-A) = K(C_1) + \cdots + K(C_i)$$

where the number $i = i(A)$ is the *component index* of A. By assumption the graph $K(A)$ is colorable in less than k colors. We denote by $\mu(A)$ the number of essentially different ways of coloring $K(A)$, that is, colorings which are not obtainable from each other by renaming the colors. In counting these ways one can always suppose that a particular vertex $a_1 \in A$ takes a specific color denoted by 1. We shall prove:

THEOREM 14.3.2. *For any subset A of the vertex set V of a critical graph K one has*

$$(14.3.3) \qquad i(A) \leqq \mu(A).$$

PROOF. By assumption the graph $G(V-C_1)$ can be colored in $k-1$ colors. Thus each of the subgraphs

$$(14.3.4) \qquad G(C_j + A), \qquad\qquad j = 2, 3, \cdots, i(A)$$

can be colored in $k-1$ colors such that the set A has the same coloring in all of them. The same argument applies to each graph $G(V-C_t)$. Thus when the number $i(A)$ of components exceeds the number of ways $\mu(A)$ in which $K(A)$ can be colored there must be pairs, say $G(V - C_1)$ and $G(V - C_2)$ in which A has the same coloring. But then all graphs (14.3.4) including $j = 1$ can be $(k-1)$-colored with a common coloring for A. This yields a coloring of K in $k-1$ colors. We conclude that (14.3.3) must hold.

When $K(A)$ is a complete graph there is essentially only one coloring, hence:

THEOREM 14.3.3. *A critical graph cannot be separated by the vertices of a complete subgraph.*

Each critical graph has associated with it maximal length arcs L_0 and maximal length circuits C_0. We denote by

$$\lambda_k(n),\ \gamma_k(n)$$

respectively the smallest lengths of L_0 and C_0 for the various k-critical graphs of order n. The following result is due to Kelly and Kelly:

THEOREM 14.3.4. *One has*

$$(14.3.5) \qquad\qquad \lim_{n\to\infty} \lambda_k(n) = \lim_{n\to\infty} \gamma_k(n) = \infty.$$

PROOF. A set A with v vertices has at most v^{v-1} essentially different colorings. From Theorem 14.3.2 we conclude

$$i(A) \leqq v^{v-1}.$$

Thus for an arc L of length l

$$i(L) \leqq (l+1)^l$$

and so for a critical graph in which the maximal arc length is l_0

$$i(L) \leqq (l_0+1)^{l_0}.$$

Theorem 2.5.4 shows that the local degrees of K are bounded for a given l_0 and the inequality (2.4.6) implies that by increasing n also l_0 must tend to infinity.

To prove the second part of (14.3.5) we rely upon an observation due to Dirac:

THEOREM 14.3.5. *In a graph without separating vertices one has*

$$(14.3.6) \qquad\qquad c_0^2 > l_0$$

where l_0 and c_0 are the lengths of the longest arcs and circuits.

PROOF. Let $L_0(a, b)$ be a longest arc. According to Theorem 5.4.1 there is a circuit C passing through a and b. The arc L_0 decomposes into sections

$L_1, \cdots, L_t$ such that each L_i either has only its endpoints on C or lies entirely on C. In either case L_i is a circuit arc so that the length c_i of L_i is less than c_0. Thus

$$l_0 = \sum c_i < tc_0$$

and since $t < c_0$ the inequality (14.3.6) follows.

Further study of the asymptotic behavior of the function $\gamma_k(n)$ in (14.3.5) have been made by Dirac and Read:

Property (2) in Theorem 14.2.1 has the following extension:

THEOREM 14.3.6. *Any critical k-chromatic graph is at least $(k-1)$-edge connected.*

PROOF. Suppose that for some set A there exists a decomposition

$$G = G(A) + G(\bar{A}) + G(A, \bar{A}), \quad A + \bar{A} = V$$

with

(14.3.7) $\rho = \rho(A, \bar{A}) < k-1.$

The graphs $G(A)$ and $G(\bar{A})$ have color functions f and $\bar{f}$ with the values $1, \cdots, k-1$. We shall show that when (14.3.7) holds they can be combined into a coloring of the whole graph G in $k-1$ colors, contrary to assumptions. Let

$$a_1, a_2, \cdots, a_e$$

be the vertices in A from which there are edges to $\bar{A}$. If they represent r different color values $f(a_i)$ we take them to be $1, 2, \cdots r$ and order the vertices such that

$$f(a_1) = 1 \leqq f(a_2) \leqq \cdots \leqq f(a_e) = r.$$

Next we order the edges

$$E_t = (a_i, \bar{a}_j), \qquad\qquad t = 1, 2, \cdots, \rho$$

in $\rho(A, \bar{A})$ in some way with non-decreasing i. For $E_1 = (a_1, \bar{a}_1)$ we rearrange the values of $\bar{f}$ such that $\bar{f}(\bar{a}_1) = 2$. For the subsequent edges we use the values

$$\bar{f}(\bar{a}_j) = t + 1$$

rearranging the previous values of $\bar{f}$ in each step whenever necessary. Since $\rho < k-1$ the process can be carried out for all edges E_t and will result in values satisfying

$$f(a_i) \neq \bar{f}(\bar{a}_j)$$

for each edge E_t. But then f and $\bar{f}$ can be combined into a $(k-1)$-coloration of G.

Among the various unsolved problems concerning critical graphs let us mention the important

Conjecture of Hadwiger. Every connected finite k-chromatic graph has some subgraph with a complete k-graph as an image under a connected homomorphism.

This conjecture is trivial for $k = 1$ and $k = 2$. For $k = 3$ every graph with a circuit has a connected homomorphism to a triangle. For $k = 4$ the conjecture has been proved by Dirac in the general form:

THEOREM 14.3.7. *When G is a finite connected graph with single edges and without separating vertices and local degrees $\rho(v) \geq 3$ then G has a subgraph homomorphic to a complete 4-graph under a connected homomorphism.*

PROOF. Let C be a circuit of greatest length γ in G; according to Theorem 2.5.3 we have $\gamma \geq 4$. We denote the vertices in C by $a_1, \cdots, a_\gamma$. A *chord* T is an arc connecting two non-neighboring vertices in C. We prove first that there are chords at each vertex in C, for instance at a_1. There is at least one edge $E = (a_1, b)$ not belonging to C. If b is on C there is nothing to prove so that we assume that b is not on C. From Theorem 5.4.3 we see that there is a circuit C_1 including E and a_2. The arc $C_1(a, b, a_2)$ must have a first vertex a_i on C and since C is a longest circuit one concludes that $a_i \neq a_2$ and $a_i \neq a_n$.

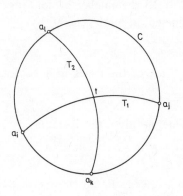
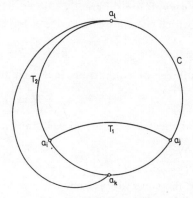

Figure 14.3.1.   Figure 14.3.2.

Assume (Figure 14.3.1) that C has two chords $T_1(a_i, a_j)$ and $T_2(a_k, a_l)$ with a common vertex t not on C. We take t as the first vertex on T_1 which is also on T_2. Then the subgraph consisting of C and T_2 together with $T_1(a_i, t)$ is homomorphic to a complete 4-graph under a connected homomorphism.

There remains the case where all chords for C are disjoint (Figure 14.3.2). Any chord $T_1(a_i, a_j)$ divides C into two arcs. We select a_i and a_j such that $C(a_i, a_j)$ is as short as possible; take a_k on this arc. There exists some chord

$T_2(a_k, a_l)$ and by our assumption a_l cannot be located on $C(a_i, a_j)$. The graph consisting of C, T_1 and T_2 is connectedly homomorphic to a complete 4-graph.

The next case is $k = 5$. Little progress has been made for such graphs and this is not surprising since it can be shown that the truth of Hadwiger's conjecture in this case would lead to a proof of the so-called 4-color map conjecture for planar graphs.

PROBLEMS

1.   When the inequality (14.3.6) is written in the form

$$c_0^2 \geqq \alpha \cdot l_0$$

determine the best possible numerical value for α.

2.   Give a necessary and sufficient condition for a graph to be connectedly homomorphic to a complete 4-graph.

14.4.   **Coloration polynomials.** Suppose that a fixed number λ of colors is available to be assigned to the vertices of a graph G with the vertex set V. When V has n elements this may be done in λ^n ways. We wish to determine the number $\pi(G; \lambda)$ of permissible colorations satisfying the condition that for each edge the endpoints are differently colored. Denote by $\mu(E)$ the number of colorings of G in which the ends of an edge E have the same color, more general, by

(14.4.1) $\mu(H) = \mu(E_{i_1}, E_{i_2}, \cdots, E_{i_s})$

the number of colorations in which the endpoints of the edges in a subgraph

(14.4.2) $H = \{E_{i_1}, \cdots, E_{i_s}\}$

receive the same color. A well-known set principle gives the formula

(14.4.3) $\pi(G; \lambda) = \lambda^n - \sum_i \mu(E_i) + \sum_{ij} \mu(E_i, E_j) \cdots$

where the sums are extended to all choices of one edge E_i, all choices of pairs of different edges E_i, E_j and so on.

To evaluate the general term (14.4.1) in the expansion (14.4.3) we decompose the subgraph H in (14.4.2) into its connected components

(14.4.4) $H = \sum H_l$, $l = 1, 2, \cdots, c(H)$.

We assume that V is the vertex set of each H. When the edges in H have the same color at both ends the vertices in any connected component H_l in (14.4.4) must all have the same colors. Thus a term (14.4.1) has the value

$$\mu(H) = \lambda^{c(H)}.$$

By substituting this in (14.4.3) the formula becomes

(14.4.5) $$\pi(G;\lambda) = \sum_{s,c} (-1)^s p(s,c)\lambda^c$$

where $p(s,c)$ is the number of subgraphs H of G with s edges and $c = c(H)$ connected components.

The formula (14.4.5) is due to G. D. Birkhoff. When this coloration polynomial $\pi(G;x)$ is known the chromatic number k_0 of G is the smallest positive integer for which

$$\pi(G;k_0) > 0.$$

In the actual computation of $\pi(G;\lambda)$ many of the terms $\mu(H)$ in (14.4.3) will cancel. The possibility of such reductions has been investigated systematically by Whitney. To deduce his results we arrange the edges in G in some definite order

(14.4.6) $$E_1, E_2, \cdots, E_N$$

where N is the number of edges in G. Let $\{C_i\}$ be the family of all circuits in G. From each we construct a *broken circuit*

(14.4.7) $$P_i = C_i - F_i$$

obtained by omitting from C_i its edge F_i of highest rank in (14.4.6). The broken circuits are arranged lexicographically

(14.4.8) $$P_1, P_2, \cdots, P_t$$

with respect to the order of those edges E_i in (14.4.6) which they contain. Then the edge F_i in (14.4.7) cannot be contained in any broken circuit P_j preceding P_i for F_i has higher rank than all edges in P_i and in P_j.

Next we place all subgraphs of G in $t + 1$ disjoint classes

(14.4.9) $$S_1, S_2, \cdots, S_{t+1}$$

defined as follows: S_1 consists of all subgraphs containing P_1; the class S_2 of all graphs containing P_2 but not P_1 and so on; S_{t+1} consists of all subgraphs containing no broken circuit.

We shall show that all terms in (14.4.3) corresponding to graphs in S_1 will cancel. One sees that the graphs in S_1 can be paired in a one-to-one manner

(14.4.10) $$H_1 \leftrightarrows H_1 + F_1$$

where H_1 excludes F_1. The two graphs in (14.4.10) have the same number of connected components since F_1 connects the two endpoints of P_1 in H_1; consequently

$$\mu(H_1) = \mu(H_1 + F_1).$$

The two terms appear with opposite signs in (14.4.3) since one has one more edge than the other.

Similarly in S_2 each graph H_2 not containing F_2 gives rise to a unique graph $H_2 + F_2$ also in S_2 since F_2 is not in P_1. The same argument shows again that the corresponding terms in (14.4.3) cancel. By repeating the process it follows that in computing (14.4.3) one can restrict oneself on the terms $\mu(H_{t+1})$ in which H_{t+1} does not include any of the broken circuits (14.4.8).

These graphs H_{t+1} can have no circuits. From this observation one concludes that

$$c(H_{t+1}) = n - s$$

and so we obtain the expression given by Whitney for the coloration polynomial

(14.4.11) $$\pi(G; x) = \sum_s (-1)^s m(s) \cdot x^{n-s}$$

where $m(s)$ is the number of subgraphs of G with s edges containing none of the broken circuits (14.4.8). By comparison of the coefficients of x^i in the two expressions (14.4.5) and (14.4.11) for $\pi(G; x)$ one obtains the formula

(14.4.12) $$(-1)^{n-i} m(n-i) = \sum_s (-1)^s p(s, i).$$

Let us mention a few simple properties of the coloration polynomials. When G has no edges evidently

$$\pi(G; x) = x^n.$$

In general, since there are no subgraphs with $c = 0$ the conditions

$$p(s, 0) = 0, \quad m(n) = 0$$

are fulfilled and $\pi(G; x)$ has the factor x. For a single edge $H = E$

$$c(E) = n - 1$$

and so

$$p(1, n-1) = N, \quad p(1, j) = 0, \qquad\qquad j \neq n-1.$$

Similarily

$$p(s, n-s) = \binom{N}{s}, \quad p(s, j) = 0, \qquad\qquad j \neq n-s$$

provided G has no circuits of length $\leq s$. A further relation is

(14.4.13) $$\sum_j p(s, j) = \binom{N}{s}$$

which is a consequence of the fact that the sum on the left represents the number of subgraphs of G with s edges. From (14.4.5) one finds

$$\pi(G;1) = \sum_{s,c}(-1)^s\, p(s,c)$$

and according to (14.4.13) this reduces to

(14.4.14) $$\pi(G;1) = \sum(-1)^s\binom{N}{s} = (1-1)^N = 0$$

provided $N > 0$.

The definition of the coloration polynomial shows that when G has a disjoint decomposition

$$G = \sum G_i \qquad\qquad\qquad i = 1, 2, \cdots, k$$

into connected components then

(14.4.15) $$\pi(G;x) = \pi(G_1;x) \cdots \pi(G_k;x).$$

Similarly let

$$G = G_1 + G_2$$

be a decomposition where G_1 and G_2 have but a single vertex a in common. Then all colorings of G are obtained from the colorings of G_1 and G_2 in which a has the same color. This immediately leads to the formula

(14.4.16) $$\pi(G;x) = \tfrac{1}{x} \cdot \pi(G_1;x) \cdot \pi(G_2;x).$$

THEOREM 14.4.1. *When E is a separating edge for G then*

(14.4.17) $$\pi(G;x) = \left(1 - \tfrac{1}{x}\right)\pi(G-E;x).$$

PROOF. We divide the subgraphs of G into two classes

$$\{H\}, \{H + E\}$$

where H runs through the subgraphs of $G-E$. The graph $H + E$ has one more edge than H and one fewer connected component so that

$$\pi(G;x) = \sum(-1)^s\mu(H) + \tfrac{1}{x}\sum(-1)^{s+1}\mu(H).$$

By summation (14.4.17) follows.

When Theorem 14.4.1 is applied to a tree T one concludes that

(14.4.18) $$\pi(T;x) = x(x-1)^{n-1}.$$

For a circuit free graph the coloration polynomial according to (14.4.15) is the product of such factors (14.4.18).

One sees that in a circuit C with n edges a subgraph H with s edges has

$$c(H) = n - s, \qquad\qquad s < n$$

components. This leads to the formula

(14.4.19) $\pi(C; x) = (x - 1)^n + (-1)^n (x - 1)$.

By combining the formulas (14.4.15) and (14.4.16) with the result in Theorem 14.4.1 the computation of the coloration polynomial of a graph is immediately reduced to the determination of the polynomials for its lobe graphs.

The color polynomials may also be computed by successive reductions by means of the formula

$$\pi(G + E; x) = \pi(G; x) - \pi(G'; x)$$

where $G + E$ is a graph obtained from G by adding a new edge $E = (a, b)$ between two of its vertices while G' is produced by letting a and b coincide. The proof is a simple consequence of the definition of the coloration polynomials. A number of other reduction procedures have been given by Whitney.

PROBLEMS

1.   Determine the coloration polynomials for the Platonic graphs.

2.   Show that when $\pi(G; x)$ is divisible exactly by x^k then k is the number of connected components in G.

3.   Prove that the condition of Theorem 14.4.1 is also sufficient for E to be a separating edge.

4.   Prove that the formula (14.4.18) also characterizes T as a tree.

CHAPTER 15

GROUPS AND GRAPHS

15.1. **Groups of automorphisms.** Each graph G, directed or undirected, has a *group of automorphisms* $\Gamma = \Gamma(G)$ consisting of the isomorphisms of G to itself. This means that the group Γ (of automorphisms) of G consists of all one-to-one correspondences α of the vertex set V to itself such that when $E = (a, b)$ is an edge in G then $E^\alpha = (a^\alpha, b^\alpha)$ is also an edge and vice versa. Thus Γ may be considered to be a permutation group on the set V. When G is defined by means of a vertex-vertex incidence matrix $M(G)$ the automorphisms are those permutation matrices M_α which commute with $M(G)$.

We shall in the following assume that G is undirected, usually with single edges and no loops. The first problem arising is the actual determination of the group $\Gamma(G)$. A complete graph U_n on n vertices has the symmetric group Σ_n as its group and conversely when the group is Σ_n the graph is complete. Another useful observation is that a graph and its complement must have the same group.

We notice next that the determination of the group can be reduced to the case where G is connected. Suppose that

$$(15.1.1) \qquad\qquad G = G_1 + G_2 + \cdots + G_r, \qquad\qquad G_i = \sum G_{ij}$$

is the decomposition of G into connected components G_{ij} arranged such that the graphs

$$(15.1.2) \qquad\qquad G_{ij}, \qquad\qquad j = 1, 2, \cdots, n_i$$

are isomorphic to each other but not to other components. By any automorphism the graphs G_i must be transformed into themselves so that the group of G is a direct product

$$(15.1.3) \qquad\qquad \Gamma(G) = \Gamma(G_1) \times \cdots \times \Gamma(G_r)$$

corresponding to (15.1.1).

The isomorphic components G_{ij} in (15.1.2) can be permuted among themselves and after this operation one can apply an automorphism h_j for each G_{ij}. Thus the automorphism group $\Gamma(G_i)$ in (15.1.3) consists of all correspondences which can be written in the form of a generalized permutation

$$P(h) = \begin{pmatrix} X_j \\ X_{k_j} \cdot h_{k_j} \end{pmatrix} \qquad\qquad (j = 1, 2, \cdots, n_i).$$

In the usual group theoretical terminology this is called the *complete monomial group* of n_i variables over a group H isomorphic to any one of the automorphism groups $\Gamma(G_{ij})$, $j = 1, \cdots, n_i$.

When G is a connected graph there are certain immediate restrictions on the possible automorphisms. Any vertex must be carried into a vertex with the same local degree; an edge into an edge with the same number of edges at either end. More general, any subgraph has an isomorphic image with isomorphically located edges and vertices of attachment. In spite of these limitations the actual determination of the group may be quite involved for large graphs.

We shall give some illustrations. The graphs in Figure 15.1.1 and Figure 15.1.2 are both regular of degree 3. The first has the unit group, the second a group of order 2 defined by the permutation

$$P = (1, 2)(3, 4)(5, 6)(7, 8)(9, 10)$$

as shown by Frucht.

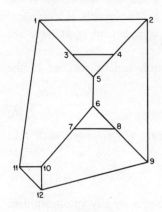

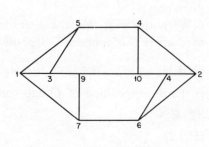

Figure 15.1.1.   Figure 15.1.2.

The graph of a circuit is the dihedral group generated by the cyclic permutation of the vertices $(1, 2, \cdots, n)$ and the reflexion $(1, n-1)(2, n-2) \cdots$.

The group of the tetrahedron is the symmetric group Σ_4 on four elements since it is the complete graph on 4 vertices. The groups of the cube and octahedron are both isomorphic to a direct product of Σ_4 and a reflexion of order 2. For the dodecahedron and icosahedron the groups are isomorphic to the direct product of the alternating group A_5 on 5 elements and a reflexion.

The so-called *Petersen graph* has the form indicated in Figure 15.1.3. It is regular of degree 3 and order 10. It was first introduced by Petersen as an illustration of a graph with $\rho = 3$ which is not the sum of 3 subgraphs of first degree. Its group is isomorphic to Σ_5 as established by Frucht.

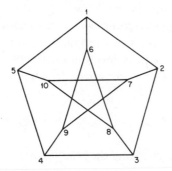

Figure 15.1.3.

A number of special graphs appear in geometric theories. As examples let us take the configuration illustrating the theorem of Pappus and Desargues in projective geometry. The groups of these graphs have been determined by Kagno. The problem is immediately reduced to the preceding cases since Desargues' graph is the complement of Petersen's graph while Pappus' graph has a complement consisting of three components, each a triangle.

Aside from the trivial case of a single vertex all graphs of the lowest orders have groups not consisting of the identity alone. According to Kagno the graph of order 6 in Figure 15.1.4 is the lowest order graph with the identical group.

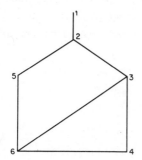

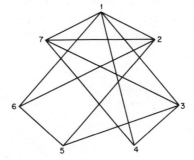

Figure 15.1.4.   Figure 15.1.5.

Kagno has also investigated all graphs of order ≤ 6 in which the local degrees satisfy the condition $\rho(v) \geq 3$. All of these have non-trival groups. Graphs of this type of order 7 may have only the identity for its group; an example is given in Figure 15.1.5.

As another illustration of graph automorphisms one may take the crystal graphs and the crystal groups. It should be noted, however, that by the determination of the crystallographical groups one is interested in a somewhat different problem, namely the automorphisms produced by orthogonal transformations of three-dimensional space. Let us mention finally also that the automorphisms of trees have been investigated in considerable detail by Pólya.

PROBLEMS

1.   Determine all graphs of order $n \leqq 7$ having only the unit element as their group.

2.   Compare the crystal group and the graph group for certain types of crystals.

15.2.   **Cayley's color graphs for groups.**   We shall describe briefly a graph representation for groups which was introduced by Cayley. Let Γ be some group of finite or infinite order N. To Γ we associate a graph G whose vertex set coincides with the set of elements in Γ. Any pair of vertices shall be connected by a directed edge $E_{ij} = (g_i, g_j)$ so that G is a complete directed graph with N incoming and outgoing edges at each vertex. In particular, there is a pair of edges (g_i, g_j) and (g_j, g_i) with opposite directions between any two vertices g_i and g_j.

We distribute the edges in G into N classes or colors by associating with each edge E_{ij} a unique group element

(15.2.1) $$c_{ij} = g_i^{-1} \cdot g_j.$$

One sees that at each vertex there is one entering and one issuing edge from each class. Thus the edges in any class form a regular subgraph of first degree, hence it is a sum of finite and infinite directed circuits. In Figure 15.2.1 one finds the color graph of the symmetric group on three elements; the form is slightly simplified since the two edges between two vertices have not been traced separately.

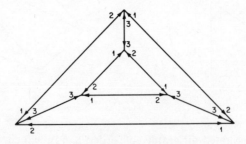

Figure 15.2.1.

Suppose now that one proceeds from a vertex g_1 in G along a directed path to some vertex g_n. Then according to (15.2.1) one must have

$$g_n = g_1 \cdot c_{12} \cdot c_{23} \cdots c_{n-1,n}.$$

Here the product

$$p = c_{12} c_{23} \cdots c_{n-1,n}$$

is the unit element e of G when the path is cyclic and $p \neq e$ otherwise. Thus the color graph may be of assistance in determining the possible relations which may exist among the elements of G.

In constructing the paths in G one has in each step the choice of taking an arbitrary new vertex not previously encountered and so it is clear that in G one can find directed Hamilton lines. To obtain some path from a vertex to another it is not necessary that the color graph include the edges for all classes. It suffices to have only those which correspond to some generating system for Γ since the other elements are produced as their products.

This brings up the problem of determining those generating systems for a group, particularly the ones which either include a minimal number of elements or which are simple in some other respect, such that their graph has Hamilton lines. Certain special cases have been considered by Rapaport. Incidentally, it may be observed that problems of this type appear in the art of bell ringing where it is the task of a team of ringers to create all permutations possible on a set of bells by moving from one to another by certain simple restrictive rules. Some references to the domain of campanology are given in the bibliography.

In the application of the color graphs in the subsequent section we shall be interested in those automorphisms which preserve the edge colorations. Such an automorphism is obtained by multiplying each element in Γ, that is, each vertex in G, on the left by a fixed group element x. Then the image of an edge $E = (g_i, g_j)$ is

$$xE = (xg_i, xg_j)$$

and according to the definition (15.2.1) both these edges have the same color. This observation leads to:

THEOREM 15.2.1.   *All automorphisms of the Cayley graph of a group which preserve the coloration of the edges are obtained by left multiplication with group elements.*

PROOF.   It remains only to show that all automorphisms are of this kind. If any color preserving automorphism α leaves a vertex g_i fixed it must also leave unchanged all outgoing and incoming edges at g_i since there is just one such edge of each color. Thus all neighboring vertices to g_i are also left invariant. By continuing the argument one concludes that $\alpha = e$ is the identity correspondence. Thus all $\alpha \neq e$ must move all vertices and there can be just one such automorphism taking one vertex into another. Since the left multiplications have this property they are the only color preserving automorphisms.

15.3. **Graphs with prescribed groups.** The following result is due to Frucht:

THEOREM 15.3.1. *To any finite group Γ one can determine a finite undirected graph G such that the group of automorphisms of G is isomorphic to Γ.*

PROOF. The first step consists in the construction of a family of non-isomorphic connected graphs H_v such that the group of each H_v is the identity. This may be done in many ways. Frucht uses the graphs illustrated in Figure 15.3.1. It consists of three edges $(1,3)$, $(3,4)$, $(4,2)$ and from each of the vertices 3 and 4 there are arcs of lengths $2v$ and $2v + 1$ respectively in $H_v, v = 1, 2, \cdots$.

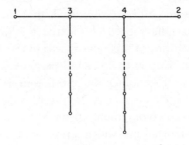

Figure 15.3.1.

Secondly a Cayley color graph $C(\Gamma)$ is constructed for Γ. The desired graph G is obtained from $C(\Gamma)$ by replacing each directed edge (g_i, g_j) of the v-th color class by the graph H_v in such a manner that g_i is identified with the vertex 1 and g_j with the vertex 2.

One sees that G is undirected and connected. It remains to show that its group is isomorphic to Γ; this may be done analogously to the proof of Theorem 15.2.1. Consider first an automorphism α leaving fixed some vertex g_i. In G the edges from g_i are of the type $(1,3)$ and $(2,4)$ depending on the direction of the corresponding edge in $C(\Gamma)$. But when g_i is invariant under α also the neighboring vertices 3 and 4 must remain unchanged because their associated paths in H_v all have different lengths. For the same reason each of the graphs H_v at g_i

remain fixed, hence also the vertex 2 corresponding to a vertex g_j. It follows successively that all vertices in G are fixed so that α is the identical correspondence.

By an automorphism of G any vertex g_i can be transferred only into some vertex g_j since all other vertices in a graph H_v have different local degrees. Furthermore, from the preceding follows that for each pair (g_i, g_j) there can at most be one automorphism taking one into the other. However, such an automorphism is induced in G by the automorphisms of $C(\Gamma)$ defined by the left multiplication with elements in Γ. This completes the proof of Theorem 15.3.1.

In principle the preceding proof is very simple, but the construction usually leads to graphs of high order. A method which is more economical in this respect was devised by Frucht in constructing regular graphs of degree 3 with a prescribed group. For any group Γ one can find a graph of this kind with $2(n + 2) N$ vertices where N is the order of Γ and n the number of its generators.

The requirement that a graph have a given group is not a severe restriction on its other properties. It has been shown by Izbicki and Sabidussi that one can take the graph regular of any degree, connectivity, chromatic number and other conditions. The same authors also extended Frucht's theorem to infinite groups.

The automorphism groups of partial orders have been examined by Birkhoff and Frucht; it can be shown that a partial order P with a given group Γ can be found such that P has at most N^2 vertices where N is the order of Γ.

In connection with the group of automorphisms of graphs one should also mention certain interesting studies by Tutte on regular graphs of degree 3. He investigated the problem of determining those graphs in which any directed arc of length s can be transferred by an automorphism into any other such arc. This is possible only when $s \leq 5$. The number s must also satisfy the condition

$$s \leq \tfrac{1}{2}m + 1$$

where m is the length of the shortest circuit. Those special graphs (cages) for which s assumes this maximal value have various remarkable properties. Coxeter proved that there is an infinity of regular graphs of degree 3 with the transitivity property for $s = 2$; an example for the case $s = 1$ was constructed by Frucht.

15.4. **Edge correspondences.** We shall say that two graphs G and G' are *edge isomorphic* when there is a one-to-one correspondence $E \leftrightarrows E'$ between their edges such that if E_1 and E_2 are incident edges in G then the corresponding edges E_1' and E_2' are incident in G' and vice versa. It is clear that any ordinary (vertex) isomorphism between G and G' also defines an edge isomorphism, but the converse need not be true. This problem has been studied by Whitney and we shall give his principal results in a somewhat simplified form.

In Figure 15.4.1 we first give an example of two graphs which are edge isomorphic without being vertex isomorphic.

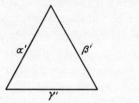
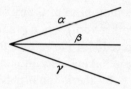

Figure 15.4.1.

Next in Figure 15.4.2 one finds three pairs of graphs of order 4 which are both vertex and edge isomorphic, but the edge isomophism is not induced by any vertex isomorphism. We leave it to the reader to verify that only in these instances can such correspondences occur in graphs whose orders do not exceed 4.

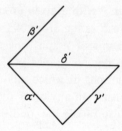
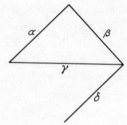

Figure 15.4.2a

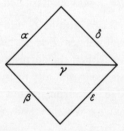
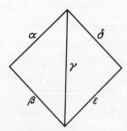

Figure 15.4.2b

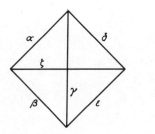 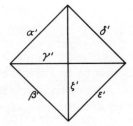

Figure 15.4.2c

The theorem of Whitney states:

THEOREM 15.4.1. *Let G be a finite connected graph not equal to any of the special graphs in Figure 15.4.1 and Figure 15.4.2. Then any edge isomorphism of G to another graph is induced by a vertex isomorphism.*

PROOF. According to the preceding observations we may assume that G has at least 5 vertices. It then contains as a subgraph some minimal connected subgraph, i.e., a tree, with 5 vertices. One checks quickly that for such graphs all edge isomorphisms are induced by vertex isomorphisms.

The general case may be proved by induction with respect to the number of edges in G. Suppose that one adds an edge $E = (a, b)$ to G such that the new graph $G + E$ is connected. We denote by

(15.4.1) $$E_1^{(a)} = (a, a_1), \ E_2^{(a)} = (a, a_2), \cdots,$$

(15.4.2) $$E_1^{(b)} = (b, b_1), \ E_2^{(b)} = (b, b_2), \cdots$$

the edges of G incident to a and b respectively. According to the induction assumption a graph which is edge isomorphic to $G + E$ must be of the form $G' + E'$ where G' is vertex isomorphic to G and E' an edge with the same edge incidences in G' as E with respect to G. Thus we may assume that the edge isomorphic graph is of the form $G + E'$ with $E' = (a', b')$.

1. E is a terminal edge attached at the vertex a. To show that $G + E$ and $G + E'$ are vertex isomorphic it suffices to demonstrate that E' is also terminal with $a = a'$. If E' were not terminal both its endpoints a' and b' would be on G so that E' would become incident to some edges in G different from those in (15.4.1). When E' is terminal $a = a'$ because otherwise E' would also be incident to some edges not in (15.4.1).

2. E has both endpoints on G.

(α) $a = a'$, $b \neq b'$. To prove that this is impossible we notice that since b' must be incident to all edges (15.4.2) there can be only one such edge

$$E^{(b)}_1 = (b, b_1) = (b, b').$$

But then E' at b' is incident to some edge in G not in (15.4.1) nor in (15.4.2); the possibility that there should be no such edge at b' is excluded by the fact that (b, b_1) cannot be an isolated edge in G.

(β) E and E' have no endpoints in common. E' is incident to all edges (15.4.1) so there can be at most two such edges

$$E^{(a)}_1 = (a, a_1), \ E^{(a)}_2 = (a, a_2), \ E' = (a_1, a_2).$$

Also the edges (15.4.2) are incident to E'. This implies that there can be at most two edges at b and these must connect b with a_1 and a_2. In either case E' is incident to other edges at a_1 and a_2 since G is connected and has more than 4 vertices.

Since the pairs of graphs in Figure 15.4.2 are isomorphic Theorem 15.4.1 implies:

THEOREM 15.4.2. *Edge isomorphic graphs are vertex isomorphic except for the graphs in Figure 15.4.1.*

We notice that two graphs are edge isomorphic if and only if their interchange graphs (Section 1.5) are isomorphic. Thus Theorem 15.4.2 is equivalent to:

THEOREM 15.4.3. *Graphs with isomorphic interchange graphs are isomorphic with the exception of the graphs in Figure 15.4.1.*

Let G be a connected graph. We say that G is *circuit isomorphic* to another graph G' when there is a one-to-one edge correspondence between the two such that the edges lying on a circuit in one graph will correspond to edges on a circuit in the other. The following theorem is essentially due to Whitney:

THEOREM 15.4.4. *Let G be connected and without separating vertices. A necessary and sufficient condition that all circuit isomorphisms with G be induced by isomorphisms is that G be 3-vertex connected.*

PROOF. We show first that when G is 3-vertex connected any circuit isomorphism is induced by an isomorphism. None of the exceptional graphs in Figure 15.4.1 and Figure 15.4.2 are 3-vertex connected. Thus according to Theorem 15.4.1 it is sufficient that any circuit isomorphism is an edge isomorphism. Suppose that under the circuit isomorphism two adjacent edges

$$E_1 = (a, b), \ E_2 = (b, c)$$

should correspond to non-adjacent edges

$$E'_1 = (a,' b'), \ E'_2 = (c', d').$$

By the connectivity assumption the graph G_1 obtained by omitting the edges from b in G can have no separating vertices. Theorem 5.4.3 shows that in G_1 there is a circuit through a and c, hence two disjoint arcs $B(a, c)$ and $C(a, c)$ not including E_1 and E_2. Since $E_1 + E_2 + B$ is a circuit its image is a circuit passing through E_1' and E_2'. We arrange the notation such that in this image circuit a' is connected with c' and b' with d' (Figure 15.4.3).

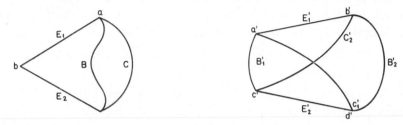

Figure 15.4.3.

Also $E_1 + E_2 + C$ is a circuit corresponding to a circuit through E_1' and E_2'. In this circuit a' must be connected to d' before c' as in the figure because a direct connection in C' from a' to c' not including E_1' and E_2' would correspond to a circuit in G consisting only of a part of the edges in B and C. We conclude that in G' there is a circuit $E_1' + C_1' + B_2'$. But the inverse image of this circuit is not a circuit, hence we have a contradiction.

Suppose next that the vertex connectivity of G is $l_0 = 2$. Then there exists a decomposition of G into two section graphs

(15.4.3) $G = G(A) + G(B), \quad A \cdot B = \{a, b\}$

where a and b are two separation vertices. Both $G(A)$ and $G(B)$ have inner vertices. If there is an edge (a, b) we assign it to $G(A)$. From the decomposition (15.4.3) we obtain a new graph G^* by *twisting* G with respect to the vertices a and b, that is, we attach $G(B)$ to $G(A)$ with the separating vertices a and b interchanged. One sees that G^* is circuit isomorphic to G but edges of $G(A)$ and $G(B)$ at a and b will not remain adjacent.

It has been shown by Whitney that if $l_0 = 2$ all circuit isomorphic graphs to G are isomorphic to a graph G^* obtained from G by successive twists with respect to various pairs of separating vertices a and b.

PROBLEMS

1.* Investigate the possibility of results analogous to the preceding for other classes of subgraphs than the circuits.

2.* Extend the preceding results to infinite graphs.

BIBLIOGRAPHY

Chapter 1

C. Berge, *Théorie des graphes et ses applications.* Paris, 1958.

D. König, *Theorie der endlichen und unendlichen Graphen.* Leipzig, 1936.

A. Sainte-Laguë, *Les réseaux (ou graphes).* Mémor. Sci. Math. v. 18, 1926.

Many collections of mathematical puzzles contain problems which may be formulated in graph terms. We shall mention only:

W. Rouse-Ball, *Mathematical recreations and problems.* London, 1892. Numerous editions.

E. Lucas, *Récréations mathématiques.* 3 v. Paris, 1882-1894.

Chapter 2

2.7

D.W. Crowe, *The n-dimensional cube and the Tower of Hanoi.* Amer. Math. Monthly, v. 63 (1956) pp. 29–30.

Chapter 3

3.1

L.Euler, *Solutio problematis ad geometriam situs pertinentis.* Commentarii Academiae Petropolitanae, v. 8 (1736) pp. 128–140.

N.G. de Bruijn, A *combinatorial problem.* Nederl. Akad. Wetensch. Proc., v. 49 (1946) pp. 758–764.

Van Aardenne-Ehrenfest and N.G. de Bruijn, *Circuits and trees in oriented graphs.* Simon Stevin, v. 28 (1951) pp. 203–217.

3.2

P. Erdös, T. Grünwald, and E. Weiszfeld, *Über Eulersche Linien unendlicher Graphen.* Mat. Fiz. Lapok, v. 43 (1936) pp. 129-140.

P. Erdös, T. Grünwald, and E. Vàzsonyi, *Über Euler-Linien unendlicher Graphen.* J. Math. Phys. Massachussets Inst. of Technology, v. 17 (1938) pp. 59–75.

E. Vàzsonyi, *Über Gitterpunkte des mehrdimensionalen Raumes.* Acta Litt. Sci. Szeged, v. 9 (1939) pp. 163–173.

G. Ringel, *Über drei kombinatorische Probleme am n-dimensionalen Würfel und Würfelgitter.* Abh. Math. Sem. Univ. Hamburg, v. 20 (1955) pp. 10–19.

3.3

C. Wiener, *Über eine Aufgabe aus der Geometria situs.* Math. Ann., v. 6 (1873) pp. 29–30.

O. Ore, *An excursion into labyrinths.* Mathematics Teacher, v. 52 (1959) pp. 367–370.

M. Beckman, C. B. McGuire, and C. B. Winsten, *Studies in the economics of transportation.* New Haven, Yale University Press, 1956.

L.R. Ford, *Network flow theory.* Rand Corp. Publ. P-23 (1956).

3.4

D. J. Newman, *A problem in graph theory.* Amer. Math. Monthly, v. 65 (1958) p. 611.

O. Ore, *Note on Hamilton circuits.* Amer. Math. Monthly, v. 67 (1960) p. 55.

W. T. Tutte, *On Hamilton circuits.* J. London Math. Soc., v. 21 (1946) pp. 98–101.

F. Supnick, *Extreme Hamilton lines.* Ann. of Math., (2) v. 66 (1957) pp. 179–201.

F. Fitting, *Doppeltsymmetrische Rösselsprünge auf Quadraten von ungeraden Felderzahl ohne Mittelfeld.* Jber. Deutsch. Math. Verein, v. 46 (1936) Abt. 1, pp. 38–43.

G. Dantzig, R. Fulkerson, and S. Johnson, *Solution of a large-scale travelling-salesman problem.* Journal Operational Research Soc. of Amer., v. 2 (1954) pp. 393–410.

I. Heller, *The travelling-salesman problem.* George Washington Univ. Logistics Research Project, 1954.

M. M. Flood, *On the travelling salesman's problem.* Journal Operational Research Soc. of Amer., v. 4 (1956) pp. 61–75.

T. S. Motzkin, and E. G. Straus, *Some combinatorial extremum problems.* Proc. Amer. Math. Soc., v. 7 (1956) pp. 1014–1021.

G. Dantzig, R. Fulkerson, and S. Johnson, *On a linear programming combinatorial approach to the travelling-salesman problem.* Journal Operational Research Soc. of Amer. v. 7 (1959) pp. 58–66.

R. Bellman, *On a routing problem.* Quart. Appl. Math., v. 16 (1958) pp. 87–90.

Chapter 4
4.1

A. Cayley, *A theorem on trees.* Quarterly Journal of Pure and Appl. Math., v. 23 (1889) pp. 376–378.

H. Prüfer, *Neuer Beweis eines Satzes über Permutationen.* Archiv der Math. und Phys., (3) v. 27 (1918) pp. 142–144.

O. Dziobek, *Eine Formel der Substitutionstheorie*. Sitzungsberichte der Berliner Math. Gesellchaft, v. 16 (1947) pp. 64–67.

G. Bol, *Über eine kombinatorische Frage*. Abh. Math. Seminar der Hansischen Univ., v. 12 (1938) pp. 242–245.

E. H. Neville, *The codifying of tree-structure*. Proc. Cambridge Philos. Soc., v. 49 (1953) pp. 381–385.

R. Bott and J. P. Mayberry, *Matrices and trees*. Also T. M. Whitin, *An economic application of "Matrices and Trees"*. Both published in O. Morgenstern: Economic Activity Analysis, New York, John Wiley and Sons, 1954.

L. Vitalbi, *Ricerche sulla teoria dei reticoli*. Giorn. Mat. Battaglini, (5) v. 4 (84) (1956) pp. 93–121.

G. Andreoli, *Preliminari topologici su gli alberi*. Giorn. Mat. Battaglini, (5) v. 2 (82) (1954) pp. 237–266.

P. J. Kelly, *A congruence theorem for trees*. Pacific J. Math., v. 7 (1957) pp. 961–968.

G. Pólya, *Kombinatorische Anzahlbestimmungen für Gruppen, Graphen und chemische Verbindungen*. Acta Math., v. 68 (1937) pp. 145–254.

J. Riordan, *An introduction to combinatorial analysis*. John Wiley and Sons, New York, 1958.

O. Boruvka, *On a minimal problem*. Práce Moraské Pridovedecké Spolecnosti, v. 3 (1926).

V. Jarnik and M. Kossler, *Sur les graphes minima contenant n points donnés*. Časopis Mat. Fys., v. 63 (1934) pp. 223–235.

G. Choquet, *Etude de certains réseaux de routes*. C. R. Acad. Sci. Paris, v. 206 (1938) pp. 310–313.

J. B. Kruskal, *On the shortest spanning subtree of a graph and the traveling salesman problem*. Proc. Amer. Math. Soc., v. 7 (1956) pp. 48–50.

D. Blanusa, *Über die Anzahl der Bedingungsgleichungen beliebigen geodätischen Netzen*. Z. Vermessungswesen, v. 73 (1944) pp. 54–62.

4.4

O. Ore, *Graphs and correspondences*. Festschrift Andreas Speiser Zurich, 1945 pp. 184–191.

— *Incidence matchings in graphs*. Journ. de Math., v. 40 (1961) pp. 123–127.

4.5

O. Ore, *A problem regarding the tracing of graphs*. Elem. Math., v. 6 (1951) pp. 49–53.

F. Bäbler, *Über eine spezielle Klasse Euler'scher Graphen.* Comment. Math., Helv., v. 27 (1953) pp. 81–100.

F. Harary, *On arbitrarily traceable graphs and directed graphs.* Scripta Math. v. 23 (1957) pp. 37–41.

Further papers on trees:

A. Kotzig, *The significance of the skeleton of a graph for the construction of composition bases of some subgraphs.* Mat. Fyz. Casopis Slovensk. Akad. Vied., v. 6 (1956) pp. 68–77.

W. T. Tutte, *A ring in graph theory.* Proc. Cambridge Philos. Soc., v. 43 (1947) pp. 26–40.

J. S. R. Chisholm, *The S-matrix for neutral PS-PV meson-nucleon interaction.* Phil. Mag., (8) v. 1 (1956) pp. 338–344.

W. H. Burge, *Sorting, trees, and measures of order.* Information and Control, v. 1 (1958) pp. 181–197.

Chapter 5

5.1

S. MacLane, *Some unique separation theorems for graphs.* Amer. J. Math., v. 57 (1935) pp. 805–820.

R. E. Nettleton, K. Goldberg, and M. S. Green, *Dense subgraphs and connectivity.* Canad. J. Math., v. 11 (1959) pp. 262–268.

5.4

H. Whitney, *Non-separable and planar graphs.* Trans. Amer. Math. Soc., v. 34 (1932) pp. 339–362.

F. Harary, *An elementary theorem on graphs.* Amer. Math. Monthly, v. 66 (1959) pp. 405–407.

K. Husimi, *Note on Mayers' theory of cluster integrals.* Journ. Chem. Phys., v. 18 (1950) pp. 682–684.

F. Harary and G. E. Uhlenbeck, *On the number of Husimi trees.* Proc. Nat. Acad. Sci. U.S.A., v. 39 (1953) pp. 315–322.

F. Harary, and R. Z. Norman, *The dissimilarity characteristic of Husimi trees.* Ann. of Math. (2) v. 59 (1953), pp. 134–141.

5.5

G. A. Dirac, *Some theorems on abstract graphs.* Proc. London Math. Soc., (3) v. 2 (1952) pp. 69–81.

P. Erdös and T. Gallai, *On maximal paths and circuits of graphs,* Acta Math. Acad. Sci. Hungar., v. 10 (1959) pp. 337–356.

Chapter 6

6.4.

O. ORE AND T. S. MOTZKIN, *Subsets and subgraphs with maximal properties.* Proc. Amer. Math. Soc., v. 10 (1959) pp. 965–969.

Chapter 7

7.1.

R. RADO, *Axiomatic treatment of rank in infinite sets.* Canad. J. Math., v. 1 (1949) pp. 337–343.

W. H. GOTTSCHALK, *Choice functions and Tychonoff's theorem.* Proc. Amer. Math. Soc., v. 2 (1951) p. 172.

7.3.

O. ORE, *Graphs and matching theorems.* Duke Math. J., v. 22 (1955) pp. 625–639.

P. HALL, *On representatives of subsets.* J. London Math. Soc., v. 10 (1935) pp. 26–30.

M. HALL, *District representatives of subsets.* Bull. Amer. Math. Soc., v. 54 (1948) pp. 922–926.

7.4.

N. G. DE BRUIJN, *Gemeenschapelijke representantensystemen van twee klassen-indeelingen van een versameling.* Nieuw Archiev voor Wiskunde, (2) v. 22 (1943) pp. 48–52.

G. GRÜNWALD, *Über einen mengentheoretischen Satz.* Mat. Fiz. Lapok, v. 44 (1937) pp. 51–53.

M. HALL, *An algorithm for distinct representatives.* Amer. Math. Monthly, v. 63 (1956) pp. 716–717.

P. R. HALMOS AND H. E. VAUGHAN, *The marriage problem.* Amer. J. Math., v. 72 (1950) pp. 214–215.

L. HENKIN, *Some interconnections between modern algebra and mathematical logic.* Trans. Amer. Math. Soc., v. 74 (1953). pp. 410–427.

P. J. HIGGINS, *Disjoint transversals of subsets.* Canad. J. Math., v. 11 (1959) pp. 280–285.

A. J. HOFFMAN AND H. W. KUHN, *Systems of distinct representatives and linear programming.* Amer. Math. Monthly, v. 63 (1956) pp. 455–460.

— *On systems of distinct representatives.* Annals of Math. Studies, No. 38 (1956).

G. KREWERAS, *Extension d'un théorème sur les répartitions en classes.* C. R.Acad Sci. Paris, v. 222 (1946) pp. 431–432.

W. MAAK, *Ein Problem der Kombinatorik in seiner Formulierung von H. Weyl.* Math.-Phys. Semesterber. Göttingen, v. 22 (1952) pp. 251–256.

H. B. MANN AND H. J. RYSER, *Systems of distinct representatives*. Amer. Math. Monthly, v. 60 (1953) pp. 397–401.

N. S. MENDELSOHN AND A. L. DULMAGE, *Some generalizations of the problem of distinct representatives*. Canad. J. Math., v. 10 (1958) pp. 230–241.

— *Coverings of bipartite graphs*. Canad. J. Math., v. 10 (1958) pp. 517–534.

R. RADO, *Factorization of even graphs*. Quart. J. Math., Oxford, v. 20 (1949) pp. 95–104.

V. SHMUSHKOVITCH, *On a combinatorial theorem of the theory of sets*. Mat. Sb., v. 6 (1939) pp. 139–146.

B. L. VAN DER WAERDEN, *Ein Satz über Klasseneinteilungen von endlichen Mengen*. Hamburger Abh., v. 5 (1927) pp. 185–187.

H. WEYL, *Almost periodic invariant vector sets in a metric vector space*. Amer. J. Math., v. 71 (1949) pp. 178–205.

7.5

G. SCORZA, *A proposito di un teorema del Chapman*. Boll. Un. Mat. Ital., v. 6 (1927) pp. 1–6.

H. W. CHAPMAN, *A note on the elementary theory of groups of finite order*. Messenger of Math., v. 42 (1913) pp. 132–134; v. 43 p. 85.

G. A. MILLER, *On a method due to Galois*. Quarterly J. Math., v. 41 (1910) pp. 382–384.

S. SHÜ, *On the common representative system of residue classes of infinite groups*. J. London Math. Soc., v. 16 (1941) pp. 101–104.

O. ORE, *On coset representatives in groups*. Proc. Amer. Math. Soc., v. 9 (1958) pp. 665–670.

— *Conditions for subgraphs of directed graphs*. J. Math. Pures Appl., v. 37 (1958) pp. 321–328.

7.7

A. L. DULMAGE AND N. S. MENDELSOHN, *The term and stochastic rank of a matrix*. Canad. J. Math., v. 11 (1959) pp. 269–279.

M. HALL, *An existence theorem for Latin squares*. Bull Amer. Math. Soc., v. 51 (1945) pp. 387–388.

H. J. RYSER, *A combinatorial theorem with an application to Latin rectangles*. Proc. Amer. Math. Soc., v. 2 (1951) pp. 550–552.

— *The term rank of a matrix*. Canad. J. Math., v. 10 (1958) pp. 57–65.

M. MARCUS, *Some properties and applications of doubly stochastic matrices*. Amer. Math. Monthly, v. 67 (1960) pp. 215–221.

J. SINGER, *A class of groups associated with Latin squares*. Amer. Math. Monthly, v. 67 (1960) pp. 235–240.

7.9.

D. König, *Graphen und matrices*. Mat. Fiz. Lapok., v. 38 (1931) pp. 116–119.

— *Über trennende Knotenpunkte in Graphen*. Acta Litt. ac Scient. Szeged, v. 6 (1933) pp. 155–179.

D. König and S. Valkó, *Über Mehrdeutige Abbildungen von Mengen*. Math. Ann., v. 95 (1926) pp. 135–138.

R. Z. Norman and M. O. Rabin, *An algorithm for a minimum cover of a graph*. Proc. Amer. Math. Soc., v. 10 (1959) pp. 315–319.

C. Berge, *Two theorems in graph theory*. Proc. Nat. Acad. Sci. U.S.A., v. 43 (1957) pp. 842–844.

7.10.

P. J. Higgins, *Disjoint transversals of subsets*. Canad. J. Math., v. 11 (1959) pp. 280–285.

H. J. Ryser, *Combinatorial properties of matrices of zeros and ones*. Canad. J. Math., v. 9 (1957) pp. 371–377.

D. Gale, *A theorem on flows in networks*. Pacific J. Math., v. 7 (1957) pp. 1073–1082.

Chapter 8
8.1.

H. E. Robbins, *A theorem on graphs with an application to a problem of traffic control*. Amer. Math. Monthly, v. 46 (1939) pp. 281–283.

L. Egyed, *Über die wohlgerichteten unendlichen Graphen*. Mat. Fiz. Lapok., v. 48 (1941) pp. 505–509.

L. Redei, *Ein kombinatorischer Satz*. Acta. Litt. Szeged, v. 7 (1934) pp. 39–43.

M. Fiedler, and J. Sedlacek, *Über Wurzelbasen von gerichteten Graphen*. Casopis Pĕst Mat., v. 83 (1958) pp. 214–225.

8.2.

R. D. Luce, *Two decomposition theorems for a class of finite oriented graphs*. Amer. J. Math. v. 74 (1952) pp. 701–722.

— *Networks satisfying minimality conditions*. Amer. J. Math., v. 75 (1953) pp. 825–838.

K. Culik, *Zur Theorie der Graphen*. Casopis Pĕst. Mat., v. 83 (1958) pp. 133–155.

8.4.

L. Redei, *Über die Kantenbasen für endliche vollständige gerichtete Graphen*. Acta. Math. Sci. Hungar., v. 5 (1954) pp. 17–25.

8.6

O. Ore, *Studies on directed graphs*. I, Ann. of Math., v. 63 (1956) pp. 383–406; II, v. 64 (1956) pp. 142–153.

W. T. Tutte, *The 1-factors of oriented graphs*. Proc. Amer. Math. Soc., v. 4 (1953) pp. 922–931.

Chapter 9

9.2.

O. Ore, *Chains in partially ordered sets*. Bull. Amer. Math. Soc., v. 49 (1943) pp. 558–566.

S. Maclane, *A conjecture of Ore in partially ordered sets*. Bull. Amer. Math. Soc. v. 49 (1943) pp. 567–568.

M. Benado, *Les ensembles partiellement ordonnés et le théorème de raffinement de O. Schreier*. Acad. R. P. Romîne Bul. Şti. Şecţ. Şti. Mat. Fiz., v. 4 (1952) pp. 585–591.

— *Bemerkungen zu einer Arbeit von Oystein Ore*. Rev. Math. Pures Appl., v. 1 (1956) pp. 5–12.

M. Kolibiar, *Bemerkung uber die Ketten in teilweise geordneten Mengen*. Acta Fac. Nat. Univ. Comenian, v. 3 (1958) pp. 17–22.

9.3

O. Ore, *Sex in graphs*. Proc. Amer. Math. Soc., v. 11 (1960) pp. 533–539.

Chapter 10

10.2

R. P. Dilworth, *A decomposition theorem for partially ordered sets*. Ann. of Math., (2) v. 51 (1950) pp. 161–166.

G. A. Moreira, *Decomposition of partially ordered systems*. Revista Cientifica, v. 1 (1950) pp. 12–18.

D. T. Fulkerson, *Note on Dilworth's decomposition theorem for partially ordered sets*. Proc. Amer. Math. Soc., v. 7 (1956) pp. 701–702.

G. B. Dantzig, and A. J. Hoffman, *Dilworth's theorem on partially ordered sets*. Annals of Math. Studies no. 38 (1956), pp. 207–214.

10.3

G. Birkhoff, *Lattice theory*. Amer. Math. Soc. Colloquium Publ., v. 25., Rev. ed. 1948.

10.4.

E. SZPILRAJN, *Sur l'extension de l'ordre partiel.* Fund. Math., v. 16 (1930) pp. 386–389.

B. DUSHNIK AND E. W. MILLER, *Partially ordered sets.* Amer. J. Math., v. 63 (1941) pp. 600–610.

B. DUSHNIK, *Concerning a certain set of arrangements.* Proc. Amer. Math. Soc., v. 1 (1950) pp. 788–796.

H. KOMM, *On the dimension of partially ordered sets.* Amer. J. Math., v. 70 (1948) pp. 507–520.

V. SEDMAK, *Dimension des ensembles partiellement ordonnés associés aux polygones et polyèdres.* Hrvatsko, Prirodoslovno Društvo Glasnik Mat.-Fiz. Astr. Ser II, v. 7 (1952) pp. 169–182.

— *Quelques applications des ensembles partiellement ordonnés.* C. R. Acad. Sci. Paris, v. 236 (1953) pp. 2139–2140.

T. HIRAGUCHI, *On the dimension of partially ordered sets.* Sci. Rep. Kanazawa University, v. 1 (1951) pp. 77–94.

— *A note on Mr. Komm's theorems.* Ibid., v. 2 (1953) No. 1 pp. 1–3.

T. HIRAGUCHI, *On the dimension of orders.* Ibid., v. 4 (1955) No. 1.

— *On the λ-dimension of the product of orders.* Ibid., v. 5 (1956) pp. 1–5.

CHAPTER 11

11.1

O. ORE, *Galois connexions.* Trans. Amer. Math. Soc., v. 55 (1944) pp. 493–513.

G. BIRKHOFF, *Lattice theory.* 2nd ed. 1948, Chapter IV.

C. J. EVERETT, *Closure operators and Galois theory in lattices.* Trans. Amer. Math. Soc., v. 55 (1944) pp. 514–525.

G. PICKERT, *Bemerkungen über Galois-Verbindungen.* Arch. Math., v. 3 (1952) pp. 285–289.

G. AUMANN, *Bemerkungen über Galois-Verbindungen.* Bayer. Akad. Wiss. M. N. Kl. (1955) pp. 281–284.

11.3

J. RIGUET, *Relations binaires, fermetures, correspondences de Galois.* Bull. Soc. Math. France, v. 76 (1948) pp. 114–155.

— *Quelques propriétés des r lations difonctionelles.* C. R. Acad. Sci. Paris, v. 230 (1950) pp. 1999–2000.

J. RIGUET, *Sur les ensembles réguliers de relations binaires.* C. R. Acad. Sci. Paris, v. 231 (1950) pp. 936–937.

M. L. DUBREIL-JACOTIN, *Quelques propriétés des applications multiformes.* C. R. Acad. Sci. Paris, v. 230 (1950) pp. 806–808.

G. Y. RAINICH, *Involution and equivalence.* Michigan Math. J., v. 2 (1954) pp. 33–34.

11.4.

J. RIGUET, *Les relations de Ferrers.* C. R. Acad. Sci. Paris, v. 232 (1951) pp. 1729–1730.

P. DUBREIL, *Relations binaires et applications.* C. R. Acad. Sci. Paris, v. 230 (1950) pp. 1028–1030.

— *Comportement des relations binaires dans une application multiforme.* C. R. Acad. Sci. Paris, v. 230 (1950) pp. 1242–1243.

R. M. THRALL, *A combinatorial problem.* Michigan Math. J., v. 1 (1952) pp. 81–88.

J. LAMBEK, *Goursat's theorem and the Zassenhaus lemma.* Canad. J. Math., v. 10 (1958) pp. 45–56.

K. ONO, *On some properties of binary relations.* Nagoya Math. J., v. 12 (1957) pp. 161–170.

CHAPTER 12
12.2.

D. KÖNIG, *Über trennende Knotenpunkte in Graphen.* Acta. Litt. Sci. Szeged v. 6 (1933) pp. 155–179.

G. HAJÖS, *Zum Mengerschen Graphensatz.* Acta. Litt. Sci. Szeged, v. 7 (1934) pp. 44–47.

T. GRÜNWALD, *Ein neuer Beweis eines Mengerschen Satzes.* J. London Math. Soc., v. 13 (1938) pp. 188–192.

G. A. DIRAC, *Connectivity theorems for graphs.* Quarterly J. Math., Oxford Ser. (2) v. 3 (1952) pp. 171–174.

CHAPTER 13
13.1.

F. SCHEID, *Some packing problems.* Amer. Math. Monthly, v. 67 (1960) pp. 231–235.

13.3

E. NETTO, *Lehrbuch der Combinatorik,* 2nd ed. 1927.

W. SIERPINSKI, *Sur un problème de la théorie des relations.* Fund. Math., v. 28 (1937) pp. 71–74.

S. Piccard, *Solution d'un problème de la théorie des relations*. Fund. Math. v. 28 (1936) pp. 197–202.

— *Sur un problème de la théorie des relations*. Mathematica, v. 13 (1937) pp. 55–58.

S. Marcus, *Sur les ensembles indépendants dans la théorie des relations*. Monatsh. Math., v. 63 (1959) pp. 244–255.

G. Fodor, *On two problems concerning the theory of binary relations*. Publ. Math. Debrecen, v. 1 (1950) pp. 199–200.

— *On a theorem in the theory of binary relations*. Compositio Math., v. 8 (1951) p. 250.

— *On a problem concerning the theory of binary relations*. Nieuw Archiv voor Wiskunde, v. 23 (1951) pp. 247–248.

D. Lázár, *On a problem in the theory of aggregates*. Compositio Math. v. 3 (1936) p. 304.

G. Grünwald, *Über einen mengentheoretischen Satz*. Math. Fiz. Lapok, v. 44 (1937) pp. 51–53.

F. Bagemihl, *The Baire Category of independent sets*. Compositio Math., v. 13 (1956) pp. 71–75.

P. Erdös and G. Fodor, *Some remarks on set theory*. V. Acta. Sci. Math Szeged, v. 17 (1956) pp. 250–260; VI. v. 18 (1957), pp. 243–260.

T. Gallai, *Über extreme Punkt-und Kantenmengen Annales*. Un. Sci. Budapest, v. 2 (1959) pp. 133–138.

13.4

P. Turàn, *Eine Extremalaufgabe aus der Graphentheorie*. Math. Fiz. Lapok, v. 48 (1941) pp. 436–452.

— *On the theory of graphs*. Colloq. Math., v. 3 (1954) pp. 19–30.

K. Zarankiewicz, *Sur les relations symétriques dans l'ensemble fini* Colloq. Math., v. 1 (1947) pp. 10–14.

P. Erdös and A. H. Stone, *On the structure of linear graphs*. Bull. Amer. Math. Soc., v. 52 (1946) pp. 1087–1091.

P. Erdös, *Some theorems on graphs*. Riveon Lematematika, v. 9 (1955) pp. 13–17.

13.5.

F. P. Ramsey, *On a problem of formal logic*. Proc. London Math. Soc., (2) v. 30 (1930) pp. 264–286.

T. Skolem, *Ein kombinatorischer Satz mit Anwendung auf ein logisches Entscheidungsproblem*. Fund. Math., v. 20 (1933) pp. 254–261.

P. Erdös and R. Rado, *A combinatorial theorem*. J. London Math. Soc., v. 25 (1950) pp. 249–255.

P. ERDÖS AND G. SZEKERES, *A combinatorial problem in geometry*. Compositio Math., v. 2 (1935) pp. 463–470.

R. RADO, *The distributive law for products of infinite series*. Quart. J. Math., Oxford Ser. v. 11 (1940) pp. 229–242.

A. W. GOODMAN, *On set of acquaintances and strangers at any party*. Amer. Math. Monthly., v. 66 (1959) pp. 778–783.

A. M. GLEASON AND R. E. GREENWOOD, *Combinatorial relations and chromatic graphs*. Canad. J. Math., v. 7 (1955) pp. 1–7.

P. ERDÖS, *Some remarks on the theory of graphs*. Bull. Amer. Math. Soc., v. 53 (1947) pp. 292–294.

P. ERDÖS, AND R. RADO, *Combinatorial theorems on classifications of subsets of a given set*. Proc. London Math. Soc., v. 2 (1951) pp. 417–439.

— *A partition calculus in set theory*. Bull. Amer. Math. Soc., v. 62 (1956) pp. 427–489.

13.6.

C. E. SHANNON, *The zero error capacity of a noisy channel*. Transactions 1956 Symposium Information Theory, Institute of Radio Engineers. v. IT.-2, pp. 8–19.

CHAPTER 14

14.1.

P. ERDÖS, AND N. G. DE BRUIJN, *A colour problem for infinite graphs and a problem in the theory of relations*. Indagationes Math., v. 13 (1951) pp. 369–373.

P. ERDÖS AND R. RADO, *Partition relations connected with the chromatic number of graphs*, J. London Math. Soc., v. 34 (1959) pp. 63–72.

R. L. BROOKS, *On colouring the nodes of a network*. Cambridge Philos. Soc., v. 37 (1941) pp. 194–197.

J. MYCIELSKI, *Sur le coloriage des graphes*. Colloq. Math., v. 3 (1955) pp. 161–162.

14.2.

E. A. NORDHAUS AND J. W. GADDUM, *On complementary graphs*. Amer. Math. Monthly., v. 63 (1956) pp. 175–177.

A. A. ZYKOV, *On some properties of linear complexes*. Mat. Sb., v. 24 (66) (1949) pp. 163–188. Amer. Math. Soc. Translations No. 79.

14.3.

G. A. DIRAC, *Note on the colouring of graphs*. Math. Z., v. 54 (1951) pp. 347–353.

— *Some theorems on abstract graphs*. Proc. London Math. Soc., (3) v. 2 (1952) pp. 69–81.

— *A property of 4-chromatic graphs and some remarks on critical graphs.* J. London Math. Soc., v. 27 (1952) pp. 85–92.

— *The structure of k-chromatic graphs.* Fund. Math., v. 40 (1953) pp. 42–55.

— *Circuits in critical graphs.* Monatsh. Math., v. 59 (1955) pp. 178–187.

— *A theorem of R. L. Brooks and a con²ecture of H. Hadwiger.* Proc. London Math. Soc., (3) v. 7 (1957) pp. 161–195.

J. B. KELLY AND L. M. KELLY, *Paths and circuits in critical graphs.* Amer. J. Math., v. 76 (1954) pp. 786–792.

R. C. READ, *Maximal circiuits in critical graphs.* J. London Math. Soc., v. 32 (1957) pp. 456–462.

B. ZEIDL, *Über 4- und 5-chrome Graphen.* Monatsh. Math., v. 62 (1958) pp. 212–218.

14.4.

G. D. BIRKHOFF, *A determinant formula for the number of ways of colouring a map.* Ann. of Math., (2) v. 14 (1912) pp. 42–46.

— *On the number of ways of coloring a map.* Proc. Edinburgh Math. Soc., (2) v. 2 (1930) pp. 83–91.

H. WHITNEY, *A logical expansion in mathematics.* Bull. Amer. Math. Soc., v. 38 (1932) pp. 572–579.

— *The coloring of graphs.* Ann. of Math., (2) v. 33 (1932) pp. 688–718.

— *A set of topological invariants for graphs.* Amer. J. Math., v. 55 (1933) pp. 231–235.

CHAPTER 15

15.1.

R. FRUCHT, *Die Gruppe des Petersenschen Graphen und der Kantensysteme der regulären Polyeder.* Comment. Math. Helv., v. 9 (1937) pp. 217–223.

I. N. KAGNO, *Desargues' and Pappus' graphs and their groups.* Amer. J. Math., v. 69 (1947) pp. 859–862.

— *Linear graphs of degree ≦6 and their groups.* Corrections ibid., v. 69 (1947) p. 872; v. 77 (1955) p. 392.

G. PÓLYA, *Kombinatorische Anzahlbestimmungen für Gruppen, Graphen und chemische Verbindungen.* Acta. Math., v. 68 (1937) pp. 145–254.

15.2.

A. CAYLEY, *The theory of groups, graphical representation.* Math. Papers, v. 10 pp. 403–405.

— *On the theory of groups.* Ibid., v. 10 pp. 323–330; v. 11 pp. 365–367.

R. A. RANKIN, *A campanological problem in group theory.* Proc. Cambridge Philos. Soc., v. 44 (1948) pp. 17–25.

T. J. FLETCHER, *Campanological groups.* Amer. Math. Monthly, v. 63 (1956) pp. 619–626.

D. J. DICKINSON, *On Fletcher's paper: "Campanological groups".* Amer. Math. Monthly, v. 64 (1957) pp. 331–332.

E. S. RAPAPORT, *Cayley color groups and Hamilton lines.* Scripta Math., v. 24 (1959) pp. 51–58.

15.3.

R. FRUCHT, *Herstellung von Graphen mit vorgegebener abstrakter Gruppe.* Compositio Math., v. 6 (1938) pp. 239–250.

— *Graphs of degree three with a given abstract group.* Canad. J. Math., v. 1 (1949) pp. 365–378.

— *On groups of repeated graphs.* Bull. Amer. Math. Soc., v. 55 (1949) pp. 418–420.

— *On the construction of partially ordered systems with a given group of automorphisms.* Rev. Un. Mat. Argentina, v. 13 (1948) pp. 12–18.

G. T. TRANQUE, *The type in cubic graphs.* Gaceta Mat., (1) v. 5 (1953) pp. 11–23.

H. IZBICKI, *Reguläre Graphen 3. 4. und 5. Grades mit vorgegebenen abstrakten Automorphismengruppen, Farbenzahlen und Zusammenhängen.* Monatsh. Math., v. 61 (1957) pp. 42–50.

— *Unendliche Graphen endlichen Grades mit vorgegebenen Eigenshaften.* Ibid., v. 63 (1959) pp. 298–307.

— *Reguläre Graphen beliebigen Grades mit vorgegebenen Eigenschaften.* Ibid., v. 64 (1960) pp. 15–21.

G. SABIDUSSI, *Graphs with given group and given graph-theoretical properties.* Canad. J. Math., v. 9 (1957) pp. 515–525.

— *On the minimum order of graphs with given automorphism group.* Monatsh. Math., v. 63 (1959) pp. 124–127.

— *Graphs with given infinite groups.* Ibid., v. 64 (1960) pp. 64–67.

— *Graph multiplication.* Math. Z., v. 72 (1960) pp. 446–457.

— *On a class of fixed-point-free graphs.* Proc. Amer. Math. Soc., v. 9 (1958) pp. 800–804.

— *The composition of graphs.* Duke Math. J., v. 26 (1959) pp. 693–696.

F. HARARY, *On the group of the composition of two graphs.* Duke Math. J., v. 26 (1959) pp. 29–34.

G. BIRKHOFF, *On groups of automorphisms.* Rev. Un. Mat. Argentina, v. 11 (1946) pp. 155–157.

W. T. TUTTE, *A family of cubical graphs.* Proc. Cambridge Philos. Soc., v. 43 (1947) pp. 459–474.

H. S. M. Coxeter, *Self-dual configurations and regular graphs*. Bull. Amer. Math. Soc., v. 56 (1950) pp. 413–455.

R. Frucht, *A one-regular graph of degree three*. Canad. J. Math., v. 4 (1952) pp. 240–247.

15.4.

H. Whitney, *Congruent graphs and the connectivity of graphs*. Amer. J. Math., v. 54 (1932) pp. 150–168.

— *On the classification of graphs*. Ibid., v. 55 (1933) pp. 236–244.

— *2-isomorphic graphs*. Ibid., v. 55 (1933) pp. 245–254.

R. M. Foster, *Geometrical circuits of electrical networks*. Bell Tel. Syst. Techn. Publ. B-653; also Transactions Amer. Inst. Elec. Eng., v. 51 (1932) pp. 309–317.

J. Krausz, *Démonstration nouvelle d'un théorème de Whitney sur les réseaux*. Mat. Fiz. Lapok, v. 50 (1943) pp. 75–85.

LIST OF CONCEPTS

intersection 15, mutually transitive 192, null 14, order 17, product 191, progeny 166, proper inclusion 18, reflexive 15, self-transitive 193, sum 15, symmetric 14, transitive 15, universal 14, weakly symmetric 190, weakly transitive 193.
Root 59.

Scaffolding 101.
Section 23, lower, upper 172.
Sequence 22, cyclic 23, directed, undirected 23, one-way, two-way infinite 22, proper 168, reverse cross- 200, 203, section 23.
Set, conformal 138, covering 208, critical 109, 204, deficient 134, dependent, completely dependent, independent, related, unrelated 210, distinct representatives 116, dividing 93, dominating 206, finitely minimal 139, G-12, generating 146, 172, inclusion 17, matching 132, maximal independent 211, maximal ordered 95, M-image 135, minimal critical 109, 136, minimal δ-135, ordered 17, representatives 113, separating 138, 200, separating edge 202, strongly dependent 173, vertex 1, without deficiency 110, 204.
Sex dichotomy 167, Skeleton 101, Skein 59, Stochastic matrix 129.
Subgraph 12, proper 210, edge disjoint 12, vertex disjoint 12.

Term rank 126.
Transfinite induction 92, construction 95.
Transposition 27, 60, basis 60.
Traveling Salesman Problem 53.
Tree 58, rooted 59, maximal 101.

Union 175.

Variance 30.
Vertex 1, accessible 145, 156, 200, 203, accessibly equivalent 145, 158, attachment 79, 80, attachment number 80, connectivity 80, covering number 210, cut 87, cyclic edge connected 146, deficient 133, 160, deviation 30, disjoint 13, immediate predecessor, successor 162, incident 2, independence number 211, initial 1, 22, inner 22, intermediate 22, 162, isolated 3, median 30, mutually connected 145, separating 87, separation theorem 200, strongly circuit connected 86, terminal 1, 22, 58.

Well-ordering 92.
Weight 65, branch 65.

Zermelo's theorem 92.
Zorn's lemma 95.

INDEX OF NAMES